CED

# DIGITAL COMPUTER
## ENGINEERING

PRENTICE-HALL INTERNATIONAL SERIES
IN ELECTRICAL ENGINEERING
*William L. Everitt, editor*

PRENTICE-HALL, INC.
PRENTICE-HALL INTERNATIONAL, INC., UNITED KINGDOM AND EIRE
PRENTICE-HALL OF CANADA, LTD., CANADA

PRENTICE-HALL INTERNATIONAL, INC., *London*
PRENTICE-HALL OF AUSTRALIA, PTY., LTD., *Sydney*
PRENTICE-HALL OF CANADA, LTD., *Toronto*
PRENTICE-HALL FRANCE, S.A.R.L., *Paris*
PRENTICE-HALL OF JAPAN, INC., *Tokyo*
PRENTICE-HALL DE MEXICO, S.A., *Mexico City*

**HARRY J. GRAY**

*Associate Professor*
*Moore School of Electrical Engineering*
*University of Pennsylvania*

# DIGITAL COMPUTER
# ENGINEERING

**PRENTICE-HALL, INC.**
*Englewood Cliffs, N.J.*

Library of Congress Catalog Card Number: 63-14842

Printed in the United States of America

C

*To my wife, Cecilia*

# FOREWORD

The increasing demand for instruction in the field of digital computer engineering has already stimulated a wide variety of technical publications, many intended as textbooks for beginners. However, newcomers have been more and more at a disadvantage. Rapid advances in computer technology make obsolete those texts which put emphasis on particular systems rather than on guiding principles. Moreover, as technical specialization increases, it becomes harder for authors to write for beginners.

In *Digital Computer Engineering*, Dr. Gray has carefully restricted the content and has omitted many things that others might be tempted to include. However, there are many literature references which will enable any good student to push well beyond the subjects explicitly treated. The result is a clear account of the basic stock-in-trade needed by a good computer designer.

Too often the subject has been presented as a set of immutable principles which are directly and inexorably applied to satisfy predefined specifications. Rarely has the beginner been permitted a glimpse of computer design as a back-and-forth play involving artistic creation using imperfectly understood components. Dr. Gray avoids any pretense on this score by emphasizing from the outset that there is an art to be learned. I share his hope that this book will serve to advance that art.

JOHN W. MAUCHLY

# PREFACE

This book was written for the engineer interested in the electronic digital computer. Its purpose is to deal with the art of engineering rather than dwell heavily on circuits and logical design features. It is an attempt to give an integrated picture of the engineering problems involved, and a strong effort is made to present information adequate to that purpose.

Much of the material presented herein reflects teaching experience in a four semester-credit graduate engineering program taken by students with and without previous computer experience. Requirements include a prior knowledge of programming principles, computer arithmetic, and an elementary acquaintance with logic. Understanding of transient circuit analysis and some familiarity with field theory is also necessary.

The introductory chapter presents a brief history of the development of the electronic digital computer. ENIAC and EDVAC are described because of their historical importance and because they represent two different types of computer organization—parallel and serial.

Chapters 2 through 4 present logical foundations in a manner emphasizing the integration of the subject matter rather than analysis in great detail. Chapter 5 contains a classification of circuits that can be termed "proven" and also provides discussion of selected circuits which have not yet attained wide commercial application.

This first portion of the book starts from the larger view (the position of computers in our civilization) and proceeds to the smaller (the logic elements). The second portion reverses this direction, concluding with computers as aids in their own design.

Acknowledgment is due to Alvin Vivatson for providing Figs. 2.18, 2.19, and the accompanying text; Gerry T. O'Halloran for assisting in the preparation of the notes; Edward Parker, aided by Renate Schultz, for the editorial work in transforming the revised notes into a readable manuscript; and, in particular, to my friend and colleague, Noah S. Prywes for writing Chapter 10 of this book, for assisting in organizing the course on which this book is based, and for his constant encouragement and advice freely given over the past years.

Others who have given assistance difficult to measure are John Warfield, whose text *Introduction to Electronic Analog Computers* served as a guide for my book, and Charles V. Freiman. Both men read the entire manuscript and their comments have proven extremely helpful and valuable. John Mauchly has also provided me with many helpful suggestions, especially in regard to the Introduction and Chapter 1, and Saul Gorn has provided comments on the organization. Carl C. Chambers and J. Presper Eckert have also aided me in improving the accuracy of the history of ENIAC. However, final responsibility as to accuracy and aptness of statements contained in this book rest with me. I am also indebted to John G. Brainerd, Director of the Moore School of Electrical Engineering for his encouragement and support given within the limitations of a private university.

The manuscript was partly typed at the Moore School, chiefly by Caroline Hadermann. I would also like to express my appreciation to my wife for typing the remainder of the manuscript and for correcting the inevitable typing errors.

HARRY J. GRAY

# CONTENTS

**9 PULSE AND D-C POWER TRANSMISSION SYSTEMS, 271**

**10 APPLICATION OF COMPUTERS TO THE DESIGN OF COMPUTERS, 309**

**APPENDICES**

**I INTRODUCTION TO SEMICONDUCTOR DIODE THEORY, 343**

DIGITAL COMPUTER
ENGINEERING

ENIAC in operation. Courtesy Moore School of Electrical Engineering.

# INTRODUCTION

A computing system is essentially a tool, and its primary use is as an aid to the solution of certain problems that have been formulated with mathematical precision. It would be safe to say that man has devised not only the computer but almost every other tool in order to meet a requirement—to increase his chances of survival or to better his position in life.

Since tools are tied in so closely with man's needs we might regard such inventions as the wheel, lever, radio, computing machine, and so on as extensions of man's personality, and in this light the wheel, like the computing machine, is an intelligent machine, but to a lesser degree. That is to say, both become "intelligent" extensions of man's personality in the sense that they become useful tools when directed by man's intelligence. Going even further, we might regard each such invention as a step towards the goal of replacing, as compared to aiding, human functions by machine functions. We will not discuss the wisdom of selecting such a goal, but we should recognize its existence.

## 1  HISTORY

The computer was developed primarily to extend human functions by means of machine functions, not to replace the former by the latter, which appears to be more an industrial predicament than a scientific intent. Ever since the origination of the abacus, computing devices have had the purpose of facilitating man's work, and modern computing devices arose to relieve personnel from the drudgery of performing extensive computations by hand so that they might spend more time in the more self-improving aspects of their specialties.

The first step was the development of the concepts of number and counting, arising from the use of objects such as fingers and stones (calculi). (Such methods could be called the beginnings of mechanized calculation, in the sense that any human action that can be described and imitated by an inanimate contrivance is mechanical.) Since man had ten fingers, it was natural that groups of ten objects acquired special significance. The second step, involving the expression of numbers greater than ten, was the development of our positional number system. This development took many centuries. The Hindu-Arabic numerals appeared in India in about the seventh century, and the numerals in nearly the form we use, together with the rules for using them, did not gain complete acceptance in Europe until just a few centuries ago. Meanwhile many other numeral systems, such as the Roman one, were developed, of which few have survived.

A third step paralleled the development of numeral systems: it was the mechanization, in the real sense, of arithmetic processes. The abacus was probably the first computing device, originating in antiquity. Basic principles were uncovered in many later developments, such as Napier's "bones" (John Napier, c. 1617), a digital device for multiplication. The first slide rule appeared shortly thereafter. About twenty-five years after the appearance of Napier's "bones" Blaise Pascal announced a stylus-operated adding machine using numbered wheels, followed in 1666 by Samuel Morland's machine that worked on approximately the same principle but was designed for both addition and subtraction. (In the *stylus-operated* machine the numbered wheels were positioned manually by a rod or pin.) In 1694, Leibnitz introduced a machine that had two features* that are still used in many mechanical computing machines, and which surpassed Morland's machine in that it also multiplied, divided, and extracted roots. However, none of these machines worked reliably because the technology of the times was not adequate. Some of these efforts were in the area we call logical design; we, too, can carry out the logical design of equipment which cannot be made to operate reliably using current technology.

Throughout the eighteenth and nineteenth centuries, others worked on mechanical computing machines, and eventually all the problems of their design were solved. Manufacture on a commercial scale probably commenced with the Thomas machine (1820). In 1885, in the United States, Dorr E. Felt completed the first successful key-operated calculator, later sold under the name *Comptometer*. The development of these devices led to the wide variety of desk calculators in existence today and also to the

* These were multiplication by repeated addition and the "stepped-wheel reckoner."

business machines marketed by IBM, Remington Rand, and other manufacturers. Business machines received impetus from the work of Herman Hollerith, who invented a rotary adder and adapted the punched card of the textile industry.

Before all the problems that arose in the mechanization of the arithmetic process had been solved, Charles Babbage (c. 1835) conceived the idea of sequencing by automatic means (punched cards) the steps performed in a long computation. He also proposed in his "analytical engine" to have three units, corresponding to the memory, arithmetic unit, and control that exist in many of today's large-scale automatic computing machines. Unfortunately, the circumstances involving his personality, his chief engineer, and government support were such that he never even completed his "difference engine," the conception of which predated the analytical engine. The first difference engine was built by George Scheutz, a Stockholm printer, shortly after Babbage published his results. The Scheutz machine was later transported to and used in this country.

It was nearly the middle of the twentieth century before Babbage's ideas could be fully realized, and this was accomplished chiefly with electronic rather than mechanical devices. His ideas were realized in computing-machine form at the beginning of World War II by the construction of the Mark I calculator, put into operation in 1944 as a cooperative effort between IBM Corporation and Harvard University; for the most part it used the electromechanical technology that had been accumulated in the business-machine industry. At about the same time, Bell Laboratories built several computers using the relay technology developed by Stibitz and Williams of that organization.

The first automatic computer successfully based on electronic technology was the ENIAC (Electronic Numerical Integrator and Computer), completed in 1945. Although this computer did not strictly follow the proposed organization of Babbage's analytical engine, it did present several advances over it. The ENIAC differed from the machine at Harvard University and its cousins in that it was the first chiefly electronic computer. The other computers were in fact totally electromechanical machines consisting of mazes of wheels, gears, shafts, relays, and so on, while the only electromechanical units of the ENIAC were the input and output devices.

At about the time of the ENIAC's completion, a newer electronic machine was proposed—the EDVAC (Electronic Discrete Variable Computer). This computer was organized along the lines of Babbage's proposed system, but because of technical difficulties it was not completed until 1949. The logical design of the EDVAC formed the foundation for the logical design of the SEAC (Standards Electronic Automatic Computer), which was constructed and put into operation by the National Bureau of Standards before the EDVAC's completion. All of these machines, ENIAC,

EDVAC, and SEAC, were "synchronous" machines, the ancestors of a line of synchronous computers that were later developed by various companies and universities both here and abroad. By "synchronous" it is meant that the times at which the elements of the system perform their functions are determined by signals derived from a source of standardized periodic signals, a "clock." At about this time, John von Neumann proposed a machine of "asynchronous" nature that was constructed at the Institute for Advanced Study, at Princeton, part of which was later sent to the Smithsonian Institute. This machine, although not truly asynchronous (see Sec. 4.10), was also the ancestor of a line of similar computers that were developed later.

We have described one phase of computing machine development, the historical, but by "computing machine development" we also mean the sequence of steps that are followed in the design, construction, and use of a computing machine. If we enumerate and study these steps we can systematically approach the problem of designing and constructing a computing system that will approach the optimum design for a given class of problems. Thus, in this text we are concerned with finding those objectives that must be considered in the engineering of a computer system prior to its detailed engineering analysis and design. In other words, our first step is to state the problem. The importance of such a procedure is this: there have occurred instances where computing machines have been built and later found to be virtually impossible to use, because the work they were to do was not properly analyzed; there have also been many instances where circuits were designed and found to be useless because the circuit requirements were not sufficiently investigated. It is the purpose of this text to illustrate to the reader how necessary it is to systematically integrate his knowledge in order to avoid such instances.

# 1

# THE ENIAC AND THE EDVAC

During World War II, the University of Pennsylvania, under contract with the Ordnance Department, U.S. Army, employed many people to compute artillery firing tables by use of desk calculators. The peculiarities of each type of gun made it necessary that several tables for varying conditions be prepared for each one. Test firings first provided information which was used to obtain initial data for the computations. It was not practicable to obtain the firing tables experimentally through constant firing because this would have used up considerable ammunition, would have worn out many guns, and so on.

For example, one problem was that of exterior ballistics; it consisted of the numerical solution of differential equations of the form (simplified):

$$\frac{d^2y}{dt^2} = -E\frac{dy}{dt} - g$$

$$\frac{d^2x}{dt^2} = -E\frac{dx}{dt}$$

where $$E = \frac{e^{-hy}G(v)}{c}, \qquad v = \sqrt{\left(\frac{dx}{dt}\right)^2 + \left(\frac{dy}{dt}\right)^2}$$

In this problem $G(v)$ is a ballistic drag function which has no simple mathematical form. (ENIAC could compute a similar shell-trajectory problem in 15 seconds while by hand it would take over 10 hours.)

## 1.1 THE ENIAC

As new developments in ballistics arose, there arose also the necessity for increased and faster computations. During that time, Dr. John Mauchly, a staff member of The Moore School of Electrical Engineering, suggested and found support for the idea of building a machine that would automatically compute the firing tables and do it much faster than the large staff of mathematicians doing it by hand. Under contract with the Ordnance Department of the U.S. Army, the Moore School undertook to design, develop, and construct the ENIAC (Electronic Numerical Integrator and Computer).* The ENIAC was completed and put into operation in 1945, delivered in late 1946, and placed into operation at the Aberdeen Proving Ground, Aberdeen, Maryland, in the spring of 1947. It was retired after about twelve years of service in 1958, since it could not compete economically with machines of more modern design.

The ENIAC contained some 18,000 to 20,000 tubes, about 70,000 resistors, about 1500 telephone-type relays, and about 6000 switches. (The relays were used in the input-output system.) Some of the vacuum tubes were double triodes of 6SN7 type such that the machine contained perhaps 24,000 tube elements.

The machine was U-shaped (see frontispiece) with a length of about one hundred feet and a width of about fifty feet. It was constructed of racks about ten feet high and three feet deep, each rack containing about 500 tubes. The ENIAC required about 80 kilowatts of vacuum-tube heater power, the output of the d-c power supplies was about 40 kilowatts, and it required about 20 kilowatts to operate the blowers that removed the heat generated by the vacuum tubes and the circuits. At that time there was very little knowledge available as to how to design a reliable system. Critics predicted that with 24,000 tube elements having a design life of 3000 hours, on the average one would expect a tube failure every eight minutes, and what with maintenance time, one would not be able to do a problem on the machine. These predictions did not come true, however, since on some days the machine would operate all day without making an error, let alone having a tube failure. This performance was the outcome of what were very conservative design practices based on worst-case design and the establishment of margins based on the prediction of system performance. Complete information was not available on the life characteristics of every type of component used. However, when possible, this and other information was obtained and used in design calculations based on the worst-case concept and checked by experiment. Knowing that the rate of evaporation of barium from the oxide-coated cathodes of the tubes

* J. P. Eckert was the chief engineer, J. G. Brainerd was the project supervisor, and H. H. Goldstine was the Ordnance Department representative.

depended on temperature and that lower operating temperatures reduced stresses and the liberation of gases from tube elements, the designers used $6 \pm 0.3$ volts on the heaters of 6.3 volt tubes (means was provided to change the heater voltage if later information made it advisable to do so), and limited the power dissipation in the tubes to 25 per cent or less of the rated value. At that time they were not aware of "cathode interface" and other phenomena which appeared later to plague the designers of reliable vacuum-tube computers. (In the cathode-interface phenomena, traces of silicon would diffuse from the nickel cathode sleeve into the oxide coating, producing a resistive layer equivalent to a parallel RC combination internally in series with the cathode.) Because of this and other phenomena that cause deterioration of cathodes of nonconducting tubes, there is at present an optimum value of heater voltage (and other operating conditions) that yields maximum life. In computer-type tubes the optimum heater voltage is usually the rated value. Margins for noise were conservatively set—for example, with a negative bias of $-14$ volts on a 6J5 having $+75$ volts on the plate; also, the maximum pulse amplitude could be as much as 50 volts.

The ENIAC was a synchronous machine using a central clock source. The clock generator operated at a nominal pulse rate of 100 kc but could be varied by using an external variable-frequency oscillator. The primary source of timing signals emitted a continuous train of pulses at the clock rate having a duration of 1 $\mu$sec. Various other pulse trains were derived from the basic clock, such as a periodic string of 9 pulses (the 9P) formed by gating the clock, the 10P, 1P, etc. Digits were represented by the number of pulses on a wire. For example, three was represented by three pulses of 1 $\mu$sec duration spaced 10 $\mu$sec apart. Number words were represented by 10 digits in parallel, with an extra wire for the sign, and by 20 digits in parallel, plus sign, for double precision operation. The basic computing elements were ten-stage vacuum-tube flip-flop "ring" counters with neon-light indicators on each stage analogous to wheels with ten discrete positions, as in Leibniz' "stepped-wheel reckoner." Hence, digits could be added using a decade counter. Since the counters could be stepped in only one direction, it was necessary to use 10's-complement representation of negative numbers for subtraction.

An accumulator, of which there were twenty in ENIAC, consisted of ten decade counters plus circuits for carry propagation, and control circuits for sequencing the operations required in addition, subtraction, the transmission of the stored number word, and for programming. Hence, an accumulator had all the elements for performing storage, arithmetic, and control. On signal, an accumulator could listen for an incoming number word, transmit "additively," or transmit "subtractively," and initiate the next step in the computation. Approximately 200 $\mu$sec were required for receiving or transmitting, of which 100 $\mu$sec were allowed for the data transmission or reception and somewhat less than 100 $\mu$sec allowed for carry propagation.

The method by which carries were handled is illustrated functionally in Fig. 1.1 for the three least significant stages. The dotted square represents

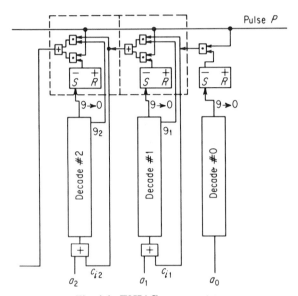

**Fig. 1.1.** ENIAC carry system.

a gate for positive signals and the square with the plus sign a buffer for positive signals. $S$ and $R$ are the set and reset inputs respectively of the flip-flops whose outputs are shown in the reset state. The signals $9_1$, $9_2$, etc., are present when the appropriate ring counter is on stage 9. The signal $9 \longrightarrow 0$ appears when the appropriate ring counter goes from stage 9 to stage 0, thus indicating a carry. The inputs to the decades are $a_0$, $a_1$, etc., corresponding to the digits of the incoming number word in order of increasing significance starting with the least significant digit. The carry network for the first stages differs from that for the other stages, two of which are shown in the dotted boxes. The carry out of a digit is stored in a flip-flop. The pulse $P$ would be passed by the energized gate to increment the next more significant digit by unity; if the next digit is 9, however, a carry is propagated to the succeeding digit by the gate activated by the "9" signal. The arrangement of Fig. 1.1 is capable of accumulating algebraic sums of either positive or negative numbers.

Because the decade counters could not be cycled in reverse, the contents of an accumulator were read out as follows:

Each decade ring counter was simultaneously cycled by the application of ten pulses to its input with carry circuits disabled. The output of flip-flops, triggered by the $9 \longrightarrow 0$ transition, would then gate the appropriate number of pulses to an output bus. By using the appropriate side of those flip-flops either the stored number or its 9's complement could be transmitted. The complement representation of correction to 10 was made by transmitting a correction pulse with the least significant digit. In this way an accumulator could transmit additively or subtractively.

In order to illustrate, by example, what has been said, suppose that $+237$ in one accumulator is to be subtracted from $+468$ held in a second accumulator. In order to do this "237" must be transmitted "subtractively," because the decade ring counters can work only in one direction; therefore, its complementary pulses, 1, 7, 6, 3, are transmitted on the four wires, and when added to 468, the results are 231. (This is very similar to the method of subtraction used on the abacus.) This fact can easily be verified by adding with the carry circuits the received pulses to the stored number, thus treating the sign as being stored in a two-stage ring counter (binary counter).

We have here an example of one of the ways in which logical and electrical design may interact. That is, 10's-complement representation was used instead of having the counters step backwards. As the reader continues through this book he will see more examples of this interaction and its relation with mechanical design. Furthermore, he will see that there may be several ways to produce a working computer, and that the choice among alternatives can be made by picking the one that maximizes some suitably chosen figure of merit.

When an accumulator transmitted, the information was carried on busses arranged in trays (digit trays) which could be physically placed so as to meet the needs of the problem. By patch cables, an accumulator or any other unit could be connected to receive from any digit tray. Thus, it was possible to perform more than one addition or subtraction in one add time (parallel programming).

Programmed transmission and reception was accomplished by routing control pulses to and from the various units by means of patch cords and program trays, as required by the problem. To illustrate this point further, if an accumulator received a program pulse on one of several inputs, it would listen on a specified one of several digit trays for an add time, and then the accumulator would emit a program pulse on an output that corresponded to the program pulse input. In order to solve a problem with this set-up the programmer would have to schedule the individual program steps in a sequential-parallel arrangement that would be commensurate with the limited storage capacity of the machine. He also would have to designate how the digit and program pulses were to be transmitted, and then specify the setting of each and every one of thousands of switches. Finally, in order to run the problem, all the specified connections and switch-settings would have to be made. In order to reduce this set-up time, John von Neumann urged that all the machine units be connected via digit and program trays, and switch settings be made so that the machine could be used as a computer of the Babbage type (provisions for this mode of operation had been made in its design). This was done and the ENIAC was operated in this fashion until it was retired.

Other units that originated with the ENIAC included a high-speed multiplier, three function tables, a divider square-rooter, a card reader, a card punch, and a master programmer. The multiplier sequenced several accumulators to perform multiplication by means of the accumulating of the left and right partial products. These products resulted from parallel multiplication of the other operand by the digits of the multiplier taken sequentially. The partial product generation was done by resistor logic networks (multiplication table). Multiplication took 14 add times.

The function tables were read-only memories in which the data contents were set up on switches occupying large panels mounted on casters. These were originally designed to hold the drag function; hence, automatic read-out of adjacent argument values was provided to simplify interpolation.

The divider square-rooter was simple in principle, in view of the fact that it sequenced several accumulators to perform division by successive additions and subtractions. (See decimal nonrestoring division algorithm in Ref. 4.)

The card reader and card punch were IBM units modified to connect onto the electronic circuits of ENIAC. The reader transmitted in a fashion similar to an accumulator (digit tray) while the card punch was limited to punching out, on command of a program pulse, the contents of eight preselected accumulators.

Loop control was achieved via the master programmer which contained several ring counters, the lengths and internal connections of which were under switch control. Thus a counter could be connected so that it could count the number of program pulses appearing on a specified program line. A given loop would then be iterated until a preset number of program pulses occurred on that line, at which time the next incoming program pulse would be shunted over to another line that provided the exit from the loop. The master programmer could also be used to direct the selection of programs in other ways besides that described.

The ENIAC contained nothing that resembled a console since the controls were distributed over the front of the entire machine. Each flip-flop and counter had a neon indicator on each stage so that the contents of every storage element could be monitored when the machine was operated one program step at a time.

Moving on from this description of the first high-speed electronic computer, a more detailed understanding of computer development and design can be gained in a discussion of the EDVAC, which altered and employed some of the features of the ENIAC.

## 1.2  THE EDVAC

While the ENIAC was being constructed at The Moore School of Electrical Engineering, the designers found some time for sundry activities including an inquiry into the design of improved computing machinery. These inquiries led to the development of EDVAC (Electronic Discrete Variable Computer) which, with one major exception, followed the "classical" pattern set by Babbage's analytical engine and by the Mark I calculator. The general basic organization can be illustrated by Fig. 1.2.

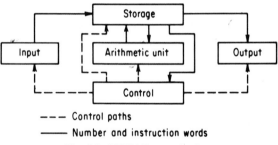

--- Control paths
—— Number and instruction words

**Fig. 1.2.** EDVAC organization.

As was conventional in this "classical" organization, the control sequenced the rest of the system as a result of the decoding of the instructions. However, instead of being obtained from an instruction tape, as proposed by Babbage and as used in the Mark I, instructions were obtained from the memory (storage) unit. In this way it became possible to modify the instructions in the arithmetic unit. This idea, called *common storage* of instructions and of data, was evolved at a round-table discussion with the designers. Because of this it is difficult to assign credit for the origination of common storage to any one man, although John von Neumann, who attended the discussions, has been acknowledged. The ability to modify instructions was necessary at that time in order to achieve loop control; however, it is now known that such techniques as indirect addressing can be used to accomplish the same end result.

The memory of the EDVAC consisted of 128 mercury acoustic delay lines. One is schematically shown in Fig. 1.3. An electrical input caused an acoustic compression wave to propagate the length of the delay line where it was detected by a piezoelectric crystal. After amplification and reshaping,

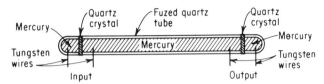

**Fig. 1.3.** EDVAC mercury acoustic delay line.

the pulses could be reapplied at the input and caused to recirculate indefinitely. The pulse rate was 1 mcps and the delay was 384 $\mu$sec so that eight words of 44 bits each could be stored, with each word separated by a 4-$\mu$sec switching blank. The word format is shown in Fig. 1.4.

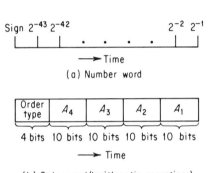

(a) Number word

(b) Order word (larithmetic operations)

**Fig. 1.4.** EDVAC word format.

As can be seen from Fig. 1.4, the EDVAC was a serial machine. Numbers were represented as signed magnitudes (binary fractions). The sign came first in time so that the arithmetic unit could be set up for addition or subtraction of magnitudes, depending on the sign of the operands—if, for example, an addition operation was ordered. (The least significant bits also came first in time since carries in addition had to propagate from the least to the most significant bits.)

In arithmetic operations, $A_1$ and $A_2$ gave the memory location of the two operands, $A_3$ gave the destination of the result, and $A_4$ gave the location of the next instruction (three plus one address code). No particular advantage accrued from placing $A_1$ first in time, since the memory could not be accessed for the first operand until the instruction had left it completely. Hence, the sequence of addresses in the order word was determined by that sequence which optimized the design of the precessing delay loop, which stored the instruction while it was being decoded.

Two separate arithmetic units performing simultaneously compared operations were used. Additional checking consisted in testing for unused order types, pulses in the switching blank, and overflow in addition, subtraction, and division.

The circuits of ENIAC were directly descended from radar technology. Vacuum tubes were used throughout for amplification and logic with the exception of the multiplication table in the high-speed multiplier, wherein resistor logic was used. The circuits of EDVAC were designed shortly after germanium semiconductor diodes became available. (The EDVAC diode buffer and gate circuits are shown in Fig. 1.5.) Normally ON 6AG7 vacuum tubes were also used to invert pulses. Other circuits used were flip-flops, transformer-coupled amplifiers, and pulse-forming blocking oscillators.

A considerable amount of effort went into the determination of design tolerances for the vacuum tubes used, but a negligible amount of effort was expended in the determination and use of the design tolerances of resistors, diodes, and other components. The result was that the margins for vacuum-tube parameter variation and degradation were not sufficient to compensate for the neglect of adequate consideration of the effect of variation of the other components. However, when the EDVAC was installed at the Aberdeen Proving Ground, an air conditioner and a line voltage regulator were provided which helped greatly to improve the reliability of the machine.

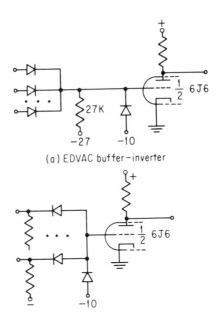

(a) EDVAC buffer–inverter

(b) EDVAC gate–inverter

Fig. 1.5.

## REFERENCES

1. Morrison, Philip and Emily, *Charles Babbage and His Calculating Engines, Selected Writings by Charles Babbage and Others* (New York: Dover Publications, Inc., 1961).

2. Babbage, H. P., *Babbage's Calculating Engines* (London: E. and F. N. Spon, 1889).

3. Montgomerie, G. A., *Digital Calculating Machines* (London: Blackie and Son, Ltd., 1956). This book is primarily concerned with desk calculators and business machines.

4. Richards, R. K., *Arithmetic Operations in Digital Computers* (Princeton, N.J.: D. Van Nostrand Co., 1955).

5. Mark I: *A Manual of Operations for the Automatic Sequence Controlled Calculator*, vol. I of the Annals of the Computation Laboratory of Harvard University.

6. ENIAC: Burks, A. W., "Electronic Computing Circuits of ENIAC," *Proceedings of the I.R.E.*, **35** (August 1947), 756–767.

7. ERA Staff, *High Speed Computing Devices* (New York: McGraw-Hill Book Co., 1950).

8. EDVAC: Gluck, S. E., "The Electronic Discrete Variable Computer," *Electrical Engineering*, **72** (February 1953), 159–162.

9. SEAC: "Computer Development (SEAC and DYSEAC) at the National Bureau of Standards, Washington, D.C.," National Bureau of Standards Circular 551, U.S. Government Printing Office.

## PROBLEMS

*These problems require the use of the references.*

1. The ENIAC add operation utilizes 20 decade counters to add two 10-digit decimal numbers.
   (a) Considering that the first number is stored in decade counters 0–9 and the second in counters 10–19, describe this add operation for the positive numbers 0000000036 and 0000000047.
   (b) Is this add operation serial, parallel, or mixed?

2. (a) How does the programming philosophy of ENIAC differ from that of EDVAC?
   (b) After ENIAC went operational, its logic was modified by the addition of a converter. How did this modification affect the programming of the computer?

3. Name the types of storage utilized in ENIAC.

4. What error-detecting system was incorporated into EDVAC? What other computer(s) utilize(s) this system?

# 2

# ORGANIZATIONAL PRINCIPLES

# OF COMPUTER DESIGN

The purpose of this chapter is to discuss some of the principles which must be taken into account in the development of a computing system. Here, as well as in the other chapters, the reader will notice the constant mention of cost factors.

Generally, in order to meet the purchaser's requirements, as well as to make the system competitive with others on the market and to assure a future market, there are specifications on system performance that have to be met. These specifications must be considered in the light of minimum cost to the manufacturer of the system and of the least possible cost for the purchaser's requirements. These considerations will be discussed later.

## 2.1 INTERACTION OF LOGICAL, MECHANICAL, AND ELECTRICAL DESIGN

Three aspects of the development of a computing system are those of logical, mechanical, and electrical design. By *logical design* we mean the steps that must be taken in order to proceed from a statement of the problems to be solved by the computer to the logical solution of these problems—by way of (1) design programming for determination of instruction requirements, (2) a consideration of the computer composition in terms of the number and types of major units, (3) a decision about the kind of information and its mode of processing, and the means of representing the information in the computer. We also include under logical design the steps that are involved under the alternate definition of the term (i.e., the detailed design of the major computer units using logical elements such as gates, buffers, etc.), such as the choice of arithmetic algorithms, the methods by which they are mechanized, and the like. By *electrical design* we mean the choice and testing of circuits, component evaluation, reliability considerations, packaging techniques, signal and power transmission systems, power supplies and control, and the electrical aspects of the framework. By *mechanical design* we mean primarily the design of packages, framework, and cooling systems.

There is an interaction between these three aspects of design. Not one can proceed independently of the others without a serious danger that the completed system will not function or at least will not meet specifications. We will proceed to indicate some of the interactions that exist.

As we have said, there is a specification on system performance that has to be met in order to meet the purchaser's requirements or to compete with other systems soon to be marketed, and these requirements often must be met at minimum cost. The state of the art indicates what units can be made, what performance improved units can have, and what their cost will be. This is one place where electrical design influences logical design. More obvious is the influence of the type of logical elements upon the cost and performance of the system; the logical designer has to keep abreast of what the technology has to offer in order that he may propose units that yield systems having maximum efficiency. (We may define efficiency as the ratio of the amount of computing done to dollar cost.) The techniques used to develop an optimum system usually involve the paper study of various alternate systems with an evaluation of their relative efficiencies.

It should be obvious that logical design affects electrical design. The specific interactions, however, need to be delineated. When the detailed design is undertaken, the logical designer needs to know the electrical characteristics of the logical elements. This includes timing, the number of places an element can drive, the number of permissible inputs, special restrictions placed because of wire lengths, etc. An important interaction that has often been overlooked is that there are optimum numbers of circuit types, permissible inputs, and drives that, in a given logical system, yield the optimum performance. A technique that has been useful is to list numerous alternatives and then to evaluate a sufficient number of them to arrive at an attractive solution. (Several methods of statistics may be of assistance here—for example, the use of Latin Squares in the design of tests.)*

Signals are voltages or currents whose variation with time can be found in principle by solving Maxwell's equations with appropriate boundary conditions.† These boundaries are determined by the mechanical structures including the size and shape of the packages containing the components, the type and configuration of the package wiring, the mounting of the packages in the framework, the geometry and conductivity of the framework itself, the signal transmission paths, and the power distribution lines. These structures affect the rise times, delays, and mutual interaction of signals propagated throughout the system. (An interaction often erroneously neglected is the mutual coupling interaction between signal and power distribution lines.) Because of this, the mechanical and electrical designs cannot proceed independently if the system is to work. The complicated geometries make the calculation of electrical interactions difficult, so that recourse must often be had to carefully controlled experiments performed on faithful replicas of the mechanical structure in the light of a good understanding of the phenomena involved. Mechanical design features also affect construction and maintenance in that connectors must be accessible and test points must be available.

Mechanical, electrical and logical design interact in that an optimum system cannot be constructed if computer subunits are placed without regard for the existing electrical problems. A certain logical function may be impossible to realize if improper placement of subunits causes excessive signal propagation delays or crosstalk.

## 2.2  FUNCTIONS OF BASIC BLOCKS

The basic units of a computing system are shown in Fig. 2.1. Control and/or data lines may pass between any or all of the units. It is helpful at this point to review the functions of each of the basic units.

The storage unit, which may be made up of various types of storage devices, can store instructions or data, or both. The data may consist of numeric, alphabetic, or alphanumeric information organized into instruction and data words. Access to any word can be achieved by supplying an address to the storage unit. This assumes that each item of information occupies an uniquely identifiable location. It is also possible to organize the

---

* See D. J. Finney, *Experimental Design and Its Statistical Basis* (Chicago: University of Chicago Press, 1955).

† For a derivation of the circuit equations as approximations from Maxwell's equations, see S. Ramo and J. R. Whinnery, *Fields and Waves in Modern Radio* (2nd ed. New York: John Wiley & Sons, 1953), chap. 5.

storage of the information so that it is accessible on the basis of content rather than location if the description is coded and stored with the word when it is put into the storage unit. This can be done by programming in an addressable storage unit or by incorporating logic with storage as in an "associative memory."

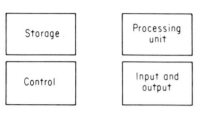

Fig. 2.1.  Basic blocks.

The processing unit may operate on data and/or instruction words when so ordered by the control. These operations may include certain arithmetic operations such as add and subtract, logical operations such as described by Boolean equations, and the rearrangement of the elements making up the word. The input unit, together with the output unit, may operate as part of the storage unit, or may read information from another medium or from some real-time communication link. This information may be temporarily stored in the input and output unit or may be rearranged there for insertion into the storage unit. The output unit may write information onto another medium or transmit to a real-time communication link, either rearranged or not. The operation of these units is directed by the control, which acts according to the instructions it receives. These instructions may come directly from the storage unit, the processing unit, an operator's console, or from the input unit.

## 2.3  CODES AND THE REPRESENTATION OF INFORMATION

We continue with a review of the system principles. Information that has to be represented in a computer consists of strings of symbols. These symbols may be numeric (numerals), alphabetic (letters, signs), or alphanumeric (both numeric and alphabetic). A symbol may be represented by a group of code elements called a *character*. For instance, the symbol 9, if it is numeric, may be represented by the character 1001, the four digits being the elements of the 8421 code discussed briefly in this chapter. A code element may be a binary digit (bit), but this is not necessary since ternary, etc., code elements are possible; however, a bit is a useful representation since it can be represented by the presence or absence of a pulse, by two distinct voltage levels, etc. The smallest string of symbols that has a specific meaning is called a *word*. As far as this system is concerned, words may be represented in serial form, as in EDVAC where all the bits of a word progress in time along a wire, or in parallel form, as in LARC where each bit has a wire of its own. Intermediate or series-parallel representations are possible, such as in ENIAC where the bits of a character appeared in serial form with the characters in parallel, or with the characters in series.

Codes for numeric information may be weighted or nonweighted. An example of a weighted code is the 8421 code for the decimal digits shown in Fig. 2.2. For the bits in a column, the weights are given at the top of the columns in Fig. 2.1.

| DIGIT | WEIGHTS<br>8421 |
|-------|---------|
| 0 | 0000 |
| 1 | 0001 |
| 2 | 0010 |
| 3 | 0011 |
| 4 | 0100 |
| 5 | 0101 |
| 6 | 0110 |
| 7 | 0111 |
| 8 | 1000 |
| 9 | 1001 |

Fig. 2.2. 8421 code.

Another useful weighted code is the biquinary code, given in Fig. 2.3.

| DIGIT | WEIGHTS<br>5043210 |
|-------|---------|
| 0 | 0100001 |
| 1 | 0100010 |
| 2 | 0100100 |
| 3 | 0101000 |
| 4 | 0110000 |
| 5 | 1000001 |
| 6 | 1000010 |
| 7 | 1000100 |
| 8 | 1001000 |
| 9 | 1010000 |

Fig. 2.3. A biquinary code.

This code is a checking code because each correct character can contain only two nonzero bits. Countless other weighted codes can be constructed, some having special properties that are useful in particular systems.

The unique assignment of groups of bits to characters, without regard to weights, yields nonweighted codes. An example of a nonweighted code is given in Fig. 2.4.

Another nonweighted code, the excess-three code, is shown in Fig. 2.5. It has, among others, the property that the carry out resulting from the addition of two code groups is the same as for the addition of the corresponding decimal digits.

Many other examples of codes may be found in the references. The choice of the proper code, or codes, for a system is a problem in optimization in

DIGIT

| 0 | 0001 |
|---|------|
| 1 | 0010 |
| 2 | 0100 |
| 3 | 1000 |
| 4 | 1001 |
| 5 | 1010 |
| 6 | 1100 |
| 7 | 1101 |
| 8 | 1110 |
| 9 | 0111 |

**Fig. 2.4.** A nonweighted code.

that the specified requirements must be met, while we must maximize at the same time some measure of efficiency.

One question that frequently arises is: what is the machine code when the memory code, the arithmetic code, the input-output code, etc., all differ? With use of Fig. 2.6 this question may be answered.

DIGIT

| 0 | 0011 |
|---|------|
| 1 | 0100 |
| 2 | 0101 |
| 3 | 0110 |
| 4 | 0111 |
| 5 | 1000 |
| 6 | 1001 |
| 7 | 1010 |
| 8 | 1011 |
| 9 | 1100 |

**Fig. 2.5.** Excess-three code.

As illustrated, there are three units in the computer with all possible information paths. However, there is no fundamental difficulty if, in a given system, all possible paths do not exist. With Fig. 2.6 we have also illustrated, for the sake of simplicity, all of the symbols that are handled by the system in giving the symbols handled by each unit. We are thus assuming that Unit 1 uses only the digits, 0–9; Unit 2 handles digits, the alphabetic symbols, A–Z, as well as special symbols involved in its internal control; Unit 3 uses only the alphabet.

Thus far there is no outstanding problem, if the units use the same code in transmitting symbols; but we will assume, as illustrated, that each unit has its own code. In short, the code in Unit 1 differs from that in Unit 2, and the code of Unit 3 differs from the other two codes. In order to transmit a digit from Unit 1 to Unit 2 it is necessary to translate from the code of Unit 1 to the code of Unit 2 for the transmitted digit. This function is provided by the code translator, TR 1-2. Similarly, Unit 2 can transmit a digit to Unit 1, or an alphabetic symbol to Unit 3, if the proper code translator, TR 2-1, or TR 2-3 in the alternative case, is interposed.

It is quite obvious that difficulty would arise if Unit 2 transmitted an alphabetic symbol to Unit 1 which handles only numeric symbols. However, this difficulty is resolved if TR 2-1 is equipped with a device (recognizer)

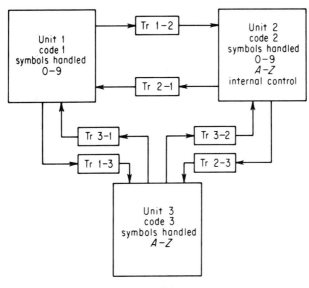

Fig. 2.6.

which would block TR 2-1 in such an event. The recognizer can be designed also to signal the control to execute some predetermined operation, such as the setting of an error alarm when it recognizes an unacceptable character. It is seen, then, that the description of a machine code consists of:

(a) the set of symbols used in each unit and the unique code for each unit (*unique* means that no two symbols used in a unit have the same representation);
(b) the rules for translation of characters to be transmitted between units that use them in common;
(c) the rules giving the control actions to be taken when the attempt is made to transmit characters to a unit that does not use them.

## 2.4 CHECKING

There are essentially two types of errors that can be detected by checking systems:

1. programming and human errors of a detectable nature, and
2. equipment malfunctions.

With regard to the first category, examples are the addressing of a nonexistent memory location, the calling for the execution of an unused order type, and the attempted activation of a nonexistent input-output unit. (It is clearly impossible to detect those program errors which could be parts of a valid program.) Since the detection of such errors can be done either by the use of built-in checking equipment or by the use of error-detecting programs, the question arises as to which way is most efficient.

In the past, most designers of computers, having the "classical" organization, have either discovered or assume that it was more efficient to build into the equipment circuits for detecting human and programming errors of the kind that we have mentioned. These detection circuits are usually rather simple since they have only to recognize the existence of certain pulse patterns for which they produce an output. Generally, it is advisable that the output of the program error-detection circuits signal either the control or the program, and if a halt is commanded that the machine halt with the information essentially undisturbed. The latter is desirable if the operator or programmer is to be allowed to diagnose the difficulty.

It may be difficult to achieve what would be an ideal machine operation, so that the compromise chosen between cost of required equipment and the achievement of the ideal of operation should be based on maximizing some suitably selected figure of merit, such as efficiency.

What is meant here by "ideal operation" is best explained by two examples. The first is that it was originally planned that the operator of EDVAC could cause the entire contents of the mercury acoustic delay line storage system to be read out automatically, onto the output medium, merely by pressing a button on the control panel. It was also intended that the address of the next instruction to be executed be placed in a nonerase-able store. After this entire process was completed, the power was to be automatically turned off. The reason given for incorporating this mode of operation in the design was that it provided a quick way of saving the contents of the storage system at the end of a day's work or when it would be expected that information would be lost in the near future because of overheating and the like. At that time the equivalence of programming and logical design had not been enunciated nor understood as a fundamental principle; hence, the designers of EDVAC attempted to perform the readout function using wired-in logic. It became apparent rather quickly that much about the state of the entire machine, at the time that computations halted in order to begin readout, had to be stored also. (The state of the machine consisted of the states of control flip-flops, alarm flip-flops, etc.) Thus it became clear that the cost of mechanization of the automatic readout process far outweighed any savings to be achieved by retaining it. In this case the figure of merit chosen in principle was that of cost (equipment cost plus operating cost).*

The second example has to do with a certain military computer wherein it was desired to safeguard the contents of the storage unit (magnetic core) if the power-supply voltages showed evidence of becoming out of tolerance. In the specific application, loss of information could be a very expensive matter from the viewpoint of national security. Also, in the event of power failure, there would have been insufficient time to carry out the preservation of the state of the machine by programming. In this case the problem was successfully solved by logical design.

In some cases, the general approach to system design is to allow the programmer and operator freedom as long as it might possibly be of use. If the programming and operating features are chosen to allow maximum flexibility to provide for problems having unknown requirements, a very rich order code will result. While such a code increases flexibility it also increases the chances of undetected program and human errors occurring. Some designers may wish to accept the increased chance of error as the price of such flexibility; others may wish to make programming studies so that the order code selected will maximize efficiency.

With regard to the second category (equipment failures) two questions to be answered often are:

(a) Should checking equipment be built-in or should checking be performed by program?

(b) To what extent should checking be performed?

The answer to the first question can be obtained, in principle, by determining the arrangement that yields maximum efficiency. In a machine, such as LARC, that has incorporated thorough built-in checking, the additional equipment required amounted to about 20 per cent of the logic circuits; since the logic circuits may account for the order of 20 per cent of the cost of the machine, the increased cost of equipment for built-in checking is small compared to the cost of the time that could be lost if undetected errors occurred. The cost of equipment for built-in checking should also be compared to the cost of incorporating checking through

---

* To a first approximation, maximizing efficiency minimizes total cost. To show this let $C_E$ be the cost of the equipment and $C_O$ be the unit operating cost. Let $E$ stand for efficiency (p. 29). Under the assumption that $C_O$ is proportional to the time taken to solve problems, $E = k/C_O C_E$. Since total cost, $C_T$, is $C_T = C_E + C_O$, then

$$C_T = C_E + \frac{k/E}{C_E}$$

which has a minimum at $C_E = \sqrt{k/E} = C_O$. Hence, maximization of efficiency minimizes total cost.

programming; the cost of programming such checks may not be in-considerable.

The extent to which checking need be performed can be determined by comparing the reliability of the equipment with the system specifications. For example, magnetic tape reading errors can consist of single errors occurring at a certain rate and double errors occurring much less frequently, etc. Let us assume that the specification for a part of a system states that the permissible error rate is an average of one detected error in 24 hours and one undetected (by the checking system) error in 168 hours. Let us assume also that single errors occur on the average of once every four hours and that other types of errors occur on the average of once every two weeks (336 hours). To meet the specifications the checking system would have to *detect* and *correct* all single errors but it need not detect the other kinds of errors. If single errors occurred less often than once in 24 hours, the checking system need only *detect* single errors in order to meet this specification with the error rate given above for other types of errors. If all types of errors occurred less often than once in 168 hours, no checking system would be needed.

Marginal checking provides a means by which the error rate may be reduced during operation for some types of equipment. It is useful when the error rate is a function of some controllable quantity that can be changed from the nominal value without damaging the components. Such a quantity might be the clock rate, or one or more power-supply voltages. The setting up of a marginal checking system requires that experiments be performed on the circuits to determine

    (a) what quantities, such as voltages, can be varied to cause a circuit to fail temporarily, if the components in a circuit have drifted out of tolerance, and

    (b) whether these quantities can be changed through a useful range without damaging the components.

In addition, the consequences of varying voltages, etc., in the system have to be determined:

    (a) Are there any circuits that will be damaged by varying a given voltage?

    (b) What margins should be expected and are obtained upon carrying out the marginal checking procedure? This aspect of the design of a marginal checking procedure establishes standard margins and is also an aid in debugging.

A marginal check is usually performed periodically on a system by varying the voltages, etc., on the system or part of it while it is being exercised by diagnostic routines until errors occur. The error-free margins are then recorded and compared to previously obtained results. If an appreciable deterioration of the margins has occurred since the last marginal check, the defective circuits are hunted down and replaced. Production of problem solutions can then be resumed with less chance of errors occurring than if marginal checking was not performed.

Clearly, marginal checking cannot reduce the number of bit pick-ups or drop-outs on magnetic tape due to dust, for example, but it is of help wherever electronic circuits are used such as in arithmetic units. Built-in checking equipment helps to simplify the task of locating the source of errors.

If the decision has been made to incorporate built-in checking equipment into a system, there still remain the questions of what units should be checked, what checking methods are possible, and how these methods can be applied.

The six categories of units that exist in computing system are storage, processing unit (arithmetic, etc.), input, output, control, and the information transfer units.

Although information transfers occur inside the five units listed above, the ones we have in mind as occurring in the information transfer units are those previously discussed that occur between the other five types of units and also between separate computing systems. If the units are close together, the checking of information transfers is simple because the chance of error in transmission is very small. However, if the units are quite far apart, elaborate checking methods may be required because of the increased chance of error—for example, where the digital information is sent over a radio communication link.

Several methods can be used for checking. In principle, they all involve "redundancy," in that more bits are used than are required for the encoding of the information to be transmitted. We can adapt any of the checking methods used in programming because of the principle of equivalence of programming and logical design. This principle states that any process that can be programmed for a digital computer can be built into the equipment if it is so desired. Hence, we need not consider questions of how the various methods of checking can be mechanized in detail, and we can postpone these considerations until later.

The information to which we wish to apply checking exists in the form of words composed of characters. Each character is made up of one or more bits. Thus, a word may be considered as a string of bits; i.e., a binary word may be regarded as a single character, as several characters containing, for example, three bits in a character, or as a word consisting of as many characters as there are bits. It is not necessary that each character have the same number of bits, nor that the code used for checking be the same code in which the information is represented. However, care must be taken in this latter respect when the unit being checked alters the information, as is done by the processing and control units.

### 2.4.1  Parity Checking

If the word is considered to be a single character, it is possible to detect single errors (and also triple, quintuple, etc. errors) by use of a parity check.

At this point we should make a distinction between "errors" and "failures." We will agree that the type of change shown in Fig. 2.7 (i.e., where a bit changes) is a single error. However, a failure is something that happens in a physical system that results in errors being produced. In the design of a built-in checking system we may want to detect the most frequent *failures* rather than the most frequent errors. To see whether or not a given checking system will detect these failures, the logical designer has to perform "thought" experiments; i.e., he assumes a component has failed and runs an experiment on paper to see if the checking equipment he has designed will detect the failure. Such experiments are at first difficult to perform, but with practice, a good logical designer can perform them easily and rapidly and can even generalize to such an extent that he can bypass the detailed steps in such an experiment. The parity checking code of Fig. 2.7 has been deliberately designed to detect some of the single *failures* that can occur in a random-access core memory, including

1. Incorrect readout of a single bit.
2. Readout of all "zeroes."
3. Readout of all "ones."

The code of Fig. 2.7 detects, of course, the first kind of failure. The second kind of failure is detected "for free" by using odd parity, and the third kind is detected by using odd parity over an even number of bits, as in Fig. 2.7. Consider the word in Fig. 2.7. An extra bit, the parity bit

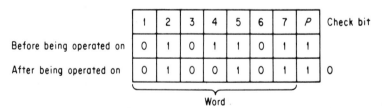

Fig. 2.7. Example of use of odd parity over an even number of bits.

(P), is included with the word to be operated on. This operation could be the storage and, later, retrieval of the word, the reading of the word from magnetic tape and its conversion into electrical signals, etc. The parity bit is so chosen in Fig. 2.7 so that the total number of 1's in the word, including the parity bit, is odd. Also, the total number of bits in the word including the parity bit is even. This is called "odd parity over an even number of bits." If an error is made in column 4, as indicated in Fig. 2.7 by the "1" in column 4 changing to a zero, the second line is obtained. Then if a check bit is computed on the second line in the same way as the parity bit was computed on the first line, it is found that the check bit does not agree with the parity bit, indicating that an error was made in the operation. The parity checking system could be mechanized as indicated in Fig. 2.8. Note the resemblance of Fig. 2.8 to a programming flow chart.

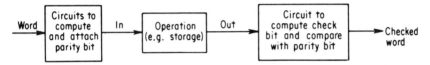

**Fig. 2.8.** Example of a parity checking system.

The difference is that in a block diagram such as in Fig. 2.8, the connecting lines carry information (control or data), while in a programming flow chart the connecting lines show the sequence of the operations or commands. (Programming theoreticians say that a logical drawing is in a "descriptive" language while a flow chart is in a "command" language.)

The block diagram for a parity checking system applied to addition is shown in Fig. 2.9. This system is logically workable. However, it may be less efficient than other methods of checking arithmetic operations.

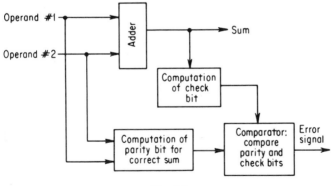

**Fig. 2.9.**

It is possible to alter the parity checking scheme to not only detect but also correct single errors. This is the method of longitudinal and transverse parity checking. For example, consider the even number of characters shown in Fig. 2.10. Let parity bits be computed on both rows and columns. When the check bits are computed and compared with the parity bits, a single error, such as one at the intersection of row 3 and column 4, will result in disagreement between check bits and parity bits in row 3 and column 4. The error then is located at the intersection of row 3 and column 4 and can be corrected.

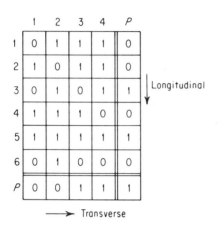

Fig. 2.10. Longitudinal and transverse parity.

If the binary word is considered to consist of as many characters as bits, then each character is a binary character. Two levels on one line serve to transmit a binary character. For checking purposes we may add not less than one more line per binary character to obtain the two-line system first suggested by John von Neumann. Since there are four possible combinations in such a system as shown in Fig. 2.11 $(a_0, a_1)$, we may have six different types of codes, two of which are shown in Figs. 2.11(a) and (b). Figure 2.11(a) may be recognized as equivalent to double transmission. If the information is doubly transmitted in parallel, twice as much equipment is required as for single transmission. If the information is transmitted in serial form, then twice the time is required as compared to single transmission.

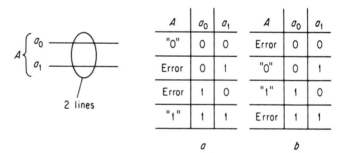

Fig. 2.11. Two-line systems.

Two principles are illustrated here. One is that time and equipment may be interchanged without changing the performance of the system. In other words, in many cases speed may be doubled by doubling the equipment. If we were to construct a figure of merit for a computing system based on efficiency $E$ as being proportional to the amount of equipment required, and if the amount of computation is assumed to be inversely proportional to time required for some typical operation, then

$$E = \frac{1}{(\text{amount of equipment})(\text{time required})}$$

The other principle illustrated is that checking systems require redundancy in the representation of information; if there is no redundancy, there can be no checking.

Figure 2.11(b) may be recognized as equivalent to a parity check on a single bit. It provides the same failure-detection properties as does the odd parity check over an even number of bits.

## 2.4.2 Error-detecting Codes

If the binary word is regarded as a single character, we may use a congruence check to some modulus (discussed below) or we may use an error-detecting code. We may also use an error-detecting code if the word is considered as a group of characters consisting of several bits per character. Methods of checking involving checking codes are applicable to arithmetic operations also, in addition to the checking of storage, etc. However, it is usually necessary to check in the same code as that in which the arithmetic is performed.

A checking code (the biquinary code) previously given as an example is useful in decimal machines. If, for example, the bits in a binary word are taken three at a time, the characters may be assigned the symbols 0, 1, 2, 3, 4, 5, 6, and 7; a code, such as a biquaternary code, could then be constructed so that one could use it as a checking code in a binary machine for checking arithmetic operations or, in general, for checking other operations in a binary or nonbinary machine.

Such a code might require six lines per character and the combination could be:

|   | B | Q |
|---|---|---|
| 0 | 01 | 0001 |
| 1 | 01 | 0010 |
| 2 | 01 | 0100 |
| 3 | 01 | 1000 |
| 4 | 10 | 0001 |
| 5 | 10 | 0010 |
| 6 | 10 | 0100 |
| 7 | 10 | 1000 |

Detection of single errors is possible because only one bit is permissible in each of the parts $B$ and $Q$ (2 out of 6 code). This code would yield a not unreasonably complex adder, but is very uneconomical as far as the memory is concerned. However, translation into and out of this code could be done with little added expense at the input and output of the arithmetic unit. For example, the translation into this code could be accomplished in the first gate-buffer level that performs the digit additions at the input of the adder. The scheme for checking addition could be as in Fig. 2.12. (The memory code is assumed to be straight binary with parity bit. Other codes could be used.)

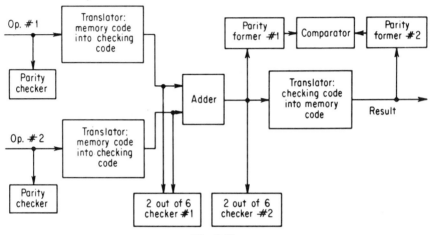

**Fig. 2.12.**

The operands have their parity checked and hence can be assumed to be error-free at the input to the translators. The first 2 out of 6 checker therefore checks the translation. The second 2 out of 6 checker checks the adder. Parity former 1 constructs the proper parity bit from the 2 out of 6 coded result. Parity former 2 constructs the proper parity bit for the result from the translated result. The comparison of these parity bits checks the translation from the 2 out of 6 code to straight binary. For failure detection, it is always necessary that the checking equipment be designed "fail-safe" so that a single failure in it gives a failure alarm also.

### 2.4.3 Congruence Checks

Congruence checks are based on the property that congruences are preserved through combinations of the arithmetic operations of addition, subtraction, and multiplication.

An integer $a$ is said to be congruent to an integer $b$ (modulo $m$) if the difference is evenly divisible by $m$. The notation introduced by Gauss is:

$$a \equiv b \qquad (\text{mod } m)$$

For example,

$$137 \equiv 37 \qquad (\text{mod } 10)$$

because $137 - 37 = 100$ is divisible by 10, leaving no remainder.

If

$$A \equiv a \ (\text{mod } m) \quad \text{and} \quad B \equiv b \ (\text{mod } m)$$

it is easy to prove that

$$A + B \equiv a + b \qquad (\text{mod } m) \qquad (2.1)$$
$$A - B \equiv a - b \qquad (\text{mod } m) \qquad (2.2)$$
$$AB \equiv ab \qquad (\text{mod } m) \qquad (2.3)$$

Consider, for example, Eq. (2.1). The addition modulo $m$

$$A \equiv a \ (\text{mod } m) \quad \text{and} \quad B \equiv b \ (\text{mod } m)$$

may be expressed

$$A = a + mr_1, \qquad B = b + mr_2$$

where $r_1$ and $r_2$ are any positive or negative integers. Thus

$$A + B = a + b + m(r_1 + r_2)$$

Letting $r_1 + r_2 = r$ we have

$$(A + B) = (a + b) + mr$$

which is just

$$A + B \equiv a + b \qquad (\text{mod } m)$$

Then $A + B \equiv a + b \ (\text{mod } m)$.

Equations (2.2) and (2.3) can be similarly proven.

In the case of division, we have

$$A = BQ + R$$

where $B$ is the divisor, $A$ is the dividend, $Q$ is the quotient, and $R$ is the remainder. Hence if

$$A \equiv a \qquad (\text{mod } m)$$
$$B \equiv b \qquad (\text{mod } m)$$
$$Q \equiv q \qquad (\text{mod } m)$$
$$R \equiv r \qquad (\text{mod } m)$$

then

$$a \equiv bq + r \qquad (\text{mod } m) \qquad (2.4)$$

Equations (2.1), (2.2), (2.3), and (2.4) provide the basis of congruence checks. For example, in Eq. (2.1) the check sums $a$ and $b$, having far fewer digits in them than do $A$ and $B$, can be added and compared to the check sum for $A + B$. Some examples follow.

*Casting Out Nines.* The checking of arithmetic by "casting out nines" can be explained as follows. A decimal integer can be written

$$N = a_0 + a_1 10^1 + a_2 10^2 + \cdots + a_n 10^n$$

We have

$$1 \equiv 1 \qquad (\text{mod } 9)$$
$$10 \equiv 1 \qquad (\text{mod } 9)$$
$$10^2 \equiv 1 \qquad (\text{mod } 9)$$
$$\cdots$$
$$10^n \equiv 1 \qquad (\text{mod } 9)$$

Therefore

$$N \equiv a_0 + a_1 + a_2 + \cdots + a_n \qquad (\text{mod } 9)$$

As an example of how the check works, consider the addition of 10375 to 93587. Now

$$10375 + 93587 = 103962$$
$$10375 \equiv 16 \equiv 7 \qquad (\text{mod } 9)$$
$$93587 \equiv 32 \equiv 5 \qquad (\text{mod } 9)$$
$$103962 \equiv 21 \equiv 3 \qquad (\text{mod } 9)$$

But $7 + 5 = 12 \equiv 3 \ (\text{mod } 9)$. That is, $7 + 5$ is congruent to the same number as 103962 is congruent to (mod 9).

Assume that an error was made in the addition such that the obtained sum was 103862. Now

$$103862 \equiv 20 \equiv 2 \qquad (\text{mod } 9)$$

which is not equal to the sum of the congruences. Thus, congruence checks can be used to detect arithmetic errors; however, such checks cannot detect all such errors. For example, suppose the sum obtained was 109362 (obtained by interchanging the third and fourth digits). We have $109362 \equiv 21 \equiv 3 \ (\text{mod } 9)$. The congruence check (mod 9) would imply the non-existence of the assumed error.

*Binary Congruence Checking.* A binary word can be written in integral form as follows:

$$N = a_0 + a_1 2^1 + a_2 2^2 + \cdots + a_n 2^n$$

Since the modulus used for the "casting out nines" check was one less than the base of 10, try a modulus of unity. We have

$$1 \equiv 0 \qquad (\text{mod } 1)$$
$$2^1 \equiv 0 \qquad (\text{mod } 1)$$
$$\cdots$$
$$2^n \equiv 0 \qquad (\text{mod } 1)$$

Hence $N \equiv 0 \pmod 1$, providing no means for checking.
$m = 2$:

$$1 \equiv 1 \qquad \pmod 2$$
$$2 \equiv 0 \qquad \pmod 2$$
$$2^2 \equiv 0 \qquad \pmod 2$$
$$\cdots$$
$$2^n \equiv 0 \qquad \pmod 2$$

Hence, $N \equiv a_0 \pmod 2$. This modulus also provides no useful check. However, one finds that useful checks can be obtained if the modulus is relatively prime to the base of 2. (Any odd number is relatively prime to 2.)
$m = 3$:

$$1 \equiv 1 \qquad \pmod 3$$
$$2 \equiv 2 \qquad \pmod 3$$
$$2^2 \equiv 1 \qquad \pmod 3$$
$$\cdots$$

Hence,
$$N \equiv a_0 + 2a_1 + a_2 + 2a_3 + \cdots \qquad \pmod 3$$
Also,
$$N \equiv a_0 - a_1 + a_2 - a_3 + \cdots \qquad \pmod 3$$

These relations can also be used to check arithmetic operations.
$m = 5$:

$$N \equiv a_0 + 2a_1 - a_2 - 2a_3 + a_4 + 2a_5 - \cdots \qquad \pmod 5$$

$m = 7$:

$$N \equiv a_0 + 2a_1 + 4a_2 + a_3 + 2a_4 + 4a_5 + \cdots \qquad \pmod 7$$

One should be aware that a congruence check does not detect all possible errors. More extensive checking is possible by using checks to more than one modulus. The decision on this is determined as before by examining the consequences of such a decision and comparing them to the consequences of alternate decisions.

Congruences have given rise to a novel number system called the *residue number system*. This system is of interest because arithmetic addition, subtraction, and multiplication require essentially the same time. Because of difficulties with division, application has been limited (see Ref. 5).

### 2.4.4 Hamming Codes

Hamming codes, called such after their originator, may be called more generally codes of *specified minimum distance*. These codes attain maximum efficiency in error detection and correction with respect to their inherent amount of redundancy. The minimum distance factor comes about by specifying in advance of the code generation the minimum number of bits which must differ between any two points or characters in the code. This distance concept is illustrated by the ring or modulo 2 addition of two numbers with distance 3:

$$101101 \quad \text{point } n$$
$$110111 \quad \text{point } m$$
$$\overline{011010} = 3 \text{ bits differ}$$

The error detecting and correcting power of these codes may be shown by Table 2.1.

TABLE **2.1.** ERROR DETECTION AND CORRECTION BY CODES

| Minimum distance | Errors detected | Errors corrected | Code |
|---|---|---|---|
| 0 | 0 | 0 | No distinct number representations |
| 1 | 0 | 0 | Distinct number representations |
| 2 | 1 | 0 | Simple parity checks |
| 3 | 1 | 1 | Hamming code |
| 4 | 2 | 1 | Hamming code plus parity |
| 5 | 2 | 2 | Distance 5 code |
| 6 | 3 | 2 | Distance 6 code |
| . . . | . . . | . . . | |

We will consider the simple Hamming code further (minimum distance three, a fact that is verifiable from the resultant code). In this code, sufficient check bits are transmitted with the message. Thus, when a checking number is computed at the receiving end by a procedure to be described, the checking number can be used to identify the bit position in error, and thereby single errors can be corrected.

Let us assume that the message contains $m$ bits. If $k$ check bits are transmitted with the message, then the checking number, which has $k$ bits, must be able to identify $m + k$ positions in addition to indicating the absence of error. This requires that

$$2^k \geq m + k + 1$$

As an example, let us consider the case for which $m = 4$, which requires that $k = 3$. We shall agree that the combinations of the checking number have the meanings given in Table 2.2. Note that if $C_1 = 1$, this means that bit $b_1$, $b_3$, $b_5$, or $b_7$ is in error; that if $C_2 = 1$, bit $b_2$, $b_3$, $b_6$, or $b_7$ is in error;

TABLE 2.2. MEANINGS OF CHECKING-NUMBER COMBINATIONS

| $C_3$ | $C_2$ | $C_1$ | Meaning |
|---|---|---|---|
| 0 | 0 | 0 | No error |
| 0 | 0 | 1 | bit 1 ($b_1$) in error |
| 0 | 1 | 0 | bit 2 ($b_2$) in error |
| 0 | 1 | 1 | bit 3 ($b_3$) in error |
| 1 | 0 | 0 | bit 4 ($b_4$) in error |
| 1 | 0 | 1 | bit 5 ($b_5$) in error |
| 1 | 1 | 0 | bit 6 ($b_6$) in error |
| 1 | 1 | 1 | bit 7 ($b_7$) in error |

and if $C_3 = 1$, then bit $b_4$, $b_5$, $b_6$, or $b_7$ is in error. We will check the accuracy of the transmission of these three groups by incorporating a parity bit in each of these groups of bits. The simplest way of doing this is to make the parity bit the first bit in each group. Then any parity bit will appear in only one of the three groups. For example, let the message be 1011. This becomes

$$b_7 \quad b_6 \quad b_5 \quad b_4 \quad b_3 \quad b_2 \quad b_1$$

$$1 \quad 0 \quad 1 \quad \phantom{0} \quad 1 \quad \phantom{0} \quad \phantom{0}$$

where bits $b_1$, $b_2$, and $b_4$ have been reserved for the parity bits. To make the parity of the group ($b_1$, $b_3$, $b_5$, $b_7$) even requires that $b_1 = 1$. In like manner, computation of the other parity bits yields

$$b_7 \quad b_6 \quad b_5 \quad b_4 \quad b_3 \quad b_2 \quad b_1$$

$$1 \quad 0 \quad 1 \quad 0 \quad 1 \quad 0 \quad 1$$

which is the total message consisting of $m + k$ bits which would be transmitted.

First, assume that it is received unchanged. Computation of the parity of each of the groups of bits ($b_1$, $b_3$, $b_5$, $b_7$), ($b_2$, $b_3$, $b_6$, $b_7$), and ($b_4$, $b_5$, $b_6$, $b_7$), shows that they are all of even parity yielding 000 for the checking number which, according to Table 2.2, means "no error." However, if $b_4$ was accidentally changed to a 1, then $1011101$ would be received. The parity of each of the groups of bits ($b_1$, $b_3$, $b_5$, $b_7$) and ($b_2$, $b_3$, $b_6$, $b_7$) is even while the parity of the group of bits ($b_4$, $b_5$, $b_6$, $b_7$) is odd, so that the checking number is seen to be $100$. According to Table 2.2 this means that $b_4$ is in error. With this knowledge, the total received message can be corrected to $1010101$, which then is as transmitted.

Clearly, the simple Hamming code with minimum distance 3 does not work if more than one error occurs. For multiple errors, codes with a minimum distance greater than three are required (see References).

## 2.5  LOGICAL DESIGN

Briefly, the steps involved may be given as follows:

1. The problem set is studied and (macro) flow charts are prepared in terms of operations that seem to be applicable to the type of problem. For scientific problems these operations might be the arithmetic operations, the processes of numerical integration, differentiation, etc. For business problems, for example, the operations might include those of filing, retrieval, sorting, and merging. Eventually, the flow chart can be expressed in terms of the arithmetic operations and certain word-dissecting and reconstructing operations. (The danger here is that if caution is not exercised one may lose awareness that the type of machine is determined by the basic operations assumed.) The relative efficiencies of various ways of solving the problem are evaluated and compared. This eventually results in some statement of the operations to be performed by the machine, the number and types of storage units, input-output units, and so forth, with flow charts describing their interaction.

2. It is desirable, then, to construct what are called "micro-flow charts." These show sufficient detail as to how the various operations are to be performed so that the transition from these charts to a detailed logical design is a routine procedure. In order to prepare the micro-flow charts, one must have a knowledge of logical design and programming, including a knowledge of arithmetic algorithms and the various ways they may be mechanized, of codes, and of checking. The preparation of these charts is a heuristic process. Various charts for a given operation would be prepared and the efficiencies of the resulting systems would be evaluated, finally yielding a set of micro-flow charts describe the operations of the system. At this point we would realize the needs for the various registers in the system and how they interact.

3. The third step is the detailed design of the system using the available logical elements. (The resulting design can be expressed as a set of drawings using a standardized set of symbols for the logical elements, or, in the absence of bridge and related networks, as a set of logical equations. A discussion of the relative merits of these two forms of representation would be beyond the scope of this book. The engineer, however, with his greater aptitude for visualization, as opposed to symbol manipulation, may prefer drawings to equations.) This step is in principle a process that can be formalized in the sense that here we interconnect what Keister, *et al.*, call "unifunctional circuits," examples of which are counters, adders, shifters, registers, flip-flops, etc. There is a one-to-one correspondence between the

operations in this step and the operations involved in building a language from base symbols such as letters. These processes are considered, theoretically, in Ref. 12 under "The Design of Mixed Formal Languages." This step involves going from the micro-flow charts which are in a "command language," as are programming flow charts, to the logical design which is in a "descriptive language." That a process can be formalized does not necessarily mean that there is a unique solution.

In principle, each solution must be obtained and evaluated with respect to its efficiency, and in practice this may be a prohibitively expensive process that must finally be based, at least in part, on past experience and personal insight.

The three steps may be schematically illustrated as a tree as in Fig. 2.13. The development of the detailed logical design consists in going from the

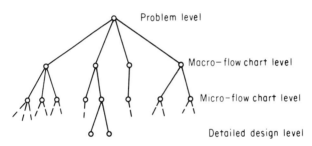

Fig. 2.13.

problem level to the detailed design level. Because of the branching, which is characteristic of synthesis, there is no unique solution unless some criterion, such as the previously defined efficiency criterion, is used to select one from the many possible designs. However, in the analysis process that consists of going from a given design, in the detailed design level, to the problem level there is a unique set of micro-flow charts, a unique set of macro-flow charts, and, if the quantities in storage are included as part of the design, a unique problem.

A formal process does exist which enables one to derive micro-flow charts from the detailed design. This is illustrated below for part of the ADD operation of the MOBIDIC, a mobile computer designed for the U.S. Army. More detailed micro-flow charts for this operation may be found in Refs. 4 and 12. The procedure is due to Gorn, and the explanation has been adapted from his work. It is not necessary to know the meanings of the symbols in order to understand the formal process; however, their meanings can be discerned by comparing Fig. 2.16 with Figs. 2.14 and 2.15, as well as with the table of logical equations, if the reader so desires.

The detailed logical design is assumed to be given in the form of logical equations. "Times" stands for "AND," "plus" stands for "OR," and "prime" for negation. The first step consists in listing the logical equations on the left-hand side of the paper as "conditions." The symbols take on the values of 0 or 1. If the condition takes on the value of 1, the following consequence or action ensues. The timing pulses occur in the sequence: $t2$ $p3$ $t3$ $p4$ $p5$ $t5$. State 2 may be read: "If MRB = 1 at $t2$, then $MOR^n$ is put into B." It is assumed that ADD = 1, AOS = 1, and MRB = 1 at all times.

LOGICAL EQUATIONS (MOBIDIC ADD INSTRUCTION)

| State | Condition: If true we have | | consequence |
|---|---|---|---|
| 2 | $(MRB)(t2)$ | : | $(MOR^n \rightarrow B)$ |
| 3 | $(ADD)(A_{sn} \oplus B_{sn})'(p3)$ | : | $(0 \rightarrow AS)$ |
| | $(ADD)(A_{sn} \oplus B_{sn})(p3)$ | : | $(1 \rightarrow AS)(B' \rightarrow B)$ |
| | $(AOS)(t3)$ | : | $(1 \rightarrow AOS^*)$ |
| 4 | $(AOS)(AS)(OF)'(p4)$ | : | $(0 \rightarrow B)(A' \rightarrow A)(A'_{sn} \rightarrow A_{sn})$ |
| 5 | $(AOS)(X_{18})'(p5)$ | : | $(0 \rightarrow OA)$ |
| | $(AOS)(AS)'(OF)(X'_{16} + X_{17})(t5)$ | : | $(1 \rightarrow OA)$ |
| | $(KEW)'(AOS)(AS)'(OF)(X'_{16})(t5)$ | : | $(1 \rightarrow TP)$ |
| | $(AOS)(AS)(OF)'(t5)$ | : | $(1 \rightarrow AOS^*)$ |

*Matrix Step.* For each timing pulse, all of the elements entering into the Boolean conditions are listed down the left-hand side of a matrix, and all of the consequences that may occur at that timing pulse are listed across the bottom. Vertical lines are drawn down to the consequences, and horizontal lines are drawn to the right from the elements. At the intersection of an element line with a consequence line which it (in conjunction with other elements) may produce, a "node" is drawn. There are two types of nodes, "AND-nodes" and "OR-nodes," having the logical function implied by their names (see Fig. 2.14).

Note the time sequence: all the Boolean equations in the first column of a time interval are handled before the actions described in the second column for that interval are taken.

Simplifications and rearrangements are made to yield Fig. 2.15. The simplifications are of two types. First, if an input to an "AND-node" is always present, it may be eliminated as superfluous (such as ADD on micro-flow chart for add instruction). If an input to an "AND-node" is always absent, the "AND-node" is never enabled and it, as well as its consequence, can be eliminated. Second, if an input to an "OR-node" is always present, it and all other inputs may be eliminated. If an input to an "OR-node" is never present, it may be eliminated. Further simplification, also within a time period, may be achieved by eliminating levels which are always "zero" or "one."

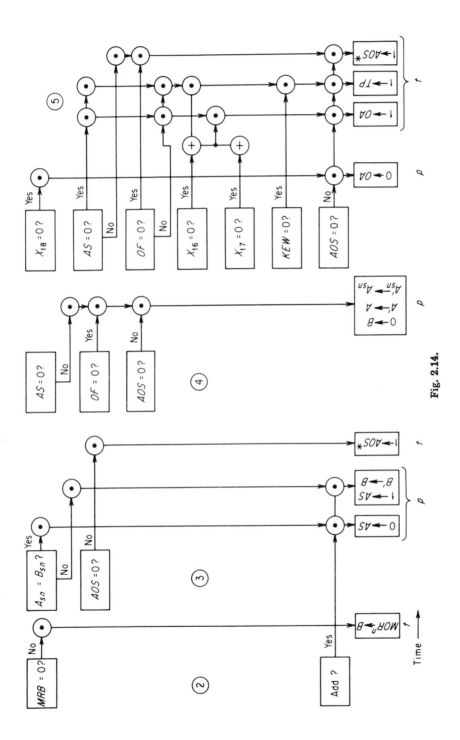

Fig. 2.14.

39

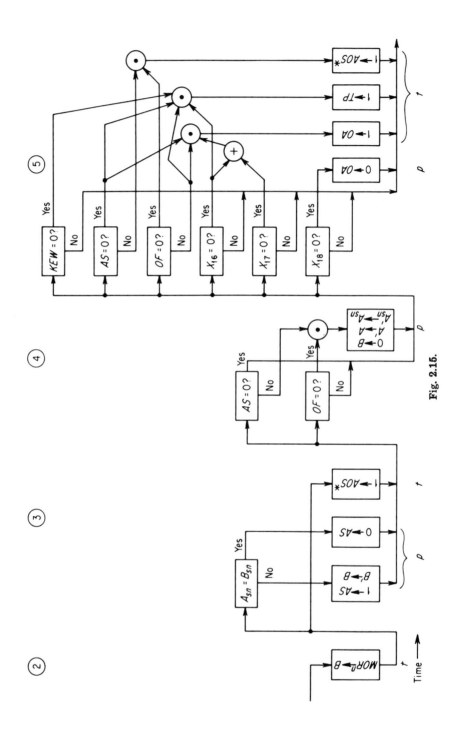

**Fig. 2.16.**

40

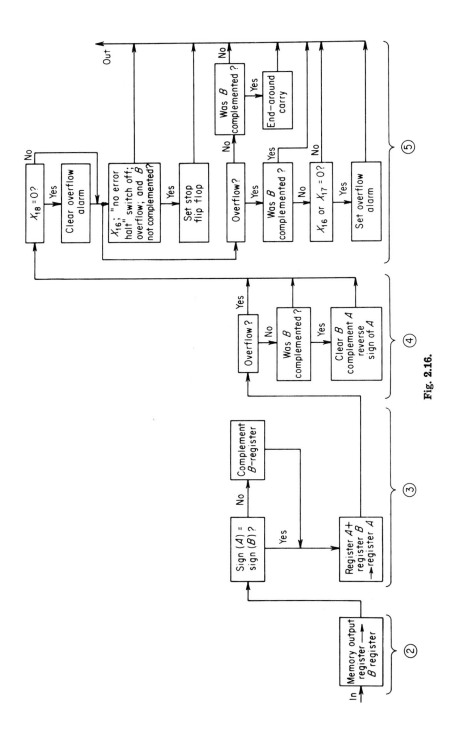

**Fig. 2.16.**

41

The rearrangement of Fig. 2.15 is simply a gathering together of all the inputs to staggered "AND-" or "OR-nodes."

The final micro-flow charts can now be made. This conversion does not yield a unique result and involves a slight liberty with the strict time sequence that has up to now been observed. It is convenient to serialize multiple-input nodes in some manner, rather than to show the questions asked simultaneously; i.e., in the sequence and the language of the programmer (Fig. 2.16).

To illustrate how the synthesis process can work, we will consider briefly the design of a 3 + 1 address binary machine using floating-point arithmetic. We will assume that we wish to go from the macro-flow chart level to the micro-flow chart level. Hence, a number word is assumed to be represented as

$$S, C, F$$

where $S$ is the sign (1 bit), $C$ is the characteristic (6 bits), and $F$ is the fraction (15 bits). The characteristic is the exponent plus 32. For example 1, 100001, 100 . . . 0 stands for $-\frac{1}{2} \times 2^1 = -1$. The micro-flow chart for the addition of two such numbers is developed as follows.

In Fig. 2.17 we have a flow chart for the addition instruction of a 3 + 1 address machine.

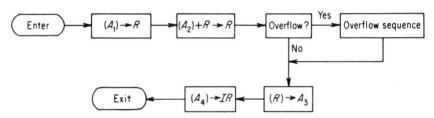

**Fig. 2.17.** 3 + 1 address flow chart.

The second box from the left in Fig. 2.17 may then be developed in more detailed form and the result is given in Fig. 2.18. It is assumed that the fractions $F_1$ and $F_2$ are normalized in that the first digit to the right of the binary point is always unity. In the flow chart shown, the overflow and underflow sequences are not developed in detail for simplicity. A good micro-flow chart would have to have these sequences developed in detail. The underflow sequence occurs when the exponent is $-32$ and the fraction is unnormal (less than $\frac{1}{2}$). One sees that such a flow chart shows an arithmetic *algorithm* for floating-point binary addition. The construction of such a flow chart and of optimum flow charts requires a knowledge of what is involved in an arithmetic process. Reference 10 contains a great deal of reference material on this subject.

It may also be noted that Fig. 2.18 could have been derived from flow

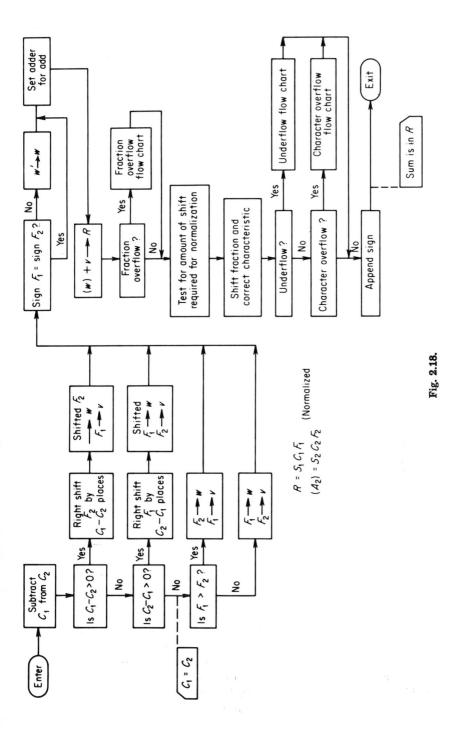

**Fig. 2.18.**

43

charts for the same operation performed on a fixed-point computer. It is true that such programs could provide material for micro-flow charts for computers having advanced automatic programming features built-in.

Figure 2.18 together with a block diagram of an arithmetic unit, such as in Fig. 2.19, describes such an arithmetic unit well enough so that it may be synthesized from logical elements.

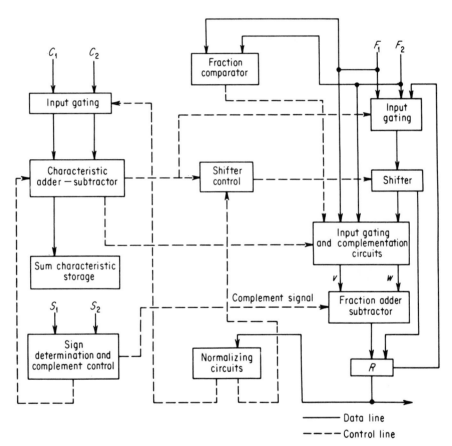

Fig. 2.19.

The operation is as follows. The first step in the add operation is a right shift of the number with the smaller characteristic until the characteristics become equal. To accomplish this, the characteristics are compared in the characteristic adder, and the result then selects the fraction to be sent to the shifter. The shifter control, using the results of the characteristic adder, determines the number of places the fraction must be shifted.

The design of the adder-subtracter is such that input $w$ can be complemented, and input $v$ cannot, which requires that the smaller fraction be gated to input $w$. This is accomplished by the signals from the characteristic adder and the fraction comparator. If the characteristics were not initially equal, the fraction coming from the shifter must be the smaller, and this fraction is gated directly to input $w$ of the adder-subtracter. However, if the characteristics were initially equal, a further test is required to determine which is the smaller fraction. This is accomplished by the fraction comparator, which is active only when the characteristics are equal. The result of the comparison of the characteristics or the result of the fraction comparator then gates the larger fraction to input $v$ and the smaller to input $w$.

Whether the fraction fed to input $w$ is complemented or not depends upon the signs of the fractions. This complement signal is determined in the component labeled "sign determination."

As soon as the inputs to the adder-subtracter are present they are added (or subtracted by complementation) and the result gated into the $R$ register. The result then must be normalized, which is accomplished by the main shifter gating, normalize control, and shift control.

If the sum has overflowed, the sixteenth bit will be unity, and the result is shifted one place to the right by the proper signal to the input gating. The normalize control, through the shift control, signals the proper number of left shifts to be performed, in order to normalize the fraction.

Of course when the fraction is being shifted right to correct for overflow the characteristic must be increased by one, and when shifted left to normalize, decreased by the proper amount. This is accomplished by the characteristic adder with the proper signal from the $R$ register and the normalize control circuit.

The fractional output of the add operation is taken directly from the shifter and gated back to the $R$ register.

The resultant characteristic and sign bit are gated back into the $R$ register.

## REFERENCES

1. Buchholz, W. (ed.), *Planning a Computer System* (New York: McGraw-Hill Book Co., 1962). Discusses design of IBM's STRETCH System.

2. Burks, A. W., and I. M. Copi, "The Logical Design of an Idealized General-Purpose Computer," *Journal of the Franklin Institute*, **261**:3 (March 1956), 4 (April 1956).

3. Caldwell, S. H., *Switching Circuits and Logical Design* (New York: John Wiley & Sons, 1958), chap. 10, "Switching Aspects of Codes."

4. Gorn, S., P. Z. Ingerman, and J. B. Crozier, "On the Construction of Micro-Flowcharts," *Communications of the Association for Computing Machinery*, **2**:10 (October 1959), 27–31.

5. Guffin, R. M., "A Computer for Solving Linear Simultaneous Equations Using the Residue Number System," *I.R.E. Transactions on Electronic Computers*, **EC-11**:2 (April 1962), 164–173.

6. Hamming, R. W., "Error Detecting and Correcting Codes," *Bell System Technical Journal*, **29** (1950), 147–160. Basic reference on Hamming codes.

7. Keister, W., A. Ritchie, and S. Washburn, *The Design of Switching Circuits* (Princeton, N. J.: D. Van Nostrand Co., 1951).

8. Patterson, G. W., "What Is a Code?" *Communications of the Association for Computing Machinery*, **3**:5 (May 1960), 315–318.

9. Plotkin, Morris, "Binary Codes with Specified Minimum Distance," Thesis, The Moore School of Electrical Engineering, University of Pennsylvania (1952).

10. Richards, R. K., *Arithmetic Operations in Digital Computers* (Princeton, N.J.: D. Van Nostrand Co., 1955). Contains a good discussion of arithmetic logic and codes.

11. Uspensky, J. V., and M. A. Heaslet, *Elementary Number Theory* (New York: McGraw-Hill Book Co., 1939), "Discussion of Congruences."

12. University of Pennsylvania, Institute for Cooperative Research, *Common Programming Language Task, Part I*, Final Report AD59UR1, Contract No. DA-36-039-sc-75047 (June 30, 1959), 25–38, 41–152. (Available from Armed Services Technical Information Agency, #AD236997.)

13. Weeg, G. P., "Uniqueness of Weighted Code Representations," *I.R.E. Transactions on Electronic Computers*, **EC-9**:4 (December 1960), 487–489.

## PROBLEMS

1. Explain the difference(s) between a weighted code and an unweighted code.

2. Design a weighted 4-bit decimal code which has a carry out of the most significant bit which corresponds to a decimal carry.

3. We have a computer which uses various codes in its input-output, control, magnetic tape, arithmetic unit, and memory. For each particular code design a checking system and discuss the relative merits of the system. Draw a block diagram of the computer showing the arithmetic unit, magnetic tape unit, memory, paper tape (input-output) unit, and control unit and show the

locations, by blocks and connecting lines, of the checking and translating units. The codes in use are as follows:

*Paper tape* (5 holes available):

| Symbols | Representation |
|---------|----------------|
| Blank | 0000 (same as blank tape) |
| Space | 0001 |
| Plus | 0010 |
| Minus | 0011 |
| Figures 0–9 | 0100–1101 |
| Unused | 1110, 1111 |

*Magnetic tape* (6 channels available):

| Symbols | Representation |
|---------|----------------|
| End of word | 0000 |
| End of block | 0001 |
| Plus | 0010 |
| Minus | 0011 |
| End of tape | 0100 |
| Figures 0–9 | 0101–1110 |
| Not used | 1111 |

*Memory unit:*

The memory unit uses a standard 8421 code and stores only the figures 0–9. The memory word is three decimal digits long plus sign bit and the parity bit.

*Arithmetic unit:*

The arithmetic unit uses a biquinary (2 out of 7) code.

*Control unit:*

Decide on some code and give support for your decision.

4. Compute the odd longitudinal and traverse parity for the following matrix and state the minimum error-detecting and error-correcting capabilities of this system.

|   | 1 | 2 | 3 | 4 | 5 | P |
|---|---|---|---|---|---|---|
| 1 | 0 | 0 | 1 | 1 | 0 |   |
| 2 | 0 | 1 | 1 | 0 | 1 |   |
| 3 | 1 | 1 | 1 | 0 | 0 |   |
| 4 | 0 | 1 | 1 | 1 | 0 |   |
| 5 | 0 | 0 | 0 | 1 | 1 |   |
| 6 | 1 | 1 | 0 | 0 | 0 |   |
| 7 | 0 | 0 | 1 | 0 | 1 |   |
| P |   |   |   |   |   |   |

**5.** Design a checking system for a selector switch which has a binary coded (421) input and eight outputs. Answer in block diagram form.

**6.** Add the following numbers and check your results using the casting out 9's method. Show enough work for clarity of method.

$$
\begin{array}{r}
7131925 \\
9873958 \\
7584902 \\
8476590 \\
6464788 \\
\underline{89487300}
\end{array}
$$

**7.** Show that $9743 \equiv 41$ (mod 99). Find minimum positive $y$ if $758493 \equiv y$ (mod 99).

**8.** In general, what errors will not be detected by a modulo 99 check coupled with a modulo 9 check?

**9.** Design a Hamming code (minimum distance 3) for a 4-bit message.

**10.** State concisely the steps involved in the formal derivation of a micro-flow chart when starting from the logical equations.

**11.** In Sec. 2.5, Fig. 2.16, there is one parallel path:
(a) Find this path.
(b) Eliminate this path by making the flow chart serial, deleting any redundancies resulting from this operation.

**12.** Flow-chart the operation which turns "end-to-end" a 5-bit character (no sign). Use any standard type registers, etc., which you consider necessary for the operation.

# 3

# COMBINATIONAL LOGIC

In this chapter we will discuss some of the principles of the design of combinational circuits. The need for combinational circuits arises because computers are sequential circuits, and sequential circuits contain combinational circuits as necessary parts.

## 3.1 DEFINITION OF A COMBINATIONAL CIRCUIT

A combinational circuit in its most general form with $m$ inputs and $n$ outputs is shown symbolically in Fig. 3.1. We will assume for our

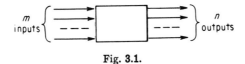

**Fig. 3.1.**

discussion that each input line and each output line may carry signals that correspond to two states (two-valued or binary inputs), although if we wished to be more general we would have to allow for the possibility of each line's carrying signals having more than two states (multivalued logics). The two states might be electrically represented by

1. "high" or "low" voltage.
2. grounded or ungrounded.

3. pulse or no pulse.
4. positive pulse or negative pulse, etc.

The definition of a combinational circuit requires that the states of the output lines at any instant depend only on the states of the inputs at the same instant. That is, previous input states have no effect on present output states. Thus there are no memory elements in a combinational circuit. However, all physical devices used for constructing combinational circuits exhibit some time delay in their operation, and time delay has a memory function. Hence, when we use physical devices in combinational circuits we must be careful to understand the effect such time delays have on the circuits' behavior. The delay and timing aspects of computer circuits will be dealt with in more detail later on.

## 3.2 UNIFUNCTIONAL AND MULTIFUNCTIONAL CIRCUITS

Keister, *et al.*, divide logic circuits into several categories that include unifunctional and multifunctional circuits. Unifunctional circuits perform single functions. Examples are

1. adders (combinational).
2. counters (sequential).
3. translators (combinational).
4. selector switches (combinational).
5. comparators (combinational).

Multifunctional circuits are defined as those circuits which perform more than one function. Examples are

1. arithmetic units.
2. computers.
3. telephone switching systems.

An adder for a single pair of binary digits can serve as an adder for a single pair of binary characters, or for the addition of a single pair of any quantities which have only two values each, provided that the binary adder is equipped with the appropriate translators which translate from the given code into the binary code and vice versa. If these translators are controlled by a device (recognizer) that recognizes the code of the input quantities and causes the translators to be set up for the proper translation, then such a device has the properties of a "processor" mechanized in hardware as defined by Gorn in his work, "On the Logical Design of Formal Mixed Languages" (Ref. 3). A digital computer can be built using sufficient numbers and types of unifunctional circuits. (In his work, Gorn shows some of the types that are necessary in principle for the design of a "string-language processor.")

## 3.3  TELEPHONE SWITCHING SYSTEMS

Early telephone switching systems and the early computers were designed by methods which rested heavily on the intuitive skill of the designer. This process, applied to telephone switching systems using electromechanical relays, required the drawing of a circuit which performed some function; the process also required the study of the circuit to see if it actually performed the function, and the reduction of the number of parts to a bare minimum. This last factor of reduction, or minimization, was primarily motivated by cost considerations, since the elimination of a single unnecessary relay contact in a unit repeated many times in a telephone switching system often represented a considerable saving. Such designs when completed were filed away for future reference.

## 3.4  OPTIMIZATION OF LOGIC CIRCUITS

Because of the importance of minimization in telephone switching systems, considerable effort was spent on the development of minimization techniques. However, we prefer to emphasize optimization rather than minimization. We may optimize a combinational circuit in several ways— for example:

1. Design for minimum cost (minimization).
2. Design for maximum speed.
3. Optimize some other parameter, e.g.,
   (a) efficiency $= 1/[(\text{cost}) \times (\text{time delay})]$,
   (b) weight,
   (c) reliability.

It should be clear that it is usually impossible, except by coincidence, to optimize more than one of the above quantities; however, we may be able to optimize some function of cost, speed, etc.

## 3.5  THE INTRODUCTION OF SWITCHING ALGEBRA

In 1938, Shannon published a paper describing an algebraic method (switching algebra) which could be used as an aid in the above design process. The chief advantage cited in the paper was that *most* (but not all—e.g., bridges) combinational circuits could be represented by the algebra, and then manipulations could be performed algebraically rather than by drawing and successive redrawing of the circuit. This paper caused the beginning of work the purpose of which was to increase the power of the algebraic methods in analysis and design of switching circuits. Some progress has also been achieved in developing new nonalgebraic methods of analysis and design—e.g., the Karnaugh map (Sec. 3.11).

## 3.6 LOGICAL SYMBOLS

Two kinds of combinational logic can be performed as determined by the characteristics of the devices used. These are

1. Contact logic. This is performed by devices that act like relays in that they close paths. Examples are (see Chap. 5)
   (a) transistors used as switches,
   (b) cryotrons.
2. Flow logic. This is performed by devices that act like vacuum tubes in that the logical quantities flow through the devices. Examples are (see Chap. 5)
   (a) diode logic,
   (b) diode-transistor logic.

Consider the relay circuit in Fig. 3.2 in conjunction with the two "truth tables" (a term borrowed from formal logic). The table on the far right is

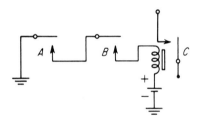

| A | B | C |
|---|---|---|
| Open | Open | Open |
| Open | Closed | Open |
| Closed | Open | Open |
| Closed | Closed | Closed |

| A | B | C |
|---|---|---|
| 0 | 0 | 0 |
| 0 | 1 | 1 |
| 1 | 0 | 0 |
| 1 | 1 | 0 |

Fig. 3.2.

an abbreviated form of the table to its left, using the symbols 0 for "open" and 1 for "closed."

If we allow the symbols 0 and 1 to have the meaning of the integers 0 and 1, then all the entries in the abbreviated table can be computed from the equation

$$C = AB \qquad (\text{"AND"}) \qquad (3.1)$$

where the ordinary arithmetic operations of equality and times are assumed. In a similar fashion we can construct the truth tables and switching-algebra equations for the two circuits in Fig. 3.3.

The operation indicated by $+$ in Eq. (3.2) is not the same as the operation of arithmetic addition, but denotes the meaning of "OR." Its characteristics are defined by the truth table accompanying it. Similarly,

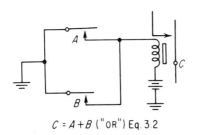

| A | B | C |
|---|---|---|
| 0 | 0 | 0 |
| 0 | 1 | 1 |
| 1 | 0 | 1 |
| 1 | 1 | 1 |

$C = A + B$ ("OR") Eq. 3.2

**Fig. 3.3.**

the characteristics of the prime operation are shown in its accompanying truth table. Some equivalent forms of Eqs. (3.1), (3.2), and (3.3) that are seen in the literature are

(1) $$C = AB = A \wedge B = A \cap B = A \cdot B$$

(2) $$C = A + B = A \vee B = A \cup B$$

(3) $$C = A' = \overline{A} = \sim A$$

Various other ways of operating relays are possible, such as multiple coils, shunting of coils by contacts, etc.; but the operation of such circuits can be described by switching-algebra equations using the four operations $(=)$, $(+)$, $(\cdot)$, $(')$.

In the case of flow logic, the first appearance was in radar where the coincidence gate was described as in Fig. 3.5.

It is possible to bias some multi-grid tubes (such as the 6AS6) to perform this function. Figure 3.6 illustrates this.

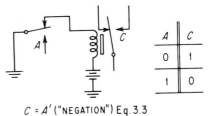

$C = A'$ ("NEGATION") Eq. 3.3

| A | C |
|---|---|
| 0 | 1 |
| 1 | 0 |

**Fig. 3.4.**

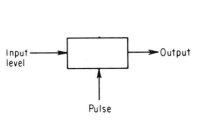

| Input level | Pulse | Output |
|---|---|---|
| Not present | Not present | Not present |
| Not present | Present | Not present |
| Present | Not present | Not present |
| Present | Present | Present |

**Fig. 3.5.**

We may define the binary variables $A$, $B$, and $C$ in Fig. 3.6 as below (the symbol $\Rightarrow$ means "if . . . then . . .").

Low voltage $\quad E_{c1} <$ CUTOFF $\Rightarrow A = 0$

High voltage $\quad E_{c1} = 0$ volts $\quad \Rightarrow A = 1$

Low voltage $\quad E_{c3} <$ CUTOFF $\Rightarrow B = 0$

High voltage $\quad E_{c3} = 0$ volts $\quad \Rightarrow B = 1$

Low voltage $\quad E_0 \ <$ CUTOFF $\Rightarrow C = 0$

High voltage $\quad E_0 \ = 0$ volts $\quad \Rightarrow C = 1$

Thus, we devise from Fig. 3.6 a truth table (Table 3.1), with an accompanying equation, that is similar to the table of Fig. 3.2.

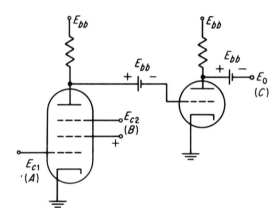

| $E_{c1}$ | $E_{c3}$ | $E_0$ |
|---|---|---|
| < cutoff | < cutoff | < cutoff |
| < cutoff | 0 volts | < cutoff |
| 0 volts | < cutoff | < cutoff |
| 0 volts | 0 volts | 0 volts |

**Fig. 3.6.**

In like manner we have Fig. 3.7. Note that the definition of $C$ is the same as the definitions of $A$ and $B$ with respect to "high voltage" and

**TABLE 3.1.** $C = AB$

| $A$ | $B$ | $C$ |
|---|---|---|
| 0 | 0 | 0 |
| 0 | 1 | 0 |
| 1 | 0 | 0 |
| 1 | 1 | 1 |

"low voltage." We can iterate (connect in cascade) such logical elements, but we also need the inverter (Fig. 3.8).

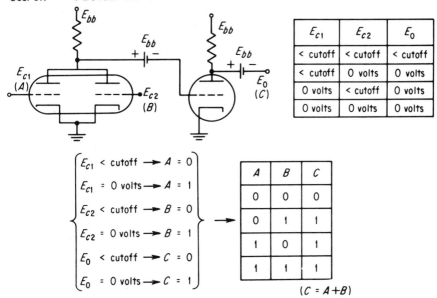

| | $E_{c1}$ | $E_{c2}$ | $E_0$ |
|---|---|---|---|
| | < cutoff | < cutoff | < cutoff |
| | < cutoff | 0 volts | 0 volts |
| | 0 volts | < cutoff | 0 volts |
| | 0 volts | 0 volts | 0 volts |

$$\left\{ \begin{array}{l} E_{c1} < \text{cutoff} \rightarrow A = 0 \\ E_{c1} = 0 \text{ volts} \rightarrow A = 1 \\ E_{c2} < \text{cutoff} \rightarrow B = 0 \\ E_{c2} = 0 \text{ volts} \rightarrow B = 1 \\ E_0 < \text{cutoff} \rightarrow C = 0 \\ E_0 = 0 \text{ volts} \rightarrow C = 1 \end{array} \right\} \rightarrow$$

| A | B | C |
|---|---|---|
| 0 | 0 | 0 |
| 0 | 1 | 1 |
| 1 | 0 | 1 |
| 1 | 1 | 1 |

$(C = A + B)$

Fig. 3.7.

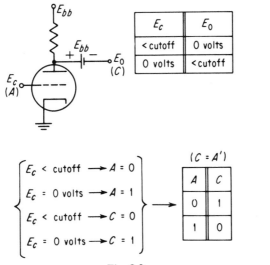

| $E_c$ | $E_0$ |
|---|---|
| < cutoff | 0 volts |
| 0 volts | < cutoff |

$$\left\{ \begin{array}{l} E_c < \text{cutoff} \rightarrow A = 0 \\ E_c = 0 \text{ volts} \rightarrow A = 1 \\ E_c < \text{cutoff} \rightarrow C = 0 \\ E_c = 0 \text{ volts} \rightarrow C = 1 \end{array} \right\} \rightarrow$$

$(C = A')$

| A | C |
|---|---|
| 0 | 1 |
| 1 | 0 |

Fig. 3.8.

## 3.7  POSTULATES OF TWO-VALUED SWITCHING ALGEBRA

From the results obtained above, it is now possible to write down the following relations.

For a variable: $A = 0$ or $A = 1$

$$0 \cdot 0 = 0 \qquad 0 + 0 = 0$$
$$0 \cdot 1 = 0 \qquad 0 + 1 = 1$$
$$1 \cdot 0 = 0 \qquad 1 + 0 = 1$$
$$1 \cdot 1 = 1 \qquad 1 + 1 = 1$$

These postulates happen to have the same formal structure as have the postulates of binary Boolean algebra. Hence, any theorems of binary Boolean algebra are also theorems of switching algebra. The postulates have been derived in this fashion in order to illustrate a process that is of more general application. For example, if three-valued instead of two-valued signals or devices had been used, by following the same procedure, we could have developed a set of postulates for three-valued logic. As another example, in Fig. 3.2, we assumed in effect that there was no delay in the operation of a relay. It was the recognition of the fact that a relay coil could be energized for a time before the relay operated that enabled D. A. Huffman to develop his theory of sequential circuits. The laws and theorems of switching algebra are as follows.

1. $A + B = B + A$                    (Associative laws)
   $AB = BA$
2. $(A + B) + C = A + (B + C)$     (Commutative laws)
   $(AB)C = A(BC)$
3. $AB + AC = A(B + C)$            (Distributive laws)
   $(A + B)(A + C) = A + BC$
4. $A + A = A$                         (Idempotent laws)
   $AA = A$
5. $1 + A = 1$                          (Special properties of 0 and 1)
   $0A = 0$
   $1A = A$
   $0 + A = A$
6. $A + AB = A$                        (Absorption laws)
   $A(A + B) = A$
7. $(A')' = A$                           (Involution)
8. $(A + B + \cdots)' = A'B' \cdots$     (de Morgan's laws)
   $(AB \cdots)' = A' + B' + \cdots$
9. $A' + A = 1$                         (Complementarity)
   $A'A = 0$
10. $(A + B')B = AB$
11. $AB' + B = A + B$
12. $(A + B)(A' + C)(B + C) = (A + B)(A' + C)$
13. $AC + A'B + BC = AC + A'B$

14. $(A + B)(A' + C) = AC + A'B$

15. $f(X) = A[f(X)$ with $A = 1, A' = 0]$
$\qquad\qquad + A'[f(X)$ with $A = 0, A' = 1]$

16. $f(X) = \{A + [f(X)$ with $A = 0, A' = 1]\}$
$\qquad\qquad \cdot \{A' + [f(X) + A = 1, A' = 0]\}$

Any law or theorem can be proven by constructing a truth table for

**TABLE 3.2.** PROOF OF $AB' + B = A + B$

|   |   | Left | Right |
|---|---|---|---|
| $A$ | $B$ | $AB' + B$ | $A + B$ |
| 0 | 0 | 0 | 0 |
| 0 | 1 | 1 | 1 |
| 1 | 0 | 1 | 1 |
| 1 | 1 | 1 | 1 |

each side of the equation. For example, for Theorem 11 Table 3.2 can be constructed.

### 3.8 SYMBOLISM

For flow logic we will at this time use the symbols for the circuits that are given in Fig. 3.9.

### 3.9 USES OF SWITCHING ALGEBRA

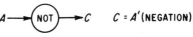

$A \longrightarrow$ (AND) $\longrightarrow C$    $C = AB$ (AND)
$B \longrightarrow$

$A \longrightarrow$ (OR) $\longrightarrow C$    $C = A + B$ (OR)
$B \longrightarrow$

$A \longrightarrow$ (NOT) $\longrightarrow C$    $C = A'$ (NEGATION)

Fig. 3.9.

Switching algebra has uses in the analysis and manipulation of combinational logic networks and in their design. Additional aids used with switching algebra in synthesis and minimization are

1. tables of combinations.
2. Karnaugh maps.
3. Quine minimization.
4. Veitch charts.
5. Harvard minimization charts.

Only the first two will be discussed in this book.

We will illustrate how switching algebra can be used in the manipulation of logical networks by considering the example of a combinational circuit

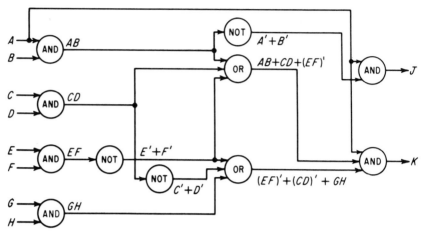

**Fig. 3.10.**

in Fig. 3.10. The expressions at the various circuit outputs illustrated in Fig. 3.10 are obtained using the rules of Fig. 3.9, and in this way we obtain

$$J = A(A' + B)$$
$$K = A[AB + CD + (EF)'][(EF)' + (CD)' + GH]$$

By using Theorem 10, we obtain

$$J = AB'$$

By using Theorem 3, we obtain

$$K = A\{(EF)' + [(CD)' + GH][CD + AB]\}$$

which by further reduction with Theorem 14 gives

$$K = A[(EF)' + (CD)'AB + CDGH]$$

As a sum of products,

$$K = AE' + AF' + ABC' + ABD' + ACDGH$$
$$J = AB'$$

This network is shown in Fig. 3.11 and is optimized for minimum delay. For the case of minimum cost, we find by minimization techniques (assuming that cost is proportional to the number of gates and buffers) that

$$J = AB'$$
$$K = A[E' + F' + BC' + BD' + CDGH]$$

If each gate, buffer, or inverter has a delay of $T$, then the delays and costs for the several designs are as in Table 3.3. (We assume that $A'$, $B'$, $C'$, etc.

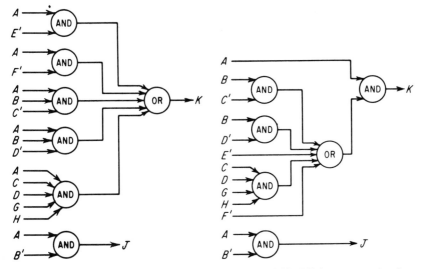

**Fig. 3.11.** Minimum delay circuit.          **Fig. 3.12.** Minimum cost circuit.

are available.) The optimization for maximum efficiency was done by trial and error.

TABLE **3.3**

| Design | Cost | Delay | Cost times delay |
|---|---|---|---|
| Original (Fig. 3.10) | 11 | $4T$ | $44T$ |
| Min. delay (Fig. 3.11) | 7 | $2T$ | $14T$ |
| Min. cost | 6 | $3T$ | $18T$ |
| Max. efficiency | 7 | $2T$ | $14T$ |

## 3.10  COMBINATIONAL CIRCUIT DESIGN

We shall present only a brief discussion of the use of Karnaugh maps and tables of combinations in the design of these circuits. Some knowledge of these design techniques is of value to those engaged in the engineering of digital computers.

As an example of the use of tables of combinations, consider the design of the binary adder in Fig. 3.13.

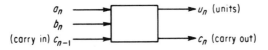

**Fig. 3.13.** Binary adder.

The truth table for the adder (Table 3.4) describes its operation.

**TABLE 3.4.** TRUTH TABLE FOR A BINARY ADDER

| $a_n$ | $b_n$ | $c_{n-1}$ | $u_n$ | $c_n$ |
|-------|-------|-----------|-------|-------|
| 0 | 0 | 0 | 0 | 0 |
| 0 | 0 | 1 | 1 | 0 |
| 0 | 1 | 0 | 1 | 0 |
| 0 | 1 | 1 | 0 | 1 |
| 1 | 0 | 0 | 1 | 0 |
| 1 | 0 | 1 | 0 | 1 |
| 1 | 1 | 0 | 0 | 1 |
| 1 | 1 | 1 | 1 | 1 |

We will consider, first, the units output. The table of input combinations which gives a units output is illustrated in Table 3.5.

**TABLE 3.5.** TABLE OF COMBINATION FOR $u_n = 1$

| $a_n$ | $b_n$ | $c_{n-1}$ |
|-------|-------|-----------|
| 0 | 0 | 1 |
| 0 | 1 | 0 |
| 1 | 0 | 0 |
| 1 | 1 | 1 |

In this table we may express $u_n$ as a sum of the terms

$$u_n = a'_n b'_n c_{n-1} + a'_n b_n c'_{n-1} + a_n b'_n c'_{n-1} + a_n b_n c_{n-1} \qquad (3.4)$$

where each term represents a line in the table.

If we write the table of combinations for which the units output is zero we have Table 3.6.

Here we may express $u'_n$ as a sum of the terms

$$u'_n = a'_n b'_n c'_{n-1} + a'_n b_n c_{n-1} + a_n b'_n c_{n-1} + a_n b_n c'_{n-1}$$

Using de Morgan's law, we obtain $u_n$ as a product of the combined terms

$$u_n = (u'_n)'$$

$$= (a_n + b_n + c_{n-1})(a_n + b'_n + c'_{n-1})(a'_n + b_n + c'_{n-1})(a'_n + b'_n + c_{n-1}) \qquad (3.5)$$

**TABLE 3.6.** Table of Combinations For $u_n = 0$

| $a_n$ | $b_n$ | $c_{n-1}$ |
|---|---|---|
| 0 | 0 | 0 |
| 0 | 1 | 1 |
| 1 | 0 | 1 |
| 1 | 1 | 0 |

Equation (3.4) is in such a form as to enable one to immediately write down the minimum delay design in Fig. 3.14. Equation (3.5) yields a minimum delay design with four OR circuits feeding a single AND circuit instead of the design of Fig. 3.14 where four AND circuits feed a single OR circuit. We note also a general principle illustrated by the above: When any Boolean function is expressed in either of the two standard forms—i.e., as a sum of products or as a product of sums—it corresponds to a minimum delay circuit. One method for obtaining solutions in these forms has just been illustrated.

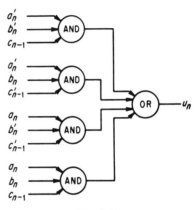

Fig. 3.14.

The table of combinations for a unity carry output is given in Table 3.7. $c_n$ expressed as a sum of products is

$$c_n = a_n' b_n c_{n-1} + a_n b_n' c_{n-1} + a_n b_n c_{n-1}' + a_n b_n c_{n-1} \qquad (3.6)$$

By using the theorems we may note that Eq. (3.6) can be simplified to obtain

$$c_n = a_n b_n + a_n c_{n-1} + b_n c_{n-1} \qquad (3.7)$$

**TABLE 3.7.** Table of Combinations For $c_n = 1$

| $a_n$ | $b_n$ | $c_{n-1}$ |
|---|---|---|
| 0 | 1 | 1 |
| 1 | 0 | 1 |
| 1 | 1 | 0 |
| 1 | 1 | 1 |

Equation (3.7) could have also been obtained from either Table 3.4 or Table 3.7 by observing that $c_n = 1$ if and only if two or three out of three of the inputs are energized.

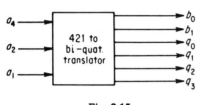

**Fig. 3.15.**

Another illustration of the design of combinational circuits which illustrates the simplification aspects of the tables of combinations is found in the design of a translator from the 421 code to the biquaternary code (Fig. 3.15). We observe from Table 3.8 that $b_0$ is unity whenever $a_4$ is zero, hence $b_0 = a_4'$. Similarly, we note also that $b_4$ is unity whenever $a_4$ is unity. Hence, $b_4 = a_4$. Now $q_0$ is unity only for the combinations 000 and 100; also the pair $a_0 = 0$ and $a_2 = 0$ occur only in these combinations; hence, $q_0$ is independent of $a_4$ and we have $q_0 = a_0'a_2'$. Continuing

**TABLE 3.8**

| Dec. Dig. | $a_4$ | $a_2$ | $a_0$ | $q_3$ | $q_2$ | $q_1$ | $q_0$ | $b_4$ | $b_0$ |
|---|---|---|---|---|---|---|---|---|---|
| 0 | 0 | 0 | 0 | 0 | 0 | 0 | 1 | 0 | 1 |
| 1 | 0 | 0 | 1 | 0 | 0 | 1 | 0 | 0 | 1 |
| 2 | 0 | 1 | 0 | 0 | 1 | 0 | 0 | 0 | 1 |
| 3 | 0 | 1 | 1 | 1 | 0 | 0 | 0 | 0 | 1 |
| 4 | 1 | 0 | 0 | 0 | 0 | 0 | 1 | 1 | 0 |
| 5 | 1 | 0 | 1 | 0 | 0 | 1 | 0 | 1 | 0 |
| 6 | 1 | 1 | 0 | 0 | 1 | 0 | 0 | 1 | 0 |
| 7 | 1 | 1 | 1 | 1 | 0 | 0 | 0 | 1 | 0 |

in this way, we can, by inspection, obtain the equations in minimum-delay form for the translation from the 421 code to the biquaternary code.

$$b_0 = a_4', \qquad q_1 = a_0a_2'$$
$$b_4 = a_4, \qquad q_2 = a_2a_0' \qquad (3.8)$$
$$q_0 = a_0'a_2', \qquad q_3 = a_0a_2$$

For a translation from the biquaternary code to the 421 code, we can also obtain from Table 3.8 by inspection the following equations.

$$a_0 = q_1 + q_3$$
$$a_2 = q_2 + q_3 \tag{3.9}$$
$$a_4 = b_4$$

To obtain these equations by writing down a sum of products, we would have to consider the 56 combinations of $b_0, \ldots, q_3$ that do not appear in Table 3.8. Since they would never occur as inputs to the translator we may or may not include the corresponding products in the equations for $a_0$, $a_2$, and $a_4$; the decision would depend on the simplifications provided.

An alternate form for Eq. (3.9) (sums of products) may be obtained as follows. We have by inspection from Table 3.8

$$a_0' = q_0 + q_2, \quad a_2' = q_0 + q_1, \quad a_4' = b_4'$$

Hence,

$$a_0 = q_0' q_2', \quad a_2 = q_0' q_1', \quad a_4 = b_4 \tag{3.10}$$

## 3.11 KARNAUGH MAP

A nonalgebraic aid to design is the Karnaugh map, which is a modification of the Veitch chart. The Karnaugh map enables a person to use the powerful pattern-recognizing properties of his brain in the synthesis of combinational logic.

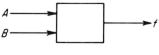

Consider the combinational circuit shown in Fig. 3.16. The inputs $(A, B)$ exist in four possible states $(0, 0)$, $(0, 1)$, $(1, 0)$, $(1, 1)$.

**Fig. 3.16.**

These may be plotted in Cartesian coordinates as in Fig. 3.17.

Each point is surrounded by a square as shown. The resulting dotted figure may be extracted to yield the two-variable map shown in Fig. 3.18.

This map may be redrawn as in Fig. 3.19.

The squares in Fig. 3.19 have an "adjacency" property in that the combinations for physically adjacent squares are at a distance of unity apart. However, to have physically adjacent all squares that represent combinations that are at a distance of unity apart we must assume that the end squares are adjacent. Three- and four-variable maps are shown in Fig. 3.20.

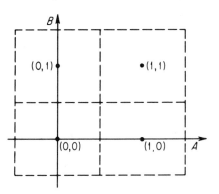

**Fig. 3.17.**

In these maps, physically adjacent squares and end squares are "adjacent." A simplified notation for the maps is shown in Fig. 3.21.

Fig. 3.18.                Fig. 3.19.

Maps for more than four variables can be constructed, but are difficult to use. Such maps are discussed in the references.

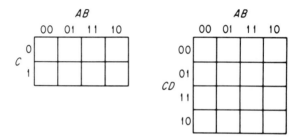

Fig. 3.20. Three- and four-variable maps.

The use of the maps in design requires that

1. A "1" is placed in each square for which an output exists for the corresponding input combination.
2. The resulting pattern is visually studied and algebraic expressions are written for the output function.

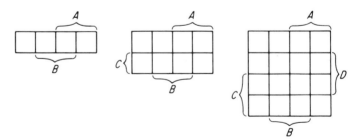

Fig. 3.21. Two-, three-, and four-variable maps.

This process will be illustrated. However, before we can work an example, we will have to learn to visually recognize the various patterns that can occur, much in the same way as one learns a new alphabet. The mapping of several products on four-variable maps is shown in Fig. 3.22.

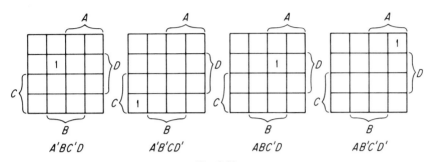

Fig. **3.22.**

Products involving one letter less than the number of variables for which the map is drawn, map as in Fig. 3.23.

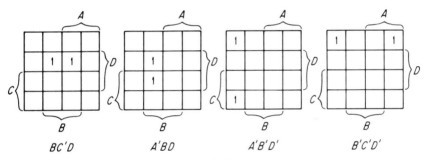

Fig. **3.23.**

Products involving two letters less than the number of variables for which the map is drawn, map as in Fig. 3.24.

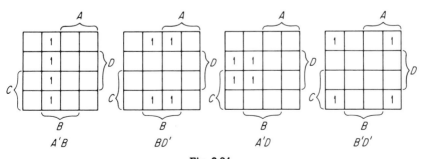

Fig. **3.24.**

Products involving three letters less than the number of variables for which the map is drawn, map as in Fig. 3.25.

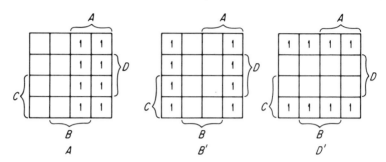

**Fig. 3.25.**

Now let us design a combinational circuit for which we are given the truth table in Table 3.9. The map for this is given in Fig. 3.26. Let us say that we wish to design a minimum-delay circuit subject to the condition it also has minimum cost. We will assume that cost is determined primarily by the number of circuits and secondarily by the number of inputs to a circuit. We will assume also both normal and inverted signal inputs are available corresponding to unprimed and primed letters. Hence, we wish to find $f$ such that it is either a sum of products or a product of sums having a minimum number of terms and a minimum number of letters in each term. We will group the marked squares in Fig. 3.26 so as to have the smallest number of groups with the largest number of marked squares in each group. The only two ways of doing this are shown in Fig. 3.27.

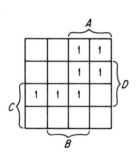

**Fig. 3.26.** Map for Table 3.9.

Using our experience, gained above, in interpreting these patterns, we can write the expressions

$$f = AC' + A'CD + BCD \qquad (3.11)$$

or

$$f = AC' + A'CD + ABD \qquad (3.12)$$

The choice between (3.11) and (3.12) would have to be based on other considerations, such as the driving capabilities of the circuits providing the input signals. For example, in Eq. (3.11) the signal $A$ goes to only one place while in (3.12) the signal $A$ goes to two places.

In like manner, we can obtain $f$ as a product of sums by writing the sum-of-products expression for the unmarked squares in Fig. 3.26. This

TABLE **3.9**

| A | B | C | D | f |
|---|---|---|---|---|
| 0 | 0 | 0 | 0 | 0 |
| 0 | 0 | 0 | 1 | 0 |
| 0 | 0 | 1 | 0 | 0 |
| 0 | 0 | 1 | 1 | 1 |
| 0 | 1 | 0 | 0 | 0 |
| 0 | 1 | 0 | 1 | 0 |
| 0 | 1 | 1 | 0 | 0 |
| 0 | 1 | 1 | 1 | 1 |
| 1 | 0 | 0 | 0 | 1 |
| 1 | 0 | 0 | 1 | 1 |
| 1 | 0 | 1 | 0 | 0 |
| 1 | 0 | 1 | 1 | 0 |
| 1 | 1 | 0 | 0 | 1 |
| 1 | 1 | 0 | 1 | 1 |
| 1 | 1 | 1 | 0 | 0 |
| 1 | 1 | 1 | 1 | 1 |

yields Eq. (3.13) which, when negated, yields the desired expression, Eq. (3.14).

$$f' = A'C' + CD' + AB'C \qquad (3.13)$$

$$f = (A + C)(C' + D)(A' + B + C') \qquad (3.14)$$

The designs for Eqs. (3.11) and (3.14) are shown in Fig. 3.28. Under the

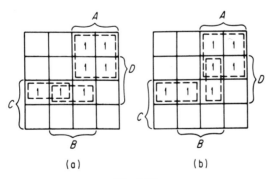

(a)                              (b)

**Fig. 3.27.**

stated assumptions, the design of Fig. 3.28(b) is the minimum-delay, minimum-cost design that is desired.

As the last example, we will consider the design of a combinational circuit which is described by the map in Fig. 3.29. A "*d*" in a square

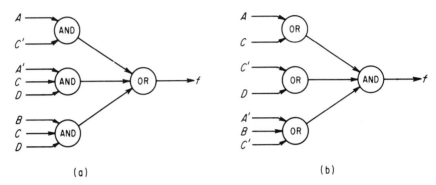

Fig. 3.28.

indicates that either the input combination does not exist or we "don't care" what the output is if the input combination does occur. The design

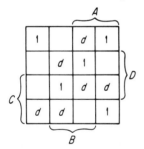

Fig. 3.29. Map illustrating "don't-care" conditions.

procedure involves the assignment of "0" or "1" to each of the *d*'s for a minimum-delay design in order to obtain the desired pattern. For a minimum-delay design with minimum cost, the result is given in Eq. (3.15) as a sum of products.

$$f = B'D' + BD \qquad (3.15)$$

It is possible to obtain factored forms by inspection of the Karnaugh map if other than minimum-delay designs are required. It is also possible to recognize symmetric functions (defined in the next section) from a map. The reader may consult the references on these aspects or, preferably, try to work out such procedures for himself.

## 3.12 LOGICAL OPERATIONS FOR COMBINATIONAL LOGIC

In order to choose a useful set of circuits for performing combinational logic, we need to know what logical functions must be performed by the logical elements.

First, consider the logical elements having two inputs (Fig. 3.30). There are sixteen different such logical elements. (In general, for an $n$-input element, there are $2^{2^n}$ different logical operations that can be performed.) The sixteen logical elements perform the functions, $f = 0, 1, A, B, A', B', A + B, A' + B, A + B', A' + B', AB, AB', A'B, A'B', A'B' + AB,$

$AB' + A'B$. It is possible to perform combinational logic with any one of several sets of operations taken from the sixteen. Several such sets are shown in Table 3.10 together with the symbols we shall choose for the operations where required.

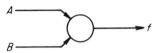

Fig. **3.30.** A two-input logical element.

We will take as axiomatic that the Group 1 functions, AND, OR, and NEGATION, are sufficient to perform combinational logic. To prove that combinational logic can be done with any one of the other groups, it is only necessary to show how the operations of Group 1 can be performed by any of the others. This is shown in Table 3.11 for all but Group 7.

In the case of Group 7, it is necessary to employ the two-line system using the two-line code mentioned in Chap. 2. Inputs $A$ and $B$ appear on two lines, as in Fig. 3.31, with the coding as shown for any variable represented by $X$.

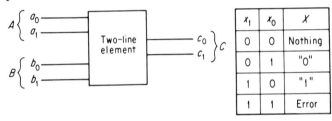

Fig. **3.31.** Two-line element.

By using tables of combinations it is a straightforward design problem to show that the two-line AND, OR, and NEGATION elements are as shown in Fig. 3.32.

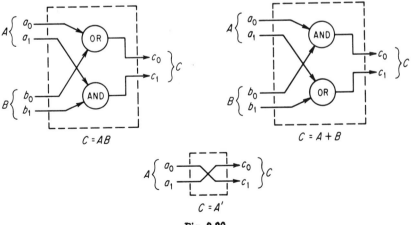

Fig. **3.32.**

TABLE 3.10

| Group no. | Name of operation | Function | Symbol |
|---|---|---|---|
| 1 | AND | $f = AB$ | |
| | OR | $f = A+B$ | |
| | NEGATION | $f = A'$ | |
| 2 | Sheffer stroke | $f = A'+B'$ | |
| 3 | Peirce stroke | $f = A'B'$ | |
| 4 | AND | $f = AB$ | |
| | NEGATION | $f = A'$ | |
| 5 | OR | $f = A+B$ | |
| | NEGATION | $f = A'$ | |
| 6 | Exclusive OR | $f = AB'+A'B$ | |
| | AND | $f = AB$ | |
| | 1 | $f = 1$ | |
| 7 | AND | $f = AB$ | |
| | OR | $f = A+B$ | |

**TABLE 3.11**

| Group no. | AND | OR | NEGATION |
|---|---|---|---|
| 2 | | | |
| 3 | | | |
| 4 | | | |
| 5 | | | |
| 6 | | | |

Multiple-input elements that can be used to perform combinational logic include the *majority organ* illustrated and defined in Fig. 3.33. If $N = 1$, in the equations of Fig. 3.33, the function performed is the OR function; if $N = M$, the function performed is the AND function. The majority organ can be used in a two-line system.

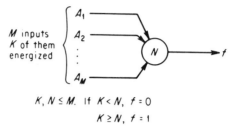

$$K, N \leq M. \text{ If } K < N, \; f = 0$$
$$K \geq N, \; f = 1$$

**Fig. 3.33.** Majority organ.

A symmetric function is a function that is unchanged for all interchanges of its variables. The logical function $f$ is a "symmetric" function of the binary variables $A_1, A_2, \ldots, A_m$. For example, if $N = 2$ and $M = 3$, it is easily shown that by using tables of combinations or Karnaugh maps,

$$f = A_1A_2 + A_1A_3 + A_2A_3 \tag{3.16}$$

If $A_1$ and $A_3$ are interchanged, Eq. (3.16) becomes

$$f_1 = A_3A_2 + A_3A_1 + A_2A_1 \tag{3.17}$$

which is equal to $f$ in Eq. (3.16).

It is interesting to note that Eq. (3.16) describes the carry digit of the three-input binary adder seen earlier in this chapter.

### 3.13 WASHBURN SYMBOLISM

A symbolism introduced by Washburn enables us to combine the symbolic logical drawings and the definitions that were treated separately in Sec. 3.7. This symbolism is helpful in determining and/or understanding the logical capabilities of a given circuit technology.

Two polarities (voltage, current, pulse, etc.) are defined. These are "plus" ($+$) and "minus" ($-$).

For the AND circuit, which we have been using in all the examples in this chapter, we would write

(a) Positive AND
Logical equation: $C = AB$
Symbol (Fig. 3.34)

The plus sign adjacent to $A$ means that that point is plus when $A = 1$, etc. The plus signs adjacent to the AND symbol mean that the operation is the AND operation in that both inputs must be plus for the output to be plus. We can also write for the same element, since by de Morgan's laws a positive AND circuit can function as a negative OR circuit,

(b) Negative OR
Logical equation: $C' = A' + B'$
Symbol (Fig. 3.35)

The minus signs adjacent to the symbol mean that the operation is the OR operation in that if either of the inputs is minus, the output will be minus.

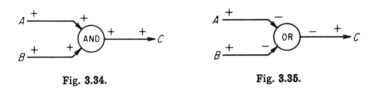

Fig. 3.34.　　　　　　　　　　　　Fig. 3.35.

Note also that the presence of the two different signs at the ends of a line indicates that the variable appears negated in the logical equation.

The positive OR circuit, which we have been using in all the examples in this chapter, is shown in Fig. 3.36(a), and its corresponding negative AND is shown in Fig. 3.36(b).

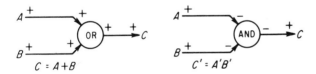

Fig. 3.36.

For the vacuum tubes in Figs. 3.6, 3.7, and 3.8 of Sec. 3.6, some of the possible symbols are shown in Fig. 3.37.

The development of the positive OR from the symbols in Fig. 3.37, and the circuit of Fig. 3.7 in Sec. 3.6, is shown in Fig. 3.38.

Let us now consider the circuit of Fig. 3.39, which consists of a diode buffer for positive signals followed by a transistor inverter.

We must assume that the resistor network $R_1$, $R_2$, $R_3$ is so designed that this circuit can be driven by and can drive similar circuits. Two equivalent symbols (AND, OR symbols) for this circuit are shown with applications in Fig. 3.40, and the reader can verify that they perform the indicated logical functions.

In the future, the symbols shown in Fig. 3.41 will be taken to be equivalent.

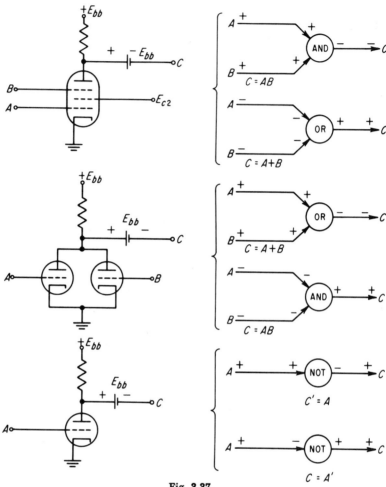

Fig. 3.37.

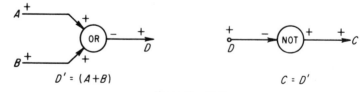

$D' = (A+B)$

$C = D'$

Hence $C = A+B$

Fig. 3.38.

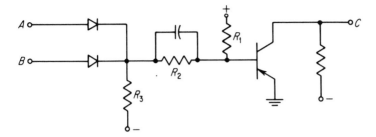

**Fig. 3.39.** Buffer-inverter.

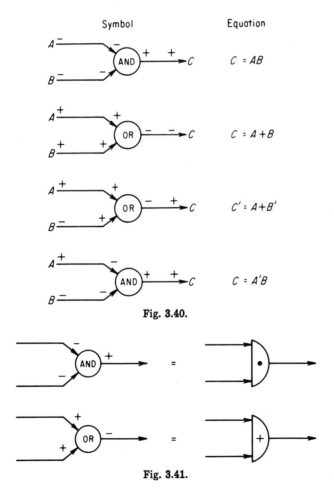

**Fig. 3.40.**

**Fig. 3.41.**

In Fig. 3.42 is shown the logical drawing of the circuit which performs
the function

$$f = (A' + B)C + (D + E + F)'G \qquad (3.18)$$

You will find it instructive to translate Eq. (3.18) by using the symbolism

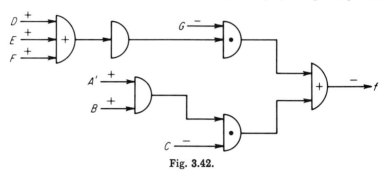

Fig. 3.42.

and equivalences of Fig. 3.41, to see if the circuit of Fig. 3.42 performs the
function of Eq. (3.18).

When the plus and minus signs, adjacent to the input letters of the
symbols in Fig. 3.42, are omitted, it is to be understood that a plus sign
in the semicircle denotes a plus sign and a dot denotes a minus sign.

### 3.14 LOADING CONSIDERATIONS

For this discussion, we will consider only the circuit in Fig. 3.43. Let us
say that a current of at least $I_{in}$ is required in order to turn the transistor $T$
off. That is, if that amount of current is furnished, the circuit is so
designed that it is completely certain that $T$ will be held off. Also, let
us say that if no input current is furnished, the transistor $T$ can
always supply a current of at least $I_{out}$ to any loads. Hence, the number
of similar circuits $N$ that this circuit can always drive is $N = I_{out}/I_{in}$.
This is a limitation on the kind of logical configurations that can be
constructed using such circuits. The problems related to the design of circuits to have a given $N$ are discussed
in Chap. 8.

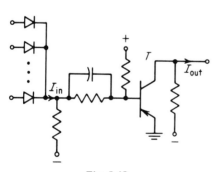

Fig. 3.43.

It is necessary to distinguish between *drives* and *places*. In the discussion
above, $N$ is the number of *drives* possessed by the circuit (we assume here

that a circuit constitutes one *load*). However, since $I_{in}$ can be furnished by more than one circuit if the conditions are favorable, a circuit can be connected to more *places* than it has drives. For example, if the logic is such that in a given circuit $I_{in}$ is always furnished by two circuits, the load on each of the two circuits can be taken to be $\frac{1}{2}$. For instance, consider the selector switch shown in Fig. 3.44 for selecting one out of four lines. We

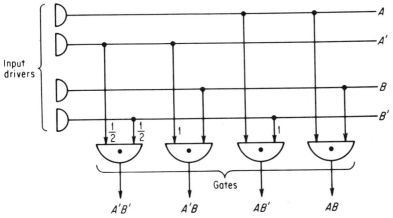

**Fig. 3.44.** One out of four selector.

wish to determine the loading on the circuits furnishing the signals $A$, $A'$, $B$, and $B'$. In this example, we can do so in two ways:

1. Observe that under all circumstances the input drivers have to hold up only three of the gates. Thus, the current furnished by the input drivers is a total of $3I_{in}$, which is divided among two of the drivers. Hence, each driver must furnish a maximum of $\frac{3}{2}I_{in}$ or, in other words, each driver drives $\frac{3}{2}$ of a load. Note, however, each driver goes to two places.

2. The effect of each possible input is examined. In the example of Fig. 3.44 this can be done by examining one case. For example, to obtain $AB$ the signals $A$ and $B$ are down (low, negative) while the signals $A'$, $B'$ are up (high, near zero). Hence, the drivers furnishing $A'$ and $B'$ must hold off the three gates producing $A'B'$, $A'B$, and $AB'$. These drivers, singly, hold off the second and third gates. Therefore, the loads for those two gates can be taken as unity for each, as shown by the numbers adjacent to the input arrows in Fig. 3.44. However $A'$ and $B'$ share the load of the gate producing $A'B'$. The division of load that produces the *minimum total load* on any of the input drivers is $\frac{1}{2}$, $\frac{1}{2}$. Hence, the total load of any of the input drivers is $1\frac{1}{2}$. This method is of general application but it may be quite difficult to apply in some cases because it involves a minimization process.

### 3.15  SOME ECONOMIC CONSIDERATIONS

In the design of minimum-delay logical networks, one frequently obtains networks of the form shown in Fig. 3.45. Here the load on the AND circuits

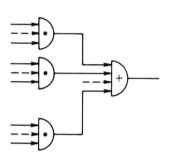

(gates) does not exceed one OR circuit (buffer) load. Because of this, it may be economically desirable to design a class of circuits that can drive only one buffer load. However, it would still be true that such gates may have to go to more than one *place*.

In those logical configurations where the gates go only to the buffer, one may think it obvious that a further saving in cost and improvement in reliability may be obtained by eliminating the diodes at the input to the buffer, since these diodes are not logi-

**Fig. 3.45.** A minimum-delay network.

cally necessary in the network of Fig. 3.45. One must exercise extreme caution in deciding whether or not to adopt component-reduction steps such as this one. Such steps are often adopted by the inexperienced without considering the effect on the total cost of the system. Such a change has the following as some of its consequences:

1. The design of another circuit. This design problem, although superficially simple, requires the determination of new operating conditions for the components, new component specifications, new reliability estimates, a long testing procedure, and possibly a long optimization procedure.

2. The packaging of another circuit with all the time-consuming considerations and tests involved.

3. The revision of the rules for using the logical elements. The additional complexity of these logical rules may result in the net lengthening of the logical design time, increasing costs.

4. Additional rigidity in the design in that errors in the logical design are more difficult to correct if more circuit types are used.

5. Additional complexity, causing increased costs in design, construction, and maintenance and a greater chance of disastrous or troublesome error in any one of these phases.

We close this section with an elementary example of the techniques involved in the selection of the number of different types of the circuit of Fig. 3.43 for a given system. The example is based on the following assumptions:

1. The cost of a circuit installed in the machine is directly proportional only to the maximum number of drives it furnishes. The reason is partly

that the drive capability depends on the current gain of the transistor and that high current gain in some transistor types commands a higher price. Five dollars a drive is assumed per circuit.

2. The cost of designing a circuit is directly proportional only to the maximum number of drives it furnishes. This is based on the fact that more possible configurations exist among the high drive circuits than among the low drive circuits and that each configuration is tested or its expected performance explored in some other way. Fifteen thousand dollars a drive is assumed for this testing.

3. The machine contains the numbers of circuits needing the drive capabilities given in Table 3.12.

TABLE **3.12.** DISTRIBUTION OF DRIVE REQUIREMENTS

| Number of drives | Number of circuits |
|:---:|:---:|
| 1 | 1000 |
| 2 | 2000 |
| 3 | 3000 |
| 4 | 2500 |
| 5 | 2000 |
| 6 | 1500 |
| 7 | 1000 |
| 8 | 500 |

Clearly we could design only one circuit furnishing eight drives and this circuit could suffice throughout the machine. We have the cost figures in this case for one system:

Design:          $8 \times \$15,000 \quad \dots \quad = \$120,000$
Construction:    $8 \times \$5 \times 13,500 = \underline{\quad 540,000}$
One design:                      TOTAL $= \$660,000$

We could, however, make two circuit designs, e.g., one design for four or less drives and another for five to eight drives. This division yields the minimum cost for two designs as determined by trial and the cost figures for one system:

Design:          $8 \times \$15,000 \quad = \$120,000$
                 $4 \times \$15,000 \quad = \quad 60,000$
Construction:    $8 \times \$5 \times 5000 = \quad 200,000$
                 $4 \times \$5 \times 8500 = \underline{\quad 170,000}$
Two designs:                     TOTAL $= \$550,000$

For three circuit designs, e.g., one design for three or less drives and another for four to five drives, and a third for six to eight drives, we obtain the cost figures:

Design:            8 × $15,000    = $120,000
                   5 × $15,000    =   75,000
                   3 × $15,000    =   45,000
Construction:      8 × $5 × 3000 =  120,000
                   5 × $5 × 4500 =  112,500
                   3 × $5 × 6000 =   90,000
Three designs:              TOTAL = $562,500

For one system, the minimum cost is obtained for two designs. However, if the design costs are spread over several systems, the cost per system in this admittedly artificial example is less for three designs than for two designs or for one design. The reader should not attempt to draw any general conclusions from this example except the following:

1. A widely used minimization procedure is illustrated, in principle, for costs.
2. Minimum cost per system usually is obtained when a limited number of circuit designs are made.

## REFERENCES

1. Caldwell, S., *Switching Circuits and Logical Design* (New York: John Wiley & Sons, 1958). Contains an extensive bibliography.

2. Flores, Ivan, *Computer Logic, The Functional Design of Digital Computers*, (Englewood Cliffs, N.J.: Prentice-Hall, Inc., 1960).

3. University of Pennsylvania, Institute for Cooperative Research, *Common Programming Language Task, Part I*, Final Report AD59UR1, Contract No. DA-36-039-sc-75047, June 30, 1959.

## PROBLEMS

1. Minimize the following expressions (i.e., minimum number of letters):
   (a) $abcd + abcd' + abc'd + abc'd' + ab'cd + a'b'cd + a'b'c'd'$
   (b) $abc'd' + abcd + a'b'cd + a'b'c'd' + ab'c'd'$
   (c) $(a' + b' + c' + d)(a' + b' + c')(a' + b + c + d')(a + b + c' + d')$

2. Design a checking circuit for a "2-out-of-7" code utilizing a table of combinations.

3. Can you add to the sets of functions of two variables listed in Table 3.10?

4. Extend the sets in Table 3.10 to functions of $n$ variables, $n > 2$.

**5.** Design a full adder for two inputs $A$ and $B$ with outputs $S$ and $C$ using only the Peirce stroke ($F = A'B'$) function. The answer should be in a logical diagram form using only the following symbol.

Fig. P3.5.

**6.** Determine the division of the number of drives for three designs, as discussed in the text, which yields a minimum total cost for one system.

## RESEARCH PROBLEMS

**1.** Study the functions of three variables for new sets of functions with which combinational logic can be performed.

# 4

# SEQUENTIAL LOGIC AND TIMING

In this chapter, we will consider the principles of sequential circuits as applied to digital computers. We will also develop those devices which are needed in addition to the logical elements, in order to build a computer. The various timing systems will be discussed with illustrative examples of timing calculations.

## 4.1 DEFINITION OF A SEQUENTIAL CIRCUIT

The logic networks discussed so far have been combinational circuits, the outputs of which are functions only of the inputs, there being therefore no effects due to time delays. In a sequential circuit, time enters in such a way that the outputs at any instant are functions not only of the inputs at that instant but also of the inputs at all previous instants in the history of the device. Thus a digital computer is a sequential circuit.

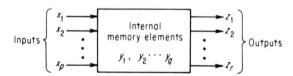

**Fig. 4.1.** Huffman-Moore model of a sequential circuit.

One model of a sequential circuit is the Huffman-Moore model. Let us look at Fig. 4.1. There are $p$ two-valued inputs, and $q$ two-valued internal stored quantities which could be stored in, for example, $q$ flip-flops. Thus, there are a maximum of $2^p$ input states, $2^q$ internal states, and $2^r$ output states, all of which may or may not exist in a given system. The outputs and the states of the internal memory elements are combinational functions of the states of the input and memory element, as given by Boolean equations of the form

$$z_j^k = f_j(x_1^k, x_2^k, \ldots, x_p^k, y_1^k, y_2^k, \ldots, y_q^k), \qquad j = 1, 2, \ldots, r$$
$$y_j^{k+1} = g_j(x_1^k, x_2^k, \ldots, x_p^k, y_1^k, y_2^k, \ldots, y_q^k), \qquad j = 1, 2, \ldots, q \qquad (4.1)$$

which give the $z_j$ at time instant $k$ and the $y_j$ at time instant $k + 1$ in terms of the $x_j$ and $y_j$ at time instant $k$. We see that the sequential circuit contains memory elements and that the design of a sequential circuit, once memory elements have been selected and assigned to the internal states, is a problem in the design of combinational circuits.

At this point, it should be mentioned that there are two types of sequential circuits. These are

(a) Synchronous (sometimes called *clocked*). In synchronous sequential circuits, the time instants are marked out by an external timing signal generator called a clock.

(b) Asynchronous (sometimes called *unclocked*). In asynchronous sequential circuits, the time instants are marked out by signals derived from the various signals in the circuit. These derived signals are sometimes called *logical clocks* when they exist explicitly.

Most digital computers are grossly synchronous and locally asynchronous.

## 4.2  ANALYSIS OF SEQUENTIAL CIRCUITS

Let us consider the sequential circuit shown in Fig. 4.2. The logical elements are all of the universal element previously discussed, i.e., the buffer-inverter. Those people familiar with such things will recognize the circuit as one stage of a double-rank shift register (to be defined) with its output negated and fed back to its input, and with the shift pulse $S_2$ obtained in a peculiar fashion from $S_1$. To analyze the operation of the circuit, one might construct a diagram showing the various time relationships among the waveforms at various points in the circuit. Such a diagram would provide a complete description of the circuit's operation, but is very difficult to draw and to interpret for complex circuits. Various other methods of analysis have been developed to make it easier to analyze such circuits, but these methods suffer from what may be drawbacks in some cases since they may not detect certain malfunctions. We will discuss, briefly, two methods that are sometimes of use in understanding the operation of a circuit: they are the sequence table and the Huffman method.

Why these methods overlook some features of the circuit's operation may be qualitatively understood by recognizing that the waveforms represent the solutions of the differential equations of the entire circuit, and any method that starts from any other starting place cannot give a complete description of the circuit's operation.

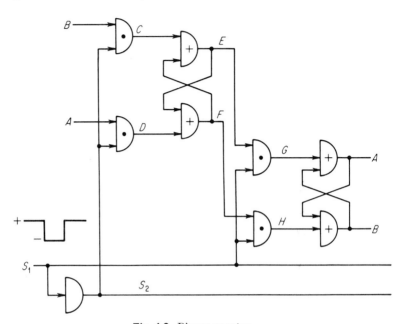

**Fig. 4.2.** Binary counter.

The sequence table gives the voltages in the circuit at discrete times which are multiples of some unit of time such as the delay of a logical element. To construct a sequence table, let 1 represent a voltage near zero, and 0 represent a negative voltage. The equations for the various quantities in Fig. 4.2 are $S_2 = S_1'$, $C = S_2'B'$, $D = S_2'A'$, $E = C'F'$, $F = D'E'$, $G = S_1'E'$, $H = S_1'F'$, $A = G'B'$ and $B = H'A'$. The signal $S_1$ starts out at 1, goes to 0, and returns to 1. Let us assume that the letters have the values shown below.

| $S_1$ | $S_2$ | $A$ | $B$ | $C$ | $D$ | $E$ | $F$ | $G$ | $H$ |
|-------|-------|-----|-----|-----|-----|-----|-----|-----|-----|
| 1     | 0     | 1   | 0   | 1   | 0   | 0   | 1   | 0   | 1   |

Since these do not check when substituted in the equations, we compute a new line from the equations using the above values of the variables and the given equations. The result is

| $S_1$ | $S_2$ | $A$ | $B$ | $C$ | $D$ | $E$ | $F$ | $G$ | $H$ |
|-------|-------|-----|-----|-----|-----|-----|-----|-----|-----|
| 1     | 0     | 1   | 0   | 1   | 0   | 0   | 1   | 0   | 0   |

(4.2)

A repetition of the computation yields the same result. Hence the condition in (4.2) is a stable state. We now apply the input—i.e., $S_1$ is changed to zero—and compute new values of the quantities from the equations using the values for all the variables as given in (4.2). The result is

| $S_1$ | $S_2$ | $A$ | $B$ | $C$ | $D$ | $E$ | $F$ | $G$ | $H$ |
|---|---|---|---|---|---|---|---|---|---|
| 0 | 0 | 1 | 0 | 1 | 0 | 0 | 1 | 0 | 0 |

The process is continued to yield the sequence table (Table 4.1). Note that

TABLE **4.1.** SEQUENCE TABLE FOR FIG. 4.2

| $S_1$ | $S_2$ | $A$ | $B$ | $C$ | $D$ | $E$ | $F$ | $G$ | $H$ | |
|---|---|---|---|---|---|---|---|---|---|---|
| 1 | 0 | 1 | 0 | 1 | 0 | 0 | 1 | 0 | 1 | INITIAL STATE (ASSUMED) |
| 1 | 0 | 1 | 0 | 1 | 0 | 0 | 1 | 0 | 0 | |
| 1 | 0 | 1 | 0 | 1 | 0 | 0 | 1 | 0 | 0 | STABLE STATE |
| 0 | 0 | 1 | 0 | 1 | 0 | 0 | 1 | 0 | 0 | INPUT CHANGED |
| 0 | 1 | 1 | 0 | 1 | 0 | 0 | 1 | 1 | 0 | |
| 0 | 1 | 0 | 0 | 0 | 0 | 0 | 1 | 1 | 0 | |
| 0 | 1 | 0 | 1 | 0 | 0 | 0 | 1 | 1 | 0 | |
| 0 | 1 | 0 | 1 | 0 | 0 | 0 | 1 | 1 | 0 | STABLE STATE |
| 1 | 1 | 0 | 1 | 0 | 0 | 0 | 1 | 1 | 0 | INPUT CHANGED |
| 1 | 0 | 0 | 1 | 0 | 0 | 0 | 1 | 0 | 0 | |
| 1 | 0 | 0 | 1 | 0 | 1 | 0 | 1 | 0 | 0 | |
| 1 | 0 | 0 | 1 | 0 | 1 | 0 | 0 | 0 | 0 | |
| 1 | 0 | 0 | 1 | 0 | 1 | 1 | 0 | 0 | 0 | |
| 1 | 0 | 0 | 1 | 0 | 1 | 1 | 0 | 0 | 0 | STABLE STATE |

both flip-flops have changed state. If we repeat the input sequence, we will return eventually to the initial stable state, illustrating the operation of the circuit as a binary counter.

We have taken as time intervals the time delay of one logical element. If more than one signal changes at a time a *race* is said to exist. Examination of the sequence table shows the existence of races. In the fifth line, both $S$ and $G$ have changed. To examine the effect of this race, one would have to expand this part of the sequence table to find the consequences of $C$'s winning the race and of $G$'s winning the race. This corresponds to the examination of the time relationships of the various waveforms as functions of the delays of the logical elements. If the outcome of the race is independent of the winner, the race is said to be *noncritical*. All races must be noncritical if any exist or else the circuit will malfunction in some circumstances.

Another binary counter is shown in Fig. 4.3. This counter uses only one flip-flop per stage but requires delay elements. It is drawn in such a way as to illustrate its relation to the single-rank shift register (to be defined). Its sequence table is given in part in Table 4.2, assuming that the outputs of the delay elements do not change during the input pulse.

Huffman has developed a method of analysis of sequential circuits which has further obscured their workings but has provided a practical means of

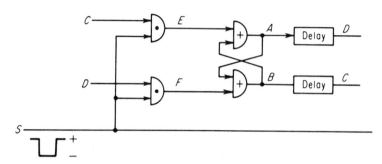

Fig. **4.3.** Binary counter.

partially analyzing complex circuits and has provided switching theoreticians with much food for thought. He has also extended his method to the synthesis of sequential circuits.

TABLE **4.2.** SEQUENCE TABLE

| $S$ | $A$ | $B$ | $C$ | $D$ | $E$ | $F$ | |
|---|---|---|---|---|---|---|---|
| 1 | 0 | 1 | 1 | 0 | 0 | 0 | INITIAL STABLE STATE |
| 0 | 0 | 1 | 1 | 0 | 0 | 0 | INPUT CHANGED |
| 0 | 0 | 1 | 1 | 0 | 0 | 1 | |
| 0 | 0 | 0 | 1 | 0 | 0 | 1 | |
| 0 | 1 | 0 | 1 | 0 | 0 | 1 | STABLE STATE |
| 0 | 1 | 0 | 1 | 0 | 0 | 1 | |
| 1 | 1 | 0 | 1 | 0 | 0 | 1 | INPUT CHANGED |
| 1 | 1 | 0 | 1 | 0 | 0 | 0 | |
| 1 | 1 | 0 | 0 | 1 | 0 | 0 | OUTPUTS OF DELAY LINES CHANGE (STABLE) |
| 1 | 1 | 0 | 0 | 1 | 0 | 0 | DEMONSTRATION OF STABILITY OF ABOVE STATE |

To analyze the binary counter of Fig. 4.2 by his method, first redraw it as in Fig. 4.4, inserting delays in all flip-flop feedback loops. Since there are several ways in which these delay elements may be placed, there will be several outcomes of the analysis, each of which should be studied in the course of developing a complete understanding of the circuit's operation. Also, the effect of delays in the other feedback loops involving the paths $A$, $B$, $E$, and $F$ should be considered. The notation used is that of Fig. 4.1. The inputs of the delays are labeled $Y_1$, $Y_2$ and the outputs are labeled $y_1$, $y_2$. We may write

$$Y_1 = x'y_2' + xy_1 + y_1y_2' = x'y_2' + xy_1$$
$$Y_2 = xy_1 + x'y_2 + y_1y_2 = xy_1 + x'y_2 \qquad (4.3)$$
$$z = y_2'$$

Take the memory elements to be the delays; the signals $Y_1$, $Y_2$ are their "excitations" and the signals $y_1$ and $y_2$ are their "responses." The terminology is taken from the relay technology for which Huffman's method was originally derived; there, $Y$ was the signal applied to a relay coil while $y$ was the state of a normally open contact on the relay.

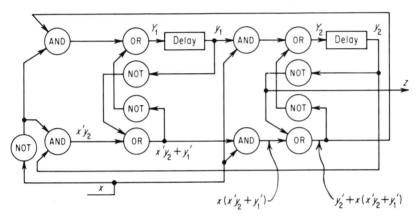

**Fig. 4.4.** Binary counter redrawn.

Now construct the $Y$ *matrix*, which is a table the entries of which are $Y_1$, $Y_2$ obtained from Eqs. (4.3). From the $Y$ matrix (Table 4.3), the $\tau$

**TABLE 4.3.** $Y$ MATRIX

|  |  | $x$ | |
|---|---|---|---|
|  |  | 0 | 1 |
|  | 00 | 10 | 00 |
|  | 01 | 01 | 00 |
| $y_1y_2$ | 11 | 01 | 11 |
|  | 10 | 10 | 11 |

*matrix* or *transition matrix* can be constructed, the entries of which are $\tau_1$, $\tau_2$ where $\tau = 1$ if $y \neq Y$. This is shown in Table 4.4. Table 4.4 shows at a glance the state of the delays in the circuit. An entry of unity means that the input and output of a delay differ. This corresponds to an unstable

**TABLE 4.4.** $\tau$ MATRIX

|  | | $x$ | |
|---|---|---|---|
|  |  | 0 | 1 |
| $y_1y_2$ | 00 | 10 | 00 |
|  | 01 | 00 | 01 |
|  | 11 | 10 | 00 |
|  | 10 | 00 | 01 |

state. Races would show up as the appearance of more than one "1" in a square.

The $z$ matrix, the entries of which are $z$, may also be constructed from Eqs. (4.3); it is shown in Table 4.5.

**TABLE 4.5.** $z$ MATRIX

|  | | $x$ | |
|---|---|---|---|
|  |  | 0 | 1 |
| $y_1y_2$ | 00 | 1 | 1 |
|  | 01 | 0 | 0 |
|  | 11 | 0 | 0 |
|  | 10 | 1 | 1 |

From the $\tau$ matrix we can construct a flow table, Table 4.6.

**TABLE 4.6.** FLOW TABLE

|  | | $x$ | |
|---|---|---|---|
|  |  | 0 | 1 |
| $y_1y_2$ | 00 | 4 | ① |
|  | 01 | ② | 1 |
|  | 11 | 2 | ③ |
|  | 10 | ④ | 3 |

The stable states in the $\tau$ matrix indicated by the entries 00 are entered in the corresponding places in the flow table and are numbered starting from one. These are the circled entries. The remaining spaces in the flow table are filled with the uncircled numbers of the stable states that will result if the circuit is in an unstable state. For example, the position corresponding to $x = 0$, $y_1 = 1$, $y_2 = 1$ contains the entry 2 because, according to the $\tau$ matrix which has the entry 10, the output of delay 1 is 1 while its input is 0. Its output will become 0 corresponding to the state $x = 0$, $y_1 = 0$, $y_2 = 1$ which has the entry ②.

With the flow table and $z$ matrix it is easy to show the sequence of operations, Table 4.7, the entries of which should be compared with those of Table 4.1.

**TABLE 4.7.** SEQUENCE TABLE

| $x$ | state | $z$ |
|-----|-------|-----|
| 0 | ② | 0 |
| 1 | 1 | 0 |
| 1 | ① | 1 |
| 0 | 4 | 1 |
| 0 | ④ | 1 |
| 1 | 3 | 1 |
| 1 | ③ | 0 |
| 0 | 2 | 0 |
| 0 | ② | 0 |

## 4.3 PULSE FORMERS

In order to design a sequential circuit as complex as a computer, we need a synthesis technique of the type used to solve many kinds of engineering problems wherein the problem is broken into smaller parts which are manageable. To do this, we will introduce a memory element called a *pulse former*. This is shown in Fig. 4.5. Notice that the pulse former samples the state of the input and sets the output to the value that the input has when sampled. Typical waveforms for such a device are shown in Fig. 4.6.

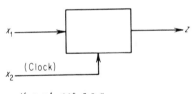

If $x_2 = 1$, set $z = x_1$

If $x_2 = 0$, fix $z$ at last value it had

**Fig. 4.5.** Pulse former.

It is possible to synthesize such a device by the method developed by Huffman, which is the reverse of his analysis procedure, just described. However, the pulse-former design problem itself can be broken into smaller parts and each handled separately. It is clear that the pulse former contains a one-bit storage element. Such an element, a flip-flop, can be constructed from buffer-inverters, as in Fig. 4.7. To use this in a pulse former, we need combinational logic to generate the SET and RESET signals. It is a simple application of the design procedures outlined in the previous chapter to obtain

$$\text{SET} = x_1 x_2$$

$$\text{RESET} = x_1' x_2$$

The resulting design is shown in Fig. 4.8.

In a synchronous sequential system using large numbers of pulse formers, it may be economically or operationally desirable to design a

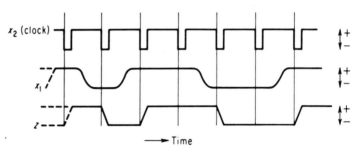

Fig. 4.6. Pulse former waveform.

special pulse former circuit. This was done in the case of Remington Rand's UNIVAC I, which was in production in the early 1950's. The UNIVAC I pulse former is shown, schematically, in Fig. 4.9. The input buffer enables one to make $x_1$ the Boolean sum of a number of variables. The network $N$ merely serves to couple the input voltage levels to the grid of $V_1$; hence, these elements form a buffer-inverter. $V_2$ and $V_3$ are connected

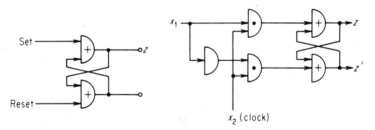

Fig. 4.7. Flip-flop.      Fig. 4.8. Pulse former using buffer-inverters.

as a *toggle-flop*, a single-bit storage element that can be triggered to either of two states at one point (the point being the grid of $V_2$) in much the same way as a toggle switch operates. The diodes $D_1, \ldots, D_6$ serve to couple the plate of $V_1$ to the grid of $V_2$ only at clock pulse time, thus providing the sampling function required in the pulse former. Diodes $D_3$ and $D_6$ normally conduct, reverse-biasing diodes $D_1$, $D_2$, $D_4$, and $D_5$. At clock pulse time (see waveform in Fig. 4.6) diodes $D_3$ and $D_5$ are reverse biased, allowing diodes $D_1$, $D_2$, $D_4$, and $D_5$ to conduct, thereby connecting the grid of $V_2$ to the plate of $V_1$. When this happens, $V_2$ is turned off when $V_1$ is on, and vice versa.

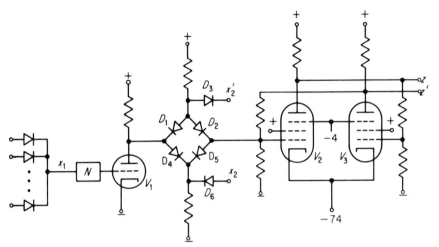

**Fig. 4.9.** UNIVAC I pulse former.

$V_3$ provides the feedback necessary to keep $V_2$ on or off after $D_1$, $D_2$, $D_4$, and $D_5$ become reverse biased. A transistorized version of the circuit of Fig. 4.9 was used in Remington Rand's UNIVAC-LARC.

If we have occasion to use a symbol for a pulse former, we will use the symbols in Fig. 4.10. Notice that both $z$ and $z'$ are assumed available.

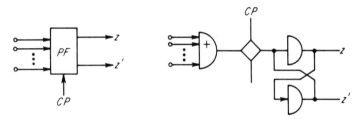

**Fig. 4.10.** Pulse former symbols.

## 4.4 SYNCHRONOUS SYSTEMS

Using pulse formers and the model of a sequential system described by Fig. 4.1 and Eqs. (4.1), we may construct the model of a synchronous sequential system shown in Fig. 4.11. For clarity, only one line is drawn for each bundle of signal lines. Figure 4.11 may be redrawn as illustrated in Fig. 4.12.

The inputs to a digital computer generally come from devices such as magnetic tape units, drums, core memories, and mechanical switches, which have their own timing; therefore, their outputs require synchronization with the clock of the computer. The devices that perform the synchronization we call *input synchronizers*. Also, since the outputs go to similar devices, we require *output synchronizers*.

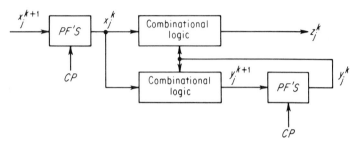

**Fig. 4.11.** Synchronous sequential system.

The closed loop shown, called the *computer loop*, can be the only closed loop in the system, excluding the closed loop through the input and output synchronizers. That is, all closed loops must contain at least one pulse former; the combinational logic cannot contain any closed loops such as

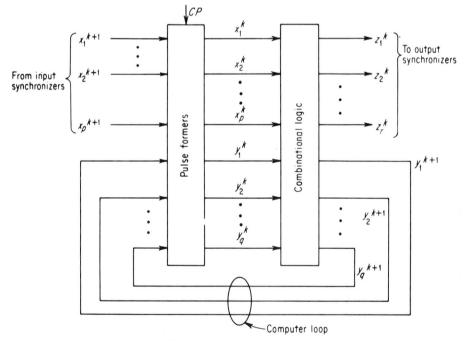

**Fig. 4.12.** Synchronous digital computer.

flip-flops. The maximum delay around the computer loop determines the maximum clock repetition rate of the system. This, together with other timing questions involving the computer loop, will be discussed later in this chapter.

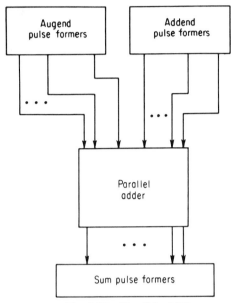

**Fig. 4.13a.** Parallel addition.

In principle, the system in Fig. 4.12 can be converted into an asynchronous system if the clock $(CP)$ is derived from the input and output signals.

How addition may be performed in synchronous systems is shown in

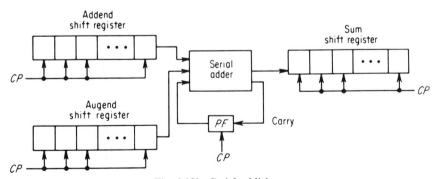

**Fig. 4.13b.** Serial addition.

Fig. 4.13(a) and 4.13(b). Each square in a shift-register block [Fig. 4.13(b)] represents a pulse former. That is, a shift register can be constructed out of pulse formers as shown in Fig. 4.14. The timing problems that exist in Fig. 4.14 will be discussed later. It can be seen, from Figs. 4.12, 4.13, and 4.14, that a computer can also be considered as a shift register with logic between the stages. Thus, if we have the elements to perform combinational logic and can build a shift register, we can build a sequential system.

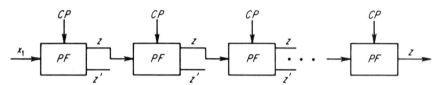

**Fig. 4.14.** Pulse former shift register.

## 4.5 MEMORY ELEMENTS

The pulse former has been used in the previous discussion because of its convenient logical properties. It performs two essential functions in a synchronous system: (a) timing (identification of pulse positions and, hence, their binary significance or meaning) and (b) reshaping of waveforms (this must be performed on a pulse train to prevent its degeneration into meaningless noise because of its distortion by the logic and wiring). Both of these functions involve some kind of memory device and need not be performed only by a pulse former. To show this, we need only show that a pulse former can be constructed from any one of several memory devices together with combinational logic devices.

Some memory elements are listed below.

1. The flip-flop.
2. The binary counter (single-stage, as in Fig. 4.2 for example).
3. A delay (one-bit).
4. The one-shot (monostable) multivibrator.
5. The pulse former.

[It will be left as an exercise to the reader to construct pulse formers and also to construct any other memory element (such as a delay) from any one of these elements.]

It is also true that combinational and sequential logic can be performed using only memories. To prove this it is only necessary to prove that a combinational circuit can be constructed from a memory. To do this construction, recall that a combinational circuit produces outputs which are Boolean functions of the inputs. Let there be a memory (addressable) having as many memory positions as there are input states, and let each address be one of the input states. At each address, store the bits for the output state corresponding to that input state.

One theory of the human brain is that it is a set of memories of this type that are interconnected, the output-state thought corresponding to an input state is stored together with the input state in the learning process.

## 4.6  SHIFT REGISTERS

We now shall consider the timing problems inherent in shift registers. The results are interpretable in terms of digital computer timing systems. A single-rank shift register using flip-flops is shown in Fig. 4.15. It is

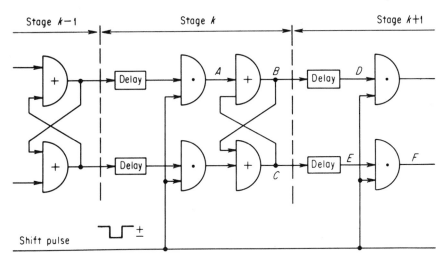

**Fig. 4.15.** Single-rank shift register.

called a single-rank shift register because it contains a single rank of flip-flops; i.e., there is one rank of flip-flops per word or per bit. However, there are two elements of storage for each bit. These consist of a flip-flop and a pair of delay lines. The demarcation between stages is located at the places where logic would be put if this shift register were the basis of a digital computer. The delays would be provided in part or entirely by the delays of the logic circuits. Since there is only one source of shift pulses, this source corresponds to the *single-phase* clock generator that would appear in a system formed around this shift register. Note that each clocking circuit requires a signal and its negation. The negation could be obtained by inverting the signal, which would yield the clocking circuit of the pulse former of Fig. 4.8.

A double-rank shift register is shown in Fig. 4.16. It is called a double-rank shift register because there is a double rank of flip-flops; i.e., there is one rank of flip-flops per word, or two flip-flops per stage or bit. If this shift register were used as the basis of a sequential system, one could place

logic between the flip-flops and the clocking gates. Two sources of shift or
clock pulses would be required, and these pulses should not overlap.

Notice that the delay lines in a stage of the single-rank shift register are
replaced by a flip-flop so that two memory elements per bit are still required. The double-rank shift register, when used as the basis of a sequential system, is the basis of the two-phase clocked system since two sources
of shift or clock pulses are required. Note also that the two-phase system
requires twice as many flip-flops as does the single-phase system. It follows

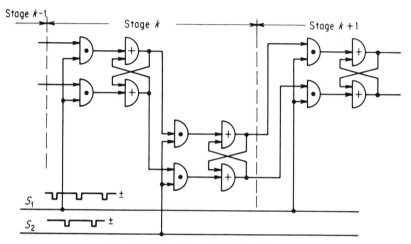

**Fig. 4.16.** Double-rank shift register.

that an $N$-phase system requires $N$ times the memory elements of a single-
phase system. This does not necessarily mean that the single-phase system
is the most inexpensive or the best, because with a given technology it may
not be possible to construct a single-phase system (see discussion of parametric elements in Chap. 5) or, with a given technology, memory elements
are obtained at such little additional cost that minimum cost occurs when
more than one clock phase is used.

We will now return to the single-rank shift register of Fig. 4.15. Any
logical element delays the signals applied to it. By careful standardization
of waveforms it is possible to assign a minimum number of delay parameters to a circuit. For the purpose of illustrating the timing calculations we
will assume that a buffer-inverter delays a rising or falling waveform by
an amount $T$ such that

$$D - \delta \leq T \leq D + \delta$$

where $D$ is its nominal delay and $\delta$ is the tolerance of $D$. With such assumptions we can draw timing diagrams using waveforms with infinitely fast
rise and fall times.

In the case of the single-rank shift register we wish to calculate (a) the clock- or shift-pulse width, (b) the size of the delay lines (minimum delay condition), and (c) the clock repetition rate for the fastest operation (maximum delay condition).

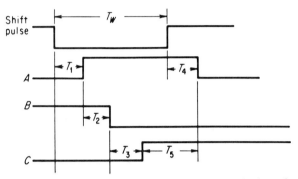

**Fig. 4.17.** Shift-pulse width determination for single-rank shift register.

First, consider the shift-pulse width. Waveforms for Fig. 4.15 are shown in Fig. 4.17. From Fig. 4.17, we have

$$T_1 + T_2 + T_3 + T_5 - T_4 = T_W \qquad (4.4)$$

For the flip-flop to stay set when set, the signal $C$ must go positive at or before the time that signal $A$ has gone negative. In other words, we must always have $T_5 \geq 0$. We shall adopt the convention for any variable $T$ that

$$T^+ \text{ means } \qquad T \leq T^+ \text{ always}$$

$$T^- \text{ means } \qquad T \geq T^- \text{ always}$$

i.e., $T^- \leq T \leq T^+$, or $T^+$ and $T^-$ are the *worst case* limits on $T$. Hence we require $T_5^- = 0$. By inspection from Eq. (4.4), we can write

$$T_5^- = T_{\overline{W}} + T_4^- - T_1^+ - T_2^+ - T_3^+ = 0$$

If, from the delay assumptions,

$$T_1^+ = T_2^+ = T_3^+ = D + \delta$$

$$T_4^- = D - \delta$$

then

$$0 = T_{\overline{W}} - 2D - 4\delta$$

or

$$T_{\overline{W}} = 2D + 4\delta \qquad (4.5)$$

Equation (4.5) defines the minimum width of the shift pulse required to set the flip-flop. Note that $T_{\overline{W}}$ is equal to the maximum delay around the flip-flop loop ($2D + 2\delta$) plus the maximum narrowing at the clock gate ($2\delta$).

The timing waveforms affecting the delay-line lengths are shown in Fig. 4.18, where $T_D$ is the delay of the delay lines. From Fig. 4.18, we have

$$T_1 + T_2 + T_D = T_W + T_6 \tag{4.6}$$

The delay line should be sufficiently long so that the signal $D$ does not change before the shift pulse has gone away. For this reason we have taken

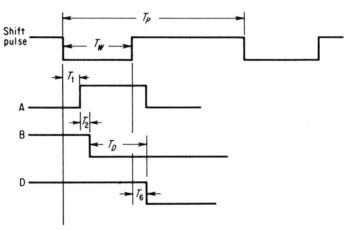

**Fig. 4.18.** Delay-line determination for single-rank shift register.

the minimum-delay path through the flip-flop. Hence, $T_6^- = 0$ is the worst-case condition. From Eq. (4.6),

$$T_1^- + T_2^- + T_D^- = T_W^+$$

or
$$T_D^- = T_W^+ - 2D + 2\delta \tag{4.7}$$

To get the maximum repetition rate, we consider the longest-delay path for information transferred from one stage to the next. This is the path $A$-$B$-$C$-$E$-$F$. The maximum delay through this path is

$$T_{A\text{-}F} = 2(D + \delta) + T_D^+ + (D + \delta)$$
$$= 3D + 3\delta + T_D^+ \tag{4.8}$$

This figure must not be greater than the minimum time between successive shift pulses, $T_P^-$. Hence,

$$T_P^- = 3D + 3\delta + T_D^+$$

and
$$f_{\max} = 1/T_P^+. \tag{4.9}$$

This is the "maximum-delay" condition.

In the case of the double-rank shift register, the clock (or shift) pulse waveforms are as in Fig. 4.19. For this shift register there are only two times to be determined: (a) the minimum clock (or shift) pulse width, and

(b) the time displacement between the successive phases which determines the maximum repetition rate, $f_{max}$ (the maximum-delay condition). There is no minimum-delay condition in multiphase systems.

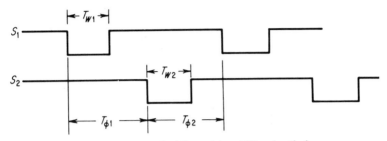

**Fig. 4.19.** Double-rank shift register shift-pulse timing.

We have by simple calculations from Fig. 4.16

$$\text{(a)} \quad T_{\bar{W}1} = T_{\bar{W}2} = 2D + 4\delta$$
$$\text{(b)} \quad T_{\phi 1}^- = T_{\phi 2}^- = 3D + 3\delta \tag{4.10}$$

Condition (a) is the requirement on the minimum pulse width and condition (b) is the maximum-delay condition. The reader should see whether there are any conditions that involve $T_{\bar{W}}^+$ and $T_{\phi}^+$. $[T_{\bar{W}}^+ \leq 2(D - \delta) + T_{\phi}^-,$ $T_{\phi}^+ < \infty.]$

## 4.7  TIMING IN SYNCHRONOUS SEQUENTIAL SYSTEMS

As mentioned above, a synchronous sequential system can be constructed by putting combinational logic between the stages of shift registers. In this way, we may construct single- or multiphase clocked systems.

The timing conditions that have to be satisfied in a single-phase system are similar to those that need to be satisfied in a single-rank shift register. The configuration in the computer loop is shown in Fig. 4.20 (a portion of Fig. 4.12). These timing conditions are

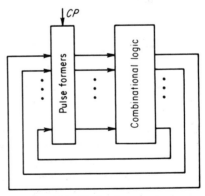

**Fig. 4.20.** Single-phase system.

1. The condition on the minimum clock-pulse width required to operate the pulse formers.
2. The minimum-delay condition. This condition sets a minimum on the amount of delay through the pulse formers and the combinational

logic (if the delay through the logic circuits is insufficient, delay elements must be provided).

3. The maximum-delay condition. (This condition sets the maximum number of logic levels that can be traversed in the combinational logic.)

The latter two paths are developed in more detail in Fig. 4.21. Let $T_{PF}^-$ be

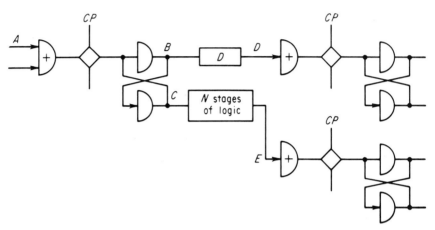

**Fig. 4.21.** Illustrating the maximum- and minimum-delay paths in a single-phase system.

the minimum delay of the pulse former through path $A$-$B$ and let $T_{PF}^+$ be the maximum delay through the pulse former through path $A$-$C$. Then the two conditions yield

1. Minimum-delay condition:

$$T_D^- = T_W^+ - T_{PF}^- \qquad \text{(path } A\text{-}B\text{-}D)$$

2. Maximum-delay condition:

$$T_P^- \geq T_{PF}^+ + N(D + \delta) \qquad \text{(path } A\text{-}B\text{-}C\text{-}E)$$

or
$$N \leq \frac{T_P^- - T_{PF}^+}{D + \delta}$$

Note that the maximum-delay condition determines the maximum permissible number of logic levels between pulse formers.

In the case of multiphase systems, there is no minimum-delay condition. However, the maximum-delay condition or conditions determine the maximum number of logic stages between pulse formers. It is important to recognize that the information rate (pulse rate) and the depth of the logic in levels or stages are not independent quantities. It is meaningless to quote an information (or pulse) rate without stating the depth of the logic in levels.

We may compare single-phase and two-phase systems using the buffer-inverter technology. Such a comparison is made in Table 4.8.

**TABLE 4.8**

| Advantages of 2-$\phi$ system over 1-$\phi$ system | Disadvantage of 2-$\phi$ system as compared to 1-$\phi$ system |
|---|---|
| 1. No minimum delay condition.<br>2. No delay elements needed.<br>3. Less work for logical designer. | 1. Twice the number of pulse formers.<br>2. Slower because of<br>    (a) Delay of additional pulse former.<br>    (b) Extra clock means additional timing tolerances.<br>3. Double the number of clock generators and clock busses. |

It is not necessary that a two-phase system be wholly two-phase through-out. It is possible to operate it in part as a single-phase system. However, the part that operates as a single-phase system has to have its timing treated as single-phase timing. When an $N$-phase system is operated in part as if there were less than $N$ phases, the process is sometimes referred to as "skipping a phase." In any event, the final choice of a system requires a comparison of speed, cost, efficiency, etc.—each case has to be considered separately.

### 4.8  NRZ VERSUS RZ SYSTEMS

Up to now, a "pulse envelope" system has been assumed. This is shown in Fig. 4.22 along with the RZ (return-to-zero) system. Other names for

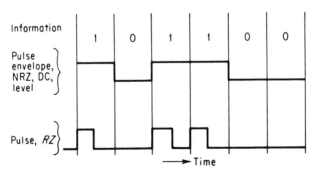

**Fig. 4.22.** RZ versus NRZ.

"pulse envelope" are NRZ (non-return-to-zero), "DC," and "level logic." Another name for the RZ system is "pulse logic." RZ operation is not usually feasible in single-phase systems. One disadvantage of the RZ system is the existence of twice as many signal transitions in a time interval, doubling the timing tolerances. Advantages of the RZ system are the possibility of the use of a-c coupling devices such as capacitors and transformers and the possibility of obtaining more power and less delay in circuit-limited operation because of the less-than-unity duty factor. It is true that some devices must operate in RZ because of their nature. It is also true that NRZ operation with such devices can be achieved by "push-push" operation wherein the output of two or more RZ elements is rectified to produce a level.

### 4.9  SPIKES IN SYNCHRONOUS SYSTEM

Consider the buffer-inverter shown in Fig. 4.23. It is quite possible that signals $A$ and $B$ may have the time relationship shown in Fig. 4.24. The

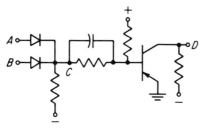

Fig. 4.23.  Buffer-inverter.

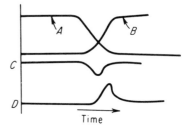

Fig. 4.24.  Spike generation.

waveforms at $C$ and $D$ will then be as shown in the same figure. The waveform $D$ shows the existence of a "spike." In the terminology of switching theory, a "hazard" exists. In clocked synchronous systems, where the logic is performed by networks of circuits like that shown in Fig. 4.23, there is ample opportunity for spike generation. Since the pulse formers sample the

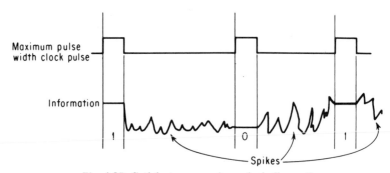

Fig. 4.25.  Satisfactory waveforms including spikes.

outputs of such logic networks, it is necessary that there be no spikes in the outputs at clock time. This can be guaranteed if the timing calculations are made as previously illustrated and if the maximum delay of a circuit, $D + \delta$, is taken as the maximum delay for either a spike or a step, whichever is greater. It is usually optimum to design the logic circuit so that the spike and step delays are the same and are greater than or equal to the delay of the trailing edge of a pulse of any other width. Under these circumstances, the signal at a clock gate of a pulse former will, in the worst case, appear as in Fig. 4.25.

### 4.10  ASYNCHRONOUS SYSTEMS

Our discussion of asynchronous systems will lead to the development of an asynchronous shift register. The technique to be presented does not necessarily yield the design which uses the minimum amount of equipment. The purpose of this section is to develop the principles involved in asynchronous systems in as simple and clear a fashion as the writer finds possible.

The definition of "asynchronous" that we use is "not synchronous," i.e., there is no source of timing signals other than those generated by the logic itself. It will be seen later that only speed-independent, double-rank shift registers are truly asynchronous. In such a register, a large capacitor placed at any point will merely slow its operation. The speed-independent class of circuits are those investigated by Muller and Bartky of the University of Illinois.

*In general, an asynchronous system must be spike-free* (spike-free means there cannot be any critical races, meaning speed independence). The conditions for obtaining a spike must not exist; these conditions are:

1. At least two inputs to a network must change state.
2. The change of inputs must give a transient output different from that before and after the transient.

For example, consider the quarter adder described by the expression

$$S = AB' + A'B$$

Let us construct a sequence table for several possible input sequences (Table 4.9). The table illustrates what happens when the inputs $(A, B)$ change from $(0, 0)$ to $(1, 1)$, both of which inputs should give an output of 1.

The question arises whether or not there are any spike-free logical elements. If there are, and if they provide a sufficient number of logical operations for the performance of combinational logic, we may be able to construct a spike-free system.

TABLE **4.9.** Sequence Table for Quarter Adder
Showing Spike Generation

| | A | B | S | |
|---|---|---|---|---|
| Time | 0 | 0 | 0 | INITIAL STATE |
| | 1 | 0 | 1 | SPIKE |
| | 1 | 1 | 0 | |
| | 1 | 1 | 0 | FINAL STATE |
| | 1 | 0 | 1 | INITIAL STATE |
| | 1 | 1 | 0 | SPIKE |
| | 0 | 1 | 1 | FINAL STATE |

Let us consider the AND circuit described by the expression

$$C = AB$$

A sequence table for several transitions may be constructed as in Table 4.10. We observe that the AND circuit is spike-free if we always start from

TABLE **4.10.** Sequence Table for AND Circuit

| | A | B | C | |
|---|---|---|---|---|
| Time | 0 | 0 | 0 | INITIAL STATE |
| | 0 | 1 | 0 | |
| | 1 | 1 | 1 | FINAL STATE |
| | 0 | 1 | 0 | INITIAL STATE |
| | 1 | 1 | 1 | SPIKE |
| | 1 | 0 | 0 | FINAL STATE |

the (0, 0) state. That is, the AND circuit is spike-free in the RZ system. It is easy to show that similarly the OR circuit and the majority organ and combinations of these are spike-free in the RZ system. However, the inverter when used with these elements produces spikes in some cases. Therefore, a spike-free system in which combinational logic can be performed is the *two-line RZ system*. (See Chap. 3, Sec. 3.12.)

The basis of a single-rank two-line RZ shift register is shown in Fig. 4.26. The reset and shift pulses, because of the presence of the delay lines, must come from a source which produces pulses having accurately controlled durations and repetition rate. Such a source has the characteristics of a clock generator; hence, the shift register of Fig. 4.26 is not asynchronous. We also conclude that if a shift register contains delay lines, it is not speed-independent, because for speed-independence the next operation must be commenced by a signal indicating the completion of the current operation.

The output of a delay line always arrives after a specific time delay and is not dependent on the completion of an operation.

A shift register satisfying all the requirements for an asynchronous system is shown in Fig. 4.27(a). We may regard this as a solution of the problem, but not necessarily as the most efficient solution.

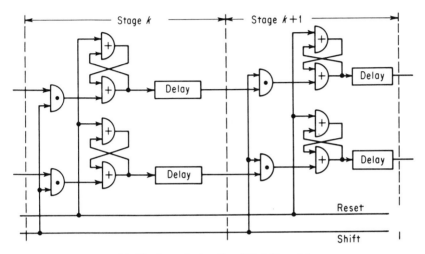

**Fig. 4.26.** Single-rank, two-line RZ shift register.

In its operation, any action must be completed before the next action is initiated. In order to understand its operation, we must assume that information is being shifted continuously along, since no provision for starting circuits has been made. The sequence of actions is shown in Fig. 4.27(b). When all odd-rank flip-flops have received information, the signal ③ will go positive, since it is negative until all flip-flops of the odd rank have received information and their last moving points have settled down. (When the signal is negative, the flip-flop lead $\alpha$ then becomes negative.) Now, if the even rank had received information in another part of the cycle, ④ would be negative. This causes $C_2$ to come on, clearing the even rank. When the even rank is cleared, ④ resets $C_2$ and ① goes negative, thus shifting the information into the even rank and making lead $\beta$ negative. When the shift is completed, ① goes positive and stops the shift. If ② is negative, $C_1$ will go positive and clear the odd rank. ② resets $C_2$ and ③ goes negative, thus shifting the information into the odd rank and making lead $\alpha$ go negative, thereby completing the cycle.

Since every action must be completed before the next action is initiated, a capacitor placed at any point will merely slow operation, and the failure of any circuit will cause operation to cease at the time in the cycle where the failed circuit should switch.

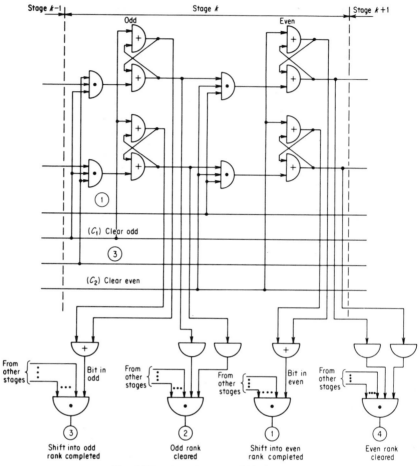

**Fig. 4.27a.** Asynchronous shift register.

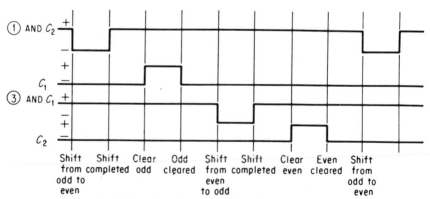

**Fig. 4.27b.** Asynchronous shift register sequence.

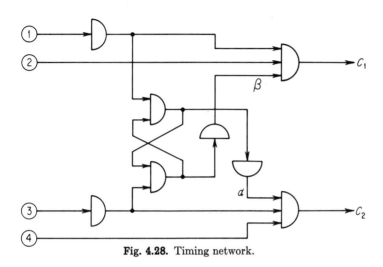

**Fig. 4.28.** Timing network.

Table 4.11 lists some of the relative advantages and disadvantages of asynchronous logic as compared to synchronous logic.

TABLE **4.11.** ADVANTAGES AND DISADVANTAGES OF ASYNCHRONOUS
LOGIC AS COMPARED TO SYNCHRONOUS LOGIC

| Advantages | Disadvantages |
|---|---|
| 1. Theoretically faster because system should operate at circuits' own speeds rather than at worst-case timing speeds.<br>2. Spike-free. | 1. Requires more equipment. Heavy loads on some circuits limit attainable speed.<br>2. More difficult to service.<br>3. More noise-sensitive. |

## 4.11 ELEMENTS REQUIRED FOR COMPUTER LOGIC

We have seen that in order to build a computer, we need to be able to perform combinational and sequential logic. In Chap. 3, the elements required for the performance of combinational logic were discussed. In this chapter we found that in order to build a computer we must also have single-bit memory elements. These memory elements can, in some cases, be constructed from the combinational logic elements. We also saw that in the single-phase synchronous system delay elements may be needed and that delay elements may also be needed in multiphase return-to-zero systems.

In the next chapter we will discuss some devices that singly or in combination can perform these necessary functions. Those combinations of wide application will also be discussed.

## REFERENCES

**1.** Caldwell, S., *Switching Circuits and Logical Design* (New York: John Wiley & Sons, 1958). Contains an extensive bibliography.

**2.** Flores, Ivan, *Computer Logic, The Functional Design of Digital Computers* (Englewood Cliffs, N.J.: Prentice-Hall, Inc., 1960).

**3.** Muller, D. E., and W. S. Bartky, "A Theory of Asynchronous Circuits," *The Annals of the Computation Laboratory of Harvard University*, **XXIX** (1959), 204–243.

## PROBLEMS

**1.** For the single-rank shift register of Fig. 4.15, we have

$$D \pm \delta = 30 \pm 10 \text{ nanoseconds}$$

Assuming that the shift-pulse width, the delay lines, and the clock period have no tolerances, find:
(a) the shift-pulse width.
(b) the size of the delay lines.
(c) the clock repetition rate for fastest operation.

**2.** Repeat the calculations of Prob. 1, if the tolerance on the shift-pulse width is $\pm 10$ nsec and the tolerances on the delay lines and the clock period are $\pm 5$ per cent. The answers to parts (a) and (b) should be nominal values. In part (c), calculate the nominal value of the maximum usable clock rate.

**3.** For the double-rank shift register of Fig. 4.16, we have

$$D \pm \delta = 30 \pm 10 \text{ nsec}$$

Assuming that the shift-pulse width and the clock period have no tolerances, find:
(a) the shift-pulse width.
(b) the clock repetition rate for fastest operation.

**4.** Repeat the calculations of Prob. 3 if the tolerance on the shift-pulse width is $\pm 10$ nsec and the tolerances on $T_{\phi 1}$ and $T_{\phi 2}$ are $\pm 5$ per cent. The answer to part (a) should be the nominal value of the shift-pulse width. In part (b), calculate the nominal value of the maximum usable clock rate.

**5.** In a single-phase clocked synchronous system (Fig. 4.21), the delay of a logical element is

$$D \pm \delta = 30 \pm 10 \text{ nsec}$$

whether in a pulse former or in logic (neglect the delay of the bidirectional clock gate). For a 2-mcps $\pm 5$ per cent single-phase clock rate, find:
(a) the clock-pulse nominal width.
(b) the maximum number of stages of logic that can be used between pulse formers. When is the minimum-delay condition violated?
The tolerance on the clock-pulse width is $\pm 10$ nsec.

**6.** Assume the conditions of Prob. 5 and that ideal lossless delay elements, having any delay, can be constructed with a delay tolerance of ±50 per cent. Determine the minimum number of types of delay elements that must be provided so that all timing conditions are satisfied when any number of logic stages, up to the maximum permissible, are placed between pulse formers.

**7.** A pulse former in a hypothetical multiphase RZ system is constructed and operated as shown below for one of the several clock phases. Determine the

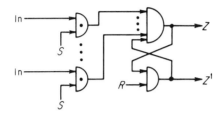

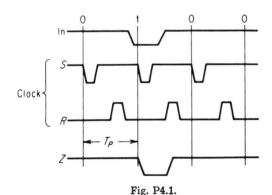

Fig. P4.1.

timing relations that must be satisfied by the various signals if the nominal width of a pulse at $Z$ ($T_Z$) satisfies the condition $T_Z = kT_P$ where $0 < k < 1$.

**8.** Show how the pulse former of Prob. 7 can be used in multiphase RZ logic. If

$$D \pm \delta = 30 \pm 10 \text{ nsec}$$

all clock tolerances are ±5 per cent, and $k = 0.5$, determine the system timing and clock phasing for the maximum information rate. If any delay elements are needed, assume a tolerance of ±5 per cent on their delay.

**9.** In the asynchronous shift register of Fig. 4.27, determine its shifting rate if the delay of a logical element is 40 nsec.

**10.** Repeat Prob. 9 for the case where the gate that produces the signal ① has a delay of 1 second. Assume that the delay of all other logical elements is 40 nsec.

# 5

# DIGITAL COMPUTER CIRCUITS

The considerations involved in the design of a digital computing system include, as we have seen thus far:

(a) The statement of the problems to be solved by the computing system.

(b) The programming of the problems.

(c) The selection of the instruction types and the determination of the major blocks of the system.

(d) The choice of suitable data codes and error-detecting systems.

(e) The choice of a consistent and complete set of operations for the performance of combinational logic.

(f) The selection of the type of sequential logic system and memory elements.

Since all of the above considerations have a bearing on circuit design, it is necessary that circuit designers have some knowledge of the various material listed above.

As an example, consider the two versions of the pulse-former shown in Fig. 5.1. One may ask which pulse former is chosen. The first one uses what might be called "the standard logical package" while the second one represents a special circuit design. One can consider each possibility with respect to its relative merits. The choice is then based on whichever circuit yields the highest value of some suitably designated figure of merit or similar quantity. The point we are making here is that the question of need for a special pulse-former circuit can be determined by following specific procedures, which can often be applied in development work to determine the choice of the combinations of electronic components that are to carry out the combinational and sequential logic operations in a computer.

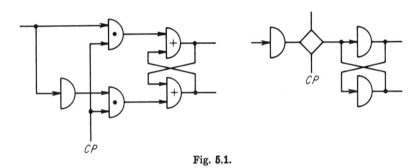

**Fig. 5.1.**

In this chapter we will discuss some of the ways in which electronic components may be connected to perform logical operations. The requirements of combinational and sequential logic place restrictions on what circuits can be used. This limits the number of possibilities that need be investigated for their relative merits by the procedures alluded to above and reduces the problem of the choice of circuits to a more manageable size.

## 5.1 TYPES OF CIRCUITS AND FUNCTIONS PERFORMED

We may ask whether or not there is any systematic procedure for determining a new circuit configuration that performs a given function using new devices. The answer that we have to give here is that this is a creative art which is, at present, not reducible to a science. The best that can be offered to the student is a review and classification of the prior art.

There are several ways to initially classify circuits. One way is by dividing them into those suited to pulse-envelope (NRZ) logic and those suited to pulse (RZ) logic. Also we may classify them on the basis of the functions that have to be performed, such as *logic* and *amplification*. The fact that the logical operations are *nonlinear* operations requires that nonlinear elements be used for the performance of this logic, or if linear elements are used, they must have nonlinear elements associated with them. Some of the elements that have been used singly or in combination to perform logic are:

(a) Diodes.
(b) Resistors; linear, used with nonlinear amplifiers.

  (c)  Magnetic cores without gain:
     (i)  single-apertured.
     (ii) multi-apertured.

Devices for providing amplification include:

  (a)  Relays.
  (b)  Vacuum tubes.
  (c)  Transistors.
  (d)  Magnetic cores (nonlinear).
  (e)  Negative resistance devices.
  (f)  Time varying inductors and capacitors (parametric amplifiers).

The operation of typical combinations will be described.

### 5.2  LOGIC USING PASSIVE ELEMENTS

Two of the passive elements listed above are the diode and the resistor. We can regard the diode as a nonlinear resistor or we can regard the resistor as a poor diode. We may replace diodes in a diode logic circuit by resistors with a corresponding loss in efficiency. A three-level diode logic circuit is shown in Fig. 5.2. A multiple-input positive OR is shown driving

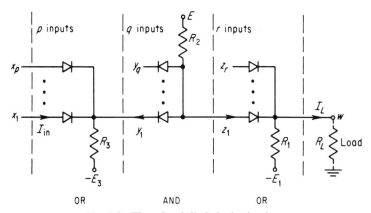

**Fig. 5.2.** Three-level diode logic circuit.

a multiple-input positive AND, which in turn drives a multiple-input positive OR. This diode circuit drives a load at $w$. Any input $x_1$ or $x_2$, etc., will make the voltage at $y_1$ rise, cutting off the corresponding diode in the AND circuit. If all inputs $y_1, y_2, \ldots, y_q$ are positive, $z_1$ will be positive. If any of the inputs $z$ are positive, $w_1$ will be positive. When all the inputs at $z$ are negative, the resistor $R_1$ will pull the point $w$ negative. The resistor $R_2$ must drive the point $w$ positive, overcoming the current in $R_1$, etc. The diodes have characteristics similar to that shown in Fig. 5.3. The forward drop is finite and there is a nonzero reverse current. We will assume that any diode in Fig. 5.2 has a drop of $V_d$ when conducting. We may then construct the table of voltages at various points in the circuit of Fig. 5.2. This will be done under the assumption that the voltage at $w$ has a maximum positive value of $V_+$ and a maximum negative value of $-V_-$. We also will obtain for these conditions the least upper and greatest lower bounds on the voltages at the various points in the circuit. The results are given in the first two lines of Table 5.1. All voltage symbols stand for magnitudes.

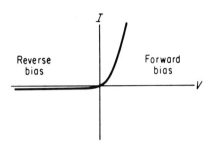

Fig. **5.3.** Diode characteristic.

TABLE **5.1**

|  | $w$ | $z_1$ | $y_1$ | $x_1$ |
|---|---|---|---|---|
| $V_{max}$ | $V_+$ | $V_+ + V_d$ | $V_+ + V_d$ | $V_+ + 2V_d$ |
| $V_{min}$ | $-V_-$ | $-V_-$ | $-V_- - V_d$ | $-V_- - V_d$ |
| $\Delta V$ | $V_+ + V_-$ | $(V_+ + V_-) + V_d$ | $(V_+ + V_-) + 2V_d$ | $(V_+ + V_-) + 3V_d$ |

The entry under $y_1$ of $V_+ + V_d$ assumes, for example, that the diodes in the AND circuit are zero-biased, allowing all the current in $R_2$ to drive the OR circuit. The third line shows the minimum voltage swings required at each point for maximum output-voltage swing, and the entries are obtained as the difference of the entries in the first two lines. Notice that there is a loss of voltage swing of amount $V_d$ in each level of diode logic. The currents (directions shown on the figure) required at the various points are given in Table 5.2 along with the current swings.

TABLE **5.2**

|  | $w$ | $z_1$ | $y_1$ | $x_1$ |
|---|---|---|---|---|
| $I(V_{max})$ | $\dfrac{V_+}{R_L}$ | $\dfrac{V_+}{R_L} + \dfrac{V_+ + E_1}{R_1}$ | $0$ | $\dfrac{V_+ + V_d + E_3}{R_3}$ |
| $I(V_{min})$ | $-\dfrac{V_-}{R_L}$ | $0$ | $\dfrac{E_2 + V_-}{R_2}$ | $0$ |
| $\Delta I$ | $\dfrac{V_+ + V_-}{R_L}$ | $\dfrac{V_+}{R_L} + \dfrac{V_+ + E_1}{R_1}$ | $\dfrac{E_2 + V_-}{R_2}$ | $\dfrac{V_+ + V_d + E_3}{R_3}$ |

The entries in Table 5.2 for $\Delta I$ may be cast into a different form by using the nodal equations for the circuit; we obtain

At $w$:
$$\frac{V_-}{R_L} + \frac{V_+}{R_L} = \frac{E_1 - V_-}{R_1} + \frac{V_+}{R_L} = |\Delta I_L|$$

At $z_1$:
$$\frac{V_+}{R_L} + \frac{V_+ + E_1}{R_1} = \frac{E_2 - V_+ - V_d}{R_2} = |\Delta I|_{z_1}$$

At $y_1$:
$$\frac{E_2 + V_-}{R_2} = \frac{E_3 - V_- - V_d}{R_3} = |\Delta I|_{y_1}$$

At $x_1$:
$$|\Delta I_{\text{in}}| = \frac{V_+ + V_d + E_3}{R_3}$$

By simple algebra, there results, neglecting component and voltage tolerances,

$$|\Delta I_{\text{in}}| = \left(\frac{E_3 + V_+ + V_d}{E_3 - V_- - V_d}\right)\left(\frac{E_2 + V_-}{E_2 - V_+ - V_d}\right)\left(\frac{E_1}{E_1 - V_-}\right)|\Delta I_L|$$

$$|\Delta I|_{y_1} = \left(\frac{E_2 + V_-}{E_2 - V_+ - V_d}\right)\left(\frac{E_1}{E_1 - V_-}\right)|\Delta I_L| \qquad (5.1)$$

$$|\Delta I|_{z_1} = \left(\frac{E_1}{E_1 - V_-}\right)|\Delta I_L|$$

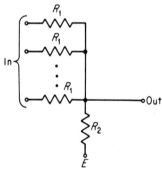

**Fig. 5.4.** Resistor logic circuit.

Each of the parenthesized factors in Eqs. (5.1) is greater than unity. Hence, there is also a loss of current through a diode gate, and, therefore, a loss of power.

A simple resistor logic circuit may be constructed as in Fig. 5.4. It may be recognized as a biased Kirchoff adder. It can perform any one of the functions of AND, OR, or MAJORITY depending on the relative values of $R_1$ and $R_2$, and the polarity of $E$. It is clear that the circuit attenuates voltage, current, and power.

## 5.3 LOGIC IN PULSE-ENVELOPE SYSTEMS

We may construct logical elements from amplifiers alone, or with amplifiers and logic circuits using passive elements as discussed in the last section. Logic circuits using passive elements exhibit a signal voltage, current, and power loss. For this reason they must be used with amplifiers having greater than unity voltage, current, *and* power gain if they are to be capable of driving other circuits of the same type.

The passive-element logic circuits pass all frequencies between some upper point determined by stray inductances and capacitances, and d-c. When used with amplifiers having a similar passband, they may be used in NRZ logic (sometimes also referred to as "baseband logic circuits"). However, if the amplifier does not pass d-c, then an RZ or pulse logic system must be used. (It is sometimes possible to use a carrier with RZ elements so that one could operate in the NRZ system.)

The only amplifying elements listed at the beginning of this chapter that pass d-c are the vacuum tube and the transistor. Hence the only elements that we can use for pulse envelope logic are:

1. Diode logic circuits with amplifiers.
2. Resistor logic circuits with amplifiers.
3. Transistor logic.
4. Vacuum-tube logic.

These, however, can also be used in RZ systems.

## 5.4  DIODE LOGIC CIRCUITS WITH AMPLIFIERS

The amplifier used in NRZ diode logic circuits, whether tube or transistor, must have greater than unity voltage, current, and power gain. Several configurations of transistors and vacuum tubes that use a single element and that amplify are given in Fig. 5.5. A p-n-p transistor is shown; the letters $e$, $b$, $c$ stand for emitter, base, and collector. Clearly, the common-emitter and the grounded-cathode connections are the only ones useful as amplifying elements if only one amplifying element is to be used in an amplifier. However, in many cases there are uses for the special properties of the other connections. In optimized systems, the other transistor connections are rarely seen because of their lower power gain. However, the cathode follower has achieved wide use in vacuum-tube computers, chiefly because of its impedance-matching properties.

There are many different ways in which, for example, two transistors may be connected. Biasing and feedback connections increase this number. One, the Darlington connection, has found some use in computers and is shown in Fig. 5.6. It is the equivalent of a transistor having a common-base current gain, $h_{FB} = \alpha$, of almost unity. If $\alpha_1$, $\alpha_2$ are the common-base current gains of $T_1$ and $T_2$, respectively, the current gain, $\alpha$, of the composite transistor is easily shown to be

$$\alpha = \alpha_1 + \alpha_2 - \alpha_1\alpha_2 \tag{5.2}$$

If we restrict our discussion at this point to a single transistor and diode logic, we are left with several possibilities. One of these is shown in Fig. 5.7. The maximum fan-out usually lies between 2 and 10 while the fan-in can be high without seriously affecting the circuit operation. ("Fan-out" is another term for drive capability, in that it is the number of

| Name of connection | Circuit | Voltage gain | Current gain | Power gain |
|---|---|---|---|---|
| Common base | 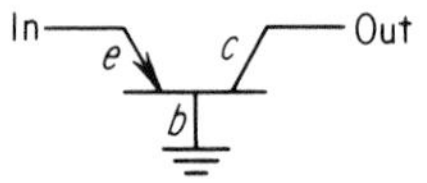 In—e—c—Out, b | ≫1 | Point contact∼2 junction<1 | >1 |
| Common emitter | 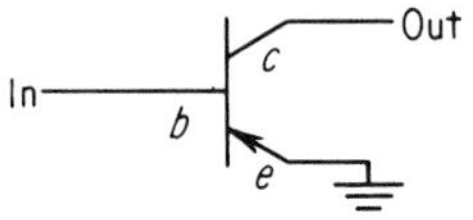 In—b, c—Out, e | ≫1 | ≫1 | ≫1 |
| Common collector | 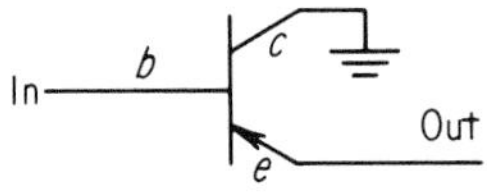 In—b, c, Out—e | <1 | ≫1 | >1 |
| Grounded grid | 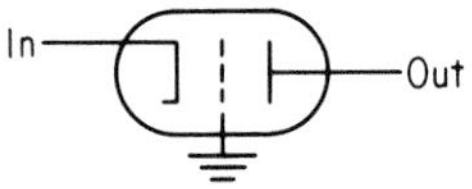 In—Out | ≫1 | <1 | >1 |
| Grounded cathode | 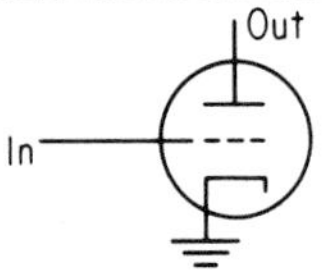 In—Out | ≫1 | ≫1 | ≫1 |
| Cathode follower | 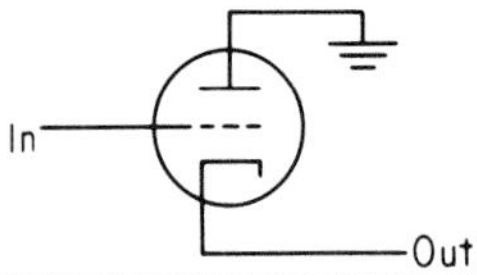 In—Out | <1 | ≫1 | ≫1 |

**Fig. 5.5.** Transistor and tube connections for a single element.

circuits that a given circuit can drive—all circuits being of the same type. "Fan-in" is a term for the number of inputs that a circuit can have.)

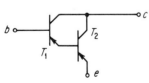

**Fig. 5.6.** Darlington connection.

Since the transistor is on when $b$ is negative and off when $b$ is positive, while $c$ is more or less negative when the transistor is respectively off and on, it is necessary to incorporate a voltage-level changing device in the base circuit. Also, since the transistor can only *charge* the load capacity, speed requirements may make it necessary to put a network in the collector to discharge the load capacity. Various kinds of networks that can be used are shown in Figs. 5.8 and 5.9. The capacitors improve the speed of operation by reducing the transient change in collector voltage of a driving stage required to affect the next stage. This effect reduces the slowing-down effect of wiring capacity. The reader should study what the characteristics of the circuit of Fig. 5.7

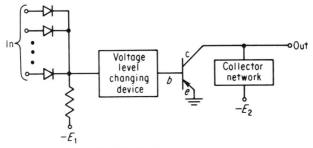

Fig. 5.7. Buffer-inverter.

would be with the various networks of Figs. 5.8 and 5.9. The effect of adding inductances in series with the various resistors in Fig. 5.7 should also be qualitatively considered.

We may reverse the input diodes in the diode circuit. One resulting

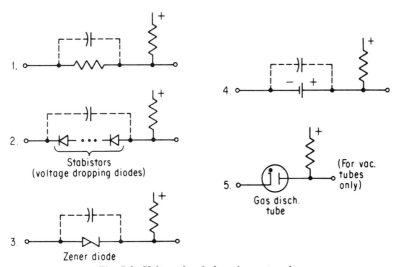

Fig. 5.8. Voltage-level changing networks.

circuit which does not have any serious operating difficulties is shown in Fig. 5.10. It performs the logical function dual to that performed by the circuit of Fig. 5.7. A source of additional delay not encountered in the circuit of Fig. 5.7 is the clipping delay introduced by the diode clamp, C.

When transistors having a higher gain than the minimum required for operation are used, these circuits *saturate*, increasing the time required for turn-off. The base current can be reduced to just that required to support the load by the feedback diode $D_F$ in Fig. 5.11.

The diode $D_F$ does not allow the collector-to-base voltage to become less than $V_2$ (less the drop of $D_F$) by reducing the base current. The spike performance of the circuit is adversely affected by the delay around the

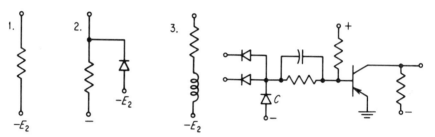

Fig. **5.9.** Collector networks.          Fig. **5.10.** Gate-inverter.

feedback loop. The turn-off time of the diode also adversely affects the turn-off time of the circuit.

With resistor logic, one configuration is shown in Fig. 5.12. It is usually not feasible to achieve additional speed by placing a capacitor across the resistances in the circuit as done in Fig. 5.8. For example, if a capacitor is placed across $R$, and a change in the number of inputs that are energized takes place, the change in voltage at $A$ will be instantaneously coupled

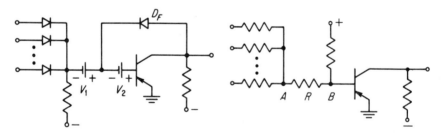

Fig. **5.11.** Collector follower.          Fig. **5.12.** Resistor-transistor logic.

to $B$ by the capacitor, and the transistor may emit a spike. The fan-in and fan-out are limited to low values of the order of two or so, because of the losses in the resistor logic circuit.

In many cases the power gain of transistors is not sufficiently high to make the use of more than one level of logic feasible. However, the power gain of vacuum tubes is sufficiently high so that multilevel diode logic circuits can and have been successfully used with them. One well-known example of this kind of circuit is the SEAC type circuit which will be discussed in the sections on pulse (RZ) logic. Single-level diode logic circuits have been used with vacuum tubes in EDVAC among others.

One important question that has to be answered frequently is which of two possible circuit configurations using similar components yields the greater efficiency. The answer depends on many circumstances including the system specifications. We will indicate by example the nature of some of the reasoning involved. In combinational logic, it is desirable, for reasons which should be clear to the reader, to be able to construct chains of AND-OR logic as in Fig. 5.13. Two essentially equivalent logical

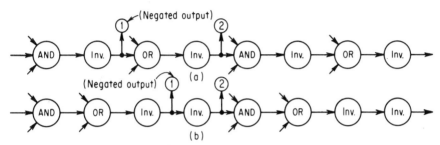

Fig. **5.13.** Two equivalent configurations.

configurations are shown in the figure. In (a), the amplification (inverter) is placed between each logical operator; in (b), two levels of logic are assumed between each amplifier. Let us say that the "power gain" of a level of diode logic is $K_D$ where $K_D < 1$ and that the power gain of an amplifier is $K_A$. Then the power gain through an AND-INV.-OR-INV. combination in (a) is $K_D K_A K_D K_A = K_D^2 K_A^2$ and through an AND-OR-INV.-INV. combination in (b) is $K_D^2 K_A^2$ [which is the same as in (a)]. Hence, for the case where no additional circuits are driven from point ① the maximum drive capability from point ② is the same in (b) as in (a).

Now let $N_a$ be the total number of AND circuits that may be driven from points ② in (a) and let $N_b$ be the corresponding quantity in (b). Then it is simple to show that the maximum values of $N_a$ and $N_b$ are $K_D^2 K_A^2$. This corresponds to no additional circuits being driven from points ① and to the AND-INV. combination in (a) operating at a power level of $1/K_D K_A$ times the power level of the OR-INV. combination.

In the case where $N(a)$, $N(b)$ additional AND circuits are driven from points ① in (a) and (b) (negated outputs), it can easily be shown that the total number of AND circuits that can be driven from point ② is

For (a):     $$N_a = K_A^2 K_D^2 - K_A K_D N(a)$$

For (b):     $$N_b = K_A^2 K_D^2 - K_A N(b)$$

These are plotted in Fig. 5.14.

The signals at points ① do not have the same logical properties; hence, the utility of these signals may not be the same. To choose between the two circuit configurations would require the investigation of typical logic networks to obtain a relation between the utility of the signals ①. This could be expressed as a ratio of the drives required $[N(a)/N(b)]$. If we assume $N(a) = N(b)$, then the configuration in (a) is superior. There are a number of other factors, however, that influence the choice between (a) and (b). With transistors, more power gain can be obtained from (a)

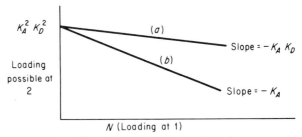

Fig. 5.14. Comparison of configurations.

than from (b) because they are better matched to their loads in (a). Also, since the first amplifier in (b) has to be turned off by a current source in the AND circuit, while the amplifiers in (a) are turned off by the preceding stage, the speed of configuration (b) will be less than that of configuration (a) with transistors even if the effect of the mismatch on speed is ignored. Furthermore, configuration (b) may be more difficult to package than configuration (a) because of the large number of possible AND-OR combinations as compared to buffer combinations.

## 5.5 TRANSISTOR LOGIC

Logic in the NRZ system can also be done with amplifying elements. We have seen how logic may be performed with vacuum tubes by paral-

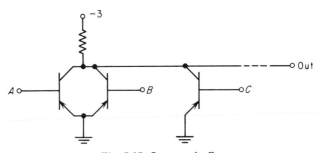

Fig. 5.15. Inverter-buffer.

leling plates to generate universal logical elements. Similar operations can be performed with transistors. For example, several transistors may be connected to produce the inverter-buffer of Fig. 5.15. This is easily seen to be a universal logical element. If the transistors are properly selected, the output of the circuit in Fig. 5.15 may be connected to other bases to form the DCTL (Direct-Coupled Transistor Logic) system. For example, if the potentials in the basic DCTL inverter are as shown in Fig. 5.16, then this direct-coupling is possible since the collector potential in the off condition can guarantee that the next inverter is on, and vice versa.

The difficulties encountered in the selection of transistors for DCTL logic are alleviated somewhat if a voltage-level changing circuit is used with the inverter. When number 1 in Fig. 5.8 is used, the resulting logic system is called RCTL (Resistor-Coupled Transistor Logic).

RCTL or DCTL inverters may be connected in series, as in Fig. 5.17,

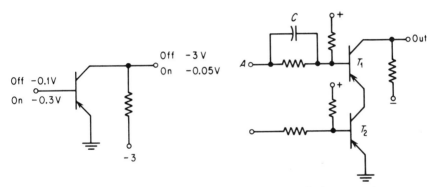

Fig. **5.16.** DCTL inverter.          Fig. **5.17.** Series connection.

in analogy to the relay contact series connection. A maximum of two DCTL inverters, with potentials illustrated in Fig. 5.16, may be connected in series. The capacitor $C$ which shunts the base resistor in RCTL may produce a "sneak" for the reason that when the point $A$ is driven in the positive direction in order to turn off $T_1$, the voltage change, coupled through $C$, and the collector-base diode of $T_1$ may produce a positive spike at the output. This is because the collector-base diode may have been conducting and may not have been able to turn off fast enough.

Such logic circuits perform "contact" logic in the manner of relay contact networks. Since contact networks can perform any combinational logic function, contact logic is potentially capable of great speed. The complexity that can be achieved in practice is limited by the fact that most existing contact-like electronic elements such as transistors are not ideal switches and do not even approach the performance of a relay contact. We shall see, when we discuss RZ logic devices, that magnetic devices can be used to perform contact logic.

Series-parallel contact networks of RCTL inverters can be constructed; such an inverter-matrix is shown in Fig. 5.18. One serious sneak circuit that exists in Fig. 5.18 can be uncovered by considering the case when $T_7$, $T_8$, and $T_9$ are on, and all other transistors are off except for the base

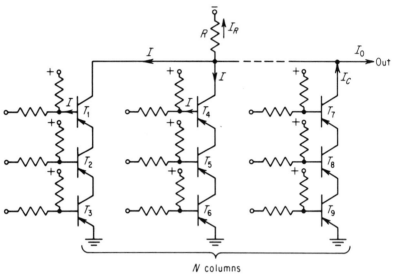

**Fig. 5.18.** Inverter-matrix.

current supplied, as shown, to the top row of transistors ($T_1$, $T_4$, in the figure). The current required from $T_7$ is seen to be

$$I_C = (N - 1)I + I_R + I_0 \tag{5.3}$$

The presence of the term $(N - 1)I$ severely limits the number of columns that may be paralleled.

The last example of NRZ transistor logic that we will consider here consists of the "current-steering" logic circuits originally proposed by IBM. A typical example is shown in Fig. 5.19 for p-n-p transistors. If any one of the transistors $T_1, \ldots, T_n$ were on, the current $I$ would be steered through its emitter to the output $B$, since $T_0$ would be off. If more than one of $T_1, \ldots, T_n$ were on, the current steered to the output $B$ would still be $I$. If all of the transistors $T_1, \ldots, T_n$ were off, the current $I$ would be steered through the output $C$. If we define minus as unity, the logical operations performed are

$$
\begin{aligned}
B &= A_1' A_2' \cdots A_n' \\
C &= A_1 + A_2 + \cdots + A_n
\end{aligned}
\tag{5.4}
$$

The first of Eqs. (5.4) is seen to be a universal logical operation. The outputs of the circuit as shown are not compatible with the input requirements of the circuit; hence, voltage-level changing networks are required. Another solution is to use the principle of *complementary symmetry* since the circuit of Fig. 5.19 can drive a similar circuit using n-p-n transistors. With the proper choice of power-supply voltages this second circuit can

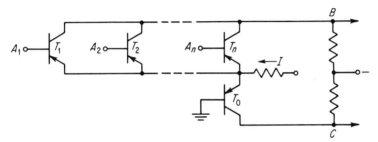

**Fig. 5.19.** Current-steering logic.

produce outputs compatible with the input requirements of the first. One advantage of the current-steering mode of operation is that the transistors operate *nonsaturated*. This mode of operation is introduced for *graded-base* transistors, which are very fast, provided that they are always operated in the active region. One disadvantage is the relatively large power consumption of such circuits. The transistor $T_0$ may be replaced by a diode, as in Fig. 5.20. Only one upper branch transistor is shown to illustrate the current-steering principle. This principle can be applied to other circuits, such as the one of Fig. 5.7.

While the current-steering principle can be used to keep the transistor out of saturation, the diode in the emitter circuit requires that additional input voltage swing be used from the circuit that drives point $A$ in Fig. 5.20. If the circuit that drives point $A$ furnishes a fixed current, the transition times of the signal at $A$ will be increased as a result of charging the wiring capacitance through a greater voltage differential. The loss in speed because of this effect will subtract from the gain in speed that is obtained from the nonsaturating operation of the transistor. In some cases there can be a net speed loss.

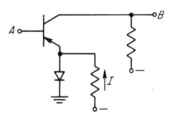

**Fig. 5.20.** Illustrating current-steering principle.

## 5.6 CLOCK GENERATION AND DISTRIBUTION

Before we consider RZ circuits, it is desirable to consider a few aspects of the clock generation and distribution problem. A typical single-phase clock system is shown in Fig. 5.21. The timing conditions that need be satisfied in the single-phase system are (a) the minimum pulse-width condition, (b) the minimum-delay condition, and (c) the maximum-delay condition. Conditions (a) and (b) are affected by the tolerance on the pulse width $T_W$, while (c) involves the minimum period $T_P^-$. Note that $T_P^+$ determines the minimum information rate in the machine. Hence, it is desirable to minimize the tolerance on $T_P$ and $T_W$ to obtain the optimum machine with given circuits.

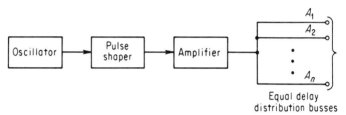

Fig. **5.21.** Single-phase clock system.

In Fig. 5.21, the tolerance on $T_W$ is determined mainly by the delay tolerances of both the pulse shaper and the amplifier, while the tolerance on $T_P$ is determined mainly by the frequency stability of the oscillator. However, if the system of Fig. 5.22 is used, the tolerance on $T_W$ is determined mainly by the delay tolerances of the pulse shaper and the amplifier, as in Fig. 5.21, while the tolerance on $T_P$ is determined by the frequency

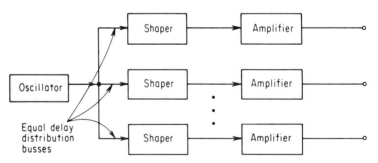

Fig. **5.22.** An alternate single-phase clock system.

stability of the oscillator and the delay tolerance of the pulse shaper and amplifier *taken twice*. Clearly, other things being equal, the system of Fig. 5.21 is preferable.

Let us now consider the two-phase system. The timing conditions that have to be satisfied are: (a) the minimum pulse-width condition, (b) the maximum-delay condition, and (c) the overlap condition. Condition (a) is affected by the tolerance on the pulse width $T_W$; (b) is affected by the tolerance on the phase displacement $T_\phi$, while (c) is affected by both tolerances. One way of developing a two-phase clock is shown in Fig. 5.23. This scheme is applicable to multiphase systems.

In Fig. 5.23, the tolerance on $T_W$ is determined mainly by the delay tolerances of the pulse shaper and the amplifier, while the tolerance on $T_\phi$

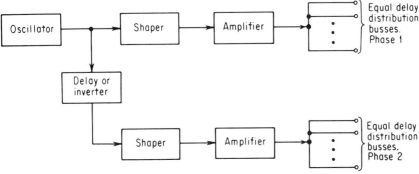

Fig. **5.23.** Two-phase clock system.

is determined mainly by the frequency stability of the oscillator, the delay tolerances of the pulse shaper and amplifier *taken twice*, and the delay tolerance of the delay or inverter. Hence, one can see qualitatively that the timing tolerance situation in multiphase clock systems is much more difficult than in the single-phase system.

## 5.7 LOGIC IN PULSE (RZ) SYSTEMS

In RZ systems, the timing tolerances are greater in number than in NRZ systems for two reasons. First, an RZ system is not usually economically feasible with a single-phase clock. Multiphase clocks are required, having the unfortunate tolerance situation seen above. Second, in an RZ system there are *two* signal transitions in a pulse time rather than the one occurring in NRZ systems, with the consequent doubling of timing tolerances.

Because of this unfortunate timing-tolerance situation it is rare to find many levels of logic between pulse formers in high-speed RZ systems. Logic can be performed with all of the passive elements previously listed and sometimes with the amplifying elements. However, most of the inventive ingenuity with respect to RZ circuits has been expended in devising amplifying elements which incorporate pulse forming or in devising circuit-element combinations which perform all three, and do them fast and cheaply. Since most successful RZ circuits are built around amplifying elements that are made to pulse-form, most of the ensuing discussion will deal with such combinations.

## 5.8 VACUUM-TUBE RZ CIRCUITS

Because of the high power gains obtainable from vacuum tubes, especially if transformers are used for impedance matching, multilevel diode logic circuits and vacuum tubes have been successfully combined in circuits of the type shown in Fig. 5.24. The logical function performed by the circuit of Fig. 5.24 is shown in Fig. 5.25.

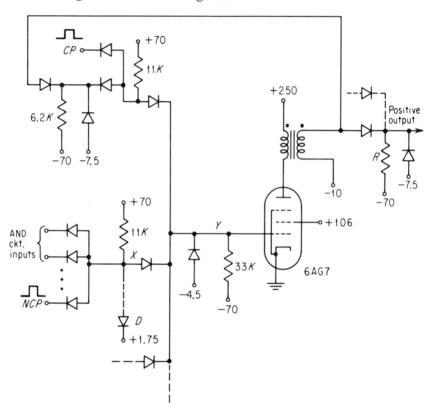

**Fig. 5.24.** An RZ circuit.

The circuit consists of a multiple-input diode AND-OR circuit driving a vacuum tube-transformer amplifier. The resistor-diode network on the transformer performs d-c restoration and couples the transformer to the load. The four functions of logic, pulse forming, clocking, and amplification are performed in the single circuit. The regeneration loop produces one-shot multivibrator action required for pulse forming. For the negation function, negative outputs can be taken from the transformer by the use of extra windings. These negative pulses are applied to the AND circuit and must overlap the NCP. Since the circuit works in a multiphase clocked system, delay lines are not needed; however, economic considerations justify their use. Circuits of this type have been used widely, in such computers as SEAC (National Bureau of Standards), FLAC (Aglin Air Force Base), MIDAC (University of Michigan), and UDOFT (University of Pennsylvania, Sylvania Electric Co., and Naval Training Devices Center). They are generally referred to as SEAC type circuits. In SEAC the 6AN5 was used, while the 404A was used in UDOFT. Both, especially the latter, are high-transconductance tubes.

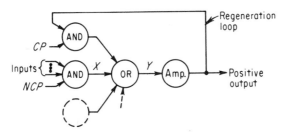

**Fig. 5.25.** Function performed.

Typical timing for a SEAC type circuit is shown in Fig. 5.26. The timing conditions require that (a) the input must arrive before NCP (the maximum-delay condition), (b) the input must be wider than the NCP (for proper inhibition), and (c) the NCP must be wide enough so that regeneration is established (the minimum pulse-width condition). There is rarely a problem in meeting the overlap condition.

Another RZ amplifier is the blocking oscillator (one-shot multivibrator), one of which is shown in Fig. 5.27 together with waveforms. The functions

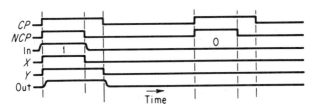

**Fig. 5.26.** SEAC type circuit timing.

of pulse forming and amplification are performed in the circuit. An input pulse causes plate current to flow. This, coupled to the grid through the transformer, turns the tube on harder until the tube represents a very low impedance. The time this takes depends on both the time constants and delays around the feedback loop and the amplitude of the input signal. The turn-on time may be as short as a nanosecond. During the pulse, the transformer magnetizing current increases approximately linearly with time until the sum of the load current, grid current, and magnetizing current exceeds what the tube can supply. Then the pulse terminates. The magnetizing current discharges into the various capacitances, thereby yielding the backswing. The pulse width is determined by the capacitance $C$, the magnetizing inductance of the transformer, and the tube characteristics. Because it depends on these three things, it is difficult to accurately control

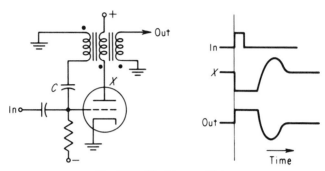

**Fig. 5.27.** Blocking oscillator.

the pulse width. A threshold must exist or the device will free-run. This threshold is provided by the bias. Because of the inherently fast nature of the device, it can trigger on the noise of the leading edge of the input pulse, causing the output waveform to jitter. This device has been used in one form or another in several computers, one of which was EDVAC.

### 5.9 TRANSISTOR RZ CIRCUITS

Because of the low power gain of transistors, it is not usually feasible to build transistorized versions of the SEAC type circuits using a single transistor. However, two-stage diode logic has been used with transistorized one-shot multivibrators using at least two transistors. Blocking oscillators or one-shot multivibrators have been built with single transistors, but they have not been too useful because of the poor rise times obtained when the power gain is adequate. The reason for this, as we shall see, is that the transistor acts as if it has an internal delay built into it in addition to a cutoff frequency. The presence of the delay degrades the performance of the feedback loop much more than one might expect (see Prob. 19 in Chap. 6).

Figure 5.28 illustrates a single-transistor/magnetic-core circuit patterned after the SEAC type circuits. Its efficiency is miniscule compared to the NRZ diode-transistor buffer-inverter and indicates the lengths to which one must go to produce a working circuit of this type.

It was designed to drive five to seven circuits of the same type, even after components and voltages had deviated five per cent from their nomi-

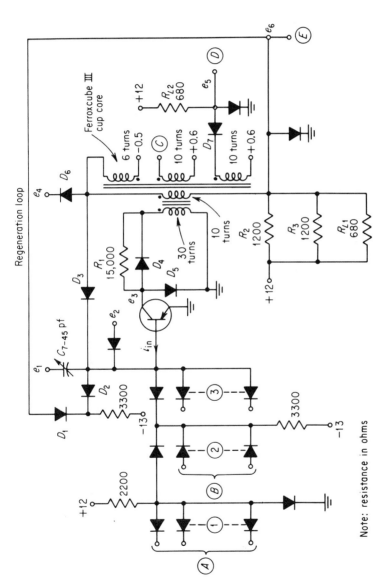

**Fig. 5.28.** A successful transistor/magnetic-core circuit.

Note: resistance in ohms

nal values. Somewhat larger allowances were made for clock variations and for diode drops and leakage currents.

The transformer, a Ferroxcube III cup core, had a magnetizing inductance of 880 μh, a leakage inductance of 4.5 μh, and a distributed capacitance of 12.5 pf, all referred to the primary winding. These characteristics were easily obtained without special winding techniques. Component variations resulted in the transformer having a net current gain of two, even though the turns ratio was three. Operation of the amplifier was in a two-phase clock system made possible by transistor hole storage and a regeneration loop. A GE model 2N135, 4.5-mcps transistor was used.

Diode network 1 is driven by unclamped outputs ($A$) while diode network 2 is driven by clamped outputs ($B$). Terminal $C$ gives an unclamped complemented output, $D$ a clamped complemented output, and $E$ a clamped direct output. Design tolerances include: resistors, ±5 per cent; and voltages, ±5 per cent. Diodes are low-drop, fast-recovery types; the clock (not shown) produces a 2-mc sine wave with a 3–4 volt peak; and the unit drives five to seven other units at 2 mcps with a 2N135 transistor ($f_F = 5$ mc).

Diodes in diode network 1 are buffing diodes which would in turn be driven by unclamped direct outputs. Clamped outputs of other circuits would drive into the gating layer, diode network 2. This gating layer in turn drives into a buffing layer, diode network 3, which drives the transistor.

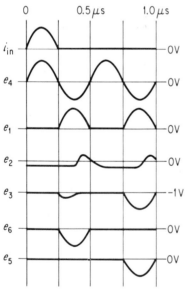

Three diodes, $D_4$, $D_6$, and $D_7$, disconnect the transformer, thus permitting self-recovery by ringing. Resistor $R_1$ shunting $D_4$ damps transformer oscillations so that the transformer is 30 per cent underdamped. This brings recovery in an approximate time of $3\sqrt{L_m C_d}$ where $L_m$ is the magnetizing inductance and $C_d$ is the net distributed capacitance, both referred to any one winding. $D_5$ serves to limit the collector voltage to that voltage which gives the greatest current gain in pulsed-collector operation.

**Fig. 5.29.** Typical waveforms for transistor/magnetic-core circuit shown in Fig. 5.28.

An input signal turns the transistor on (see Figs. 5.28 and 5.29), then hole storage (i.e., minority carrier storage) remembers the input for a short time until the collector is pulsed by clock $e_4$ through the transformer. Hole storage and high effective collector capacitance make $e_3$ substantially

$-1$ volt, causing an output at $e_6$ but not at $e_5$. The regeneration loop maintains the transistor on until the arrival of the cleanup pulse at $e_2$, which occurs at about the time that $e_4$ vanishes, and removes any remaining charge carriers in the base of the transistor. Since relatively little voltage is impressed across the transformer winding in this situation, the transformer does not need to recover.

In the absence of an input, the clock $e_4$ pulses the collector negative through the transformer. The collector-to-base capacitance that exists in an off transistor transfers some charge to the base circuit. This would cause a spurious output if not neutralized. The neutralizing clock $e_1$ furnishes an equal and opposite charge through $C$ which overcomes most of the effect of the feedback charge. An input, $i_{in}$, if it occurs, does not have to overcome the neutralizing charge. Further, the cleanup pulse occurs at the time that $de_1/dt$ is negative, preventing the neutralizing charge from injecting spurious carriers into the transistor. Owing to the small phase delay through the transformer and to other parasitic effects, the neutralizing circuit does not completely prevent a spurious output. However, the portion of the complemented output fed back through $D_3$ completes the neutralization. Thus, while neither neutralizing source alone is adequate, both together are sufficient.

After an output at $e_5$, $D_6$ is disconnected by the clock and the transformer disconnects through $D_4$ and $D_7$, making the right-hand side of the resistor across $D_4$ ring positive as the transformer goes into its recovery cycle. $R_1$ serves to damp the oscillations so that most of one positive half cycle is complete before $e_4$ goes negative again.

$R_2$ and $R_3$ prevent any sneak outputs, which could be caused partly by the charging of the collector capacitance when the transistor is off, and partly by the transformer magnetizing current. $R_{L1}$ simulates a load of three amplifiers, while $R_{L2}$ simulates the balance of a maximum load, i.e., three amplifiers.

Capacitance at $E$ causes a sneak output at $D$, and vice versa. Therefore, the full total drive capability of the amplifier cannot be utilized if both outputs are used simultaneously, and in addition, the full drive potential can be realized only if but one of the two outputs is used.

It is apparent then that the pulsed-collector operation of transistors at high frequencies requires both direct and complemented outputs from an amplifier using alloy junction transistors if the full gain of the transistors is to be realized. This is because (a) the direct output is used for external regeneration for retaining, by continued circulation, the momentary pulse input, and (b) the complemented output is used to assist in neutralizing the collector-to-base capacitance.

If one wishes to construct a transistorized blocking oscillator, one may substitute a transistor in the circuit of Fig. 5.27. However, such circuits are quite slow, the delay in the feedback loop making the rise time of the order of 0.2 μsec for the achievement of usable-power gains (>200 or so) from a transistor such as the Surface-Barrier for use in fast multistage diode logic.

If response time, in a regenerative amplifier operating at $2\frac{1}{2}$ mc, is near 0.2 μsec in order to achieve sufficient gain, and the output period also is near 0.2 μsec, then with one transformer, there is no time for the transformer to recover. At lower frequencies, where the rise time is a small portion of the total period, this problem does not exist. Furthermore, if a clamped load is driven, the feedback is not effective until the load current is overcome.

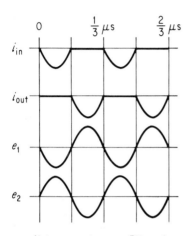

Note: $e_1$ and $e_2$ are 3V peak

**Fig. 5.30.** Typical waveforms during operation of circuit shown in Fig. 5.31.

One technique is to use one transformer for regeneration and to remove it as soon as the transistor rises to a high output state. Then a second transformer is inserted to transfer the output power to a load, and it is removed in turn at the next input period. Such switching of transformers creates the possibility of false triggering due to resonant circuits (involving the transformer windings and circuit capacities) that are shock-excited into oscillation. The use of sine-wave clocks, low-capacity (high-leakage) transformer construction, electrostatic shields, and damping circuits alleviates this problem to some extent. Such a circuit is shown in Fig. 5.31; typical waveforms are shown in Fig. 5.30.

A small current, $i_{in}$, is applied and at the same time feedback transformer $T_1$ is pulsed in by $e_1$ which draws the output current and feeds it back regeneratively to the input. At this time the amplifier is unloaded. When the transistor is fully turned on, clock $e_1$ is removed and power pulse $e_2$ is applied, thus drawing current which is transferred to the load resistor appearing as $i_{out}$. Storage is required to furnish the output; thus little or no output current is drawn while the transistor is turning on and full feedback exists. Also, little or no feedback current is drawn during the latter part of the output so that the charge storage is minimized.

The diode-resistor networks across the primaries of transformers $T_1$ and $T_2$ are for damping the backswing when $D_2$ and $D_5$ disconnect the transformers. $D_1$ prevents the backswing of $T_1$ from turning off the transistor. Diode-resistor combination $D_4$-$R_2$ forms a lower clamp, limiting the collector voltage to $-3v$, and minimizes false triggering due to charging

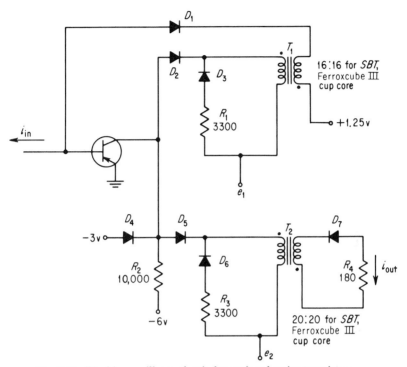

**Fig. 5.31.** Blocking oscillator circuit for surface barrier transistor.

of collector capacitance. At a 3-mcps rate with 0.15-μsec delay between input and output pulses, a power gain of 350 is obtained with a Surface-Barrier transistor.

An RZ version of the buffer-inverter is shown in Fig. 5.32. A transistor having high collector storage must be used; it is a universal logical element and includes pulse forming, amplification, timing, and logic.

## 5.10  MAGNETIC RZ LOGIC CIRCUITS

Magnetic devices are suited for RZ logic. It is possible to obtain gain from them and also to pulse-form and time. The logic may be done with the devices, or with passive elements such as diodes.

A tape-wound core may be constructed, as in Fig. 5.33. A material such as 4-79 molybdenum permalloy is rolled to a thickness of $\frac{1}{8}$ mil. It is then cut to the proper width and wound on the bobbin insulated with some inert material. The core is then subjected to an annealing cycle to develop the desired magnetic properties.

A single wrap of tape yields an unsatisfactory core, two wraps yields

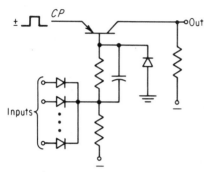

Fig. **5.32.** RZ buffer-inverter.

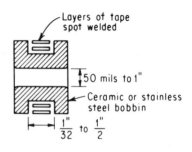

Fig. **5.33.** Tape-wound magnetic core.

occasional fair results, three wraps is better, but usually at least four to five wraps must be used for consistently good results. With $\frac{1}{8}$-mil material, the total thickness including insulation runs about a mil per wrap.

A test circuit is indicated in Fig. 5.34.

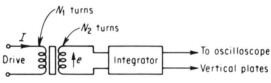

Fig. **5.34.** Test circuit.

By Faraday's law,

$$\int_1^2 e\, dt = N_2(\phi_2 - \phi_1) \times 10^{-8} \qquad \text{(CGS)}$$

$$= N_2(\phi_2 - \phi_1) \qquad\qquad \text{(MKS)}$$

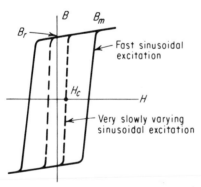

Fig. **5.35.** $B\text{-}H$ loop for square-loop core.

If the drive current is applied to a resistor across the horizontal deflection plates of the oscilloscope, we may obtain the display in Fig. 5.35, since for a toroid,

$$H = \frac{0.4\pi N_1 I}{l} \qquad \text{(CGS)}$$

$$H = \frac{N_1 I}{l} \qquad \text{(MKS)}$$

where $l$ is the mean perimeter of the core material. Cores having such "square" hysteresis loops are useful in digital devices. For logic and amplification, it is desirable that the area of the loop be as small as possible, consistent with other requirements that will be discussed.

In Fig. 5.35, $H_c$ is the coercive force, $B_r$ the residual flux density, and $B_m$ the maximum flux density produced by the drive. The shape of the loop is a function of the kind and magnitude of the drive, and for sinusoidal drive becomes wider as the frequency becomes higher. Hence, the $B$-$H$ characteristic must be described by some kind of equation. M. K. Haynes proposed the differential equation, Eq. (5.5), for polycrystalline ferrites.

$$\frac{dx}{dt} = \frac{4.82}{S}(H - H_c)(1 - x)\left[-\log \frac{(1 - x)}{2}\right]^{2/3} \tag{5.5}$$

where $x = B/B_r$ and $S$ is defined below. Chen and Papoulis have considered a similar problem for tape-wound cores. Their result, using thin magnetic tapes where eddy currents are negligible, is

$$\frac{dx}{dt} = (H - H_c)f(x)$$

where $f(x)$ is an experimentally determined function dependent only on $x$. A first-approximation description will be developed for either, which is useful for approximate calculations.

Typical voltage and current waveforms are shown for full voltage switching and full current switching in Fig. 5.36. For cores fully switched

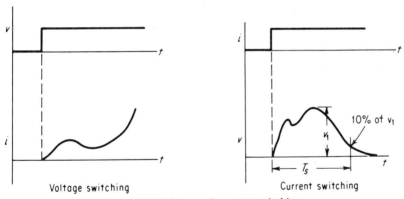

Voltage switching       Current switching

**Fig. 5.36.** Voltage and current switching.

by current steps, the switching time is defined as in this figure. Experimentally it follows for most materials that $H - H_c$ plotted versus $1/T_S$ is a straight line. Hence we may write,

$$H = H_c + \frac{S}{T_S} \tag{5.6}$$

where the constant of proportionality $S$ is the *switching constant*.

Typical data for the two classes of materials, metals and ferrites, are given below.

*Metal* (78 molybdenum permalloy)

$H_c \cong 0.1$ oersted

$\cong 0.08$ amp/cm

$S \cong 4$ oersted $\mu$sec

$\cong 3.2$ amp $\mu$sec/cm

$B_r \cong 7000$ gauss

$\cong 7 \times 10^{-5}$ webers/cm²

*Ferrite* (low-loss square-loop variety)

$H_c \cong 0.5$ oersted

$\cong 0.4$ amp/cm

$S \cong 0.8$ oersted $\mu$sec

$\cong 0.64$ amp $\mu$sec/cm

$B_r \cong 2000$ gauss

$\cong 2 \times 10^{-5}$ webers/cm²

The energy required to switch a core from one state to another is

$$\int_1^2 ei\, dt = \int_{\text{Vol. of Core}} \left[ \int_1^2 \mathbf{H} \cdot d\mathbf{B} \right] dv \qquad \text{(MKS)}$$

If the core is switched from negative remanence to positive saturation and back to negative remanence, the energy required is

$$\int_{\text{Vol}} \left[ \oint \mathbf{H} \cdot d\mathbf{B} \right] dv = \int_{\text{Vol}} \left[ \oint H\, dB \right] dv = \begin{array}{l} \text{area of hysteresis loop} \\ \times \text{ vol. of core material} \end{array}$$

This result is of fundamental importance in the design of magnetic logic devices.

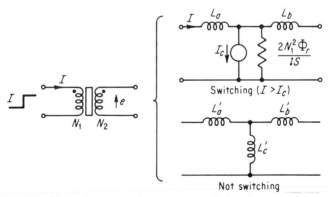

**Fig. 5.37.** Magnetic core equivalent circuits (referred to the primary winding).

To arrive at an approximate equivalent circuit for the core in Fig. 5.37, for constant-current or constant-voltage switching, there is

$$e = N_2 \frac{d\phi}{dt} \quad \text{(MKS)} \tag{5.7}$$

where $\phi$ is the magnetic flux in the core. Approximately, in current switching,

$$\frac{d\phi}{dt} = \frac{2\Phi_r}{Ts} \tag{5.8}$$

Substitution of Eqs. (5.6) and (5.8) into Eq. (5.7) yields

$$e = 2N_2\Phi_r \cdot \frac{(H - H_c)}{S} \tag{5.9}$$

Using the approximate expression for $H$ in a toroidal core

$$H = \frac{N_1 I}{l}$$

and the definition of coercive current $I_c$ referred to in the primary

$$H_c = \frac{N_1 I_c}{l}$$

Eq. (5.9) becomes $\qquad e = \frac{2N_1 N_2 \Phi_r}{lS} (I - I_c) \tag{5.10}$

The equivalent circuit in Fig. 5.37 can be deduced from Eq. (5.10). The inductances $L_a$ and $L_b$ are the leakage inductances of the primary and secondary windings. When not switching, the core may be regarded as a transformer with equivalent constants $L'_a$, $L'_b$, and $L'_c$ evaluated using the incremental permeability of the core material at the operating point. (See Sec. 6.22 on pulse transformers.) The equivalent circuits are fairly good for voltage switching operation also.

### 5.11 A MAGNETIC SHIFT REGISTER

One of the earliest shift registers developed is the Wang and Woo shift register shown in Fig. 5.38.

It has been stated that a shift register is an essential element of a sequential system. This shift register is double rank and operates with a two-phase clock.

If we refer to the hysteresis loop of Fig. 5.35, and assume that current *into* a dot drives the core *up* the loop, an input to core 1 will leave it near positive remanence. $CP1$ will then drive core 1 down the loop to negative remanence, producing a positive pulse at $A$ which is coupled into core 2. Core 2 will then be operated by $CP2$ in a similar fashion. However, if there is no input to core 1 before $CP1$ occurs, then core 1 will not yield an output when $CP1$ does occur, because it already is at negative remanence.

The diodes prevent the back transfer of information, while the resistor serves to suppress "sneaks" and to prevent the shunt diodes from shorting

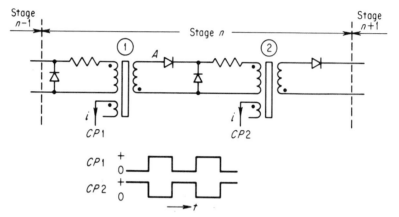

**Fig. 5.38.** Wang and Woo shift register.

the cores. The sneaks occur because a core that is not switching still yields a small output when driven (see Fig. 5.37).

### 5.12 SHUNT AND SERIES MAGNETIC AMPLIFIERS

The Wang and Woo shift register consists of a chain of *shunt* magnetic amplifiers. The basic circuit of the shunt magnetic amplifier is shown in Fig. 5.39. Positive current directions are shown, together with the directions

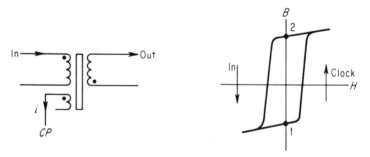

**Fig. 5.39.** Shunt magnetic amplifier.

in which the various applied signals drive the flux in the core. Its operation is seen to be identical to the operation of the cores in the Wang and Woo shift register.

Additional components must be used to suppress sneaks and to prevent the reverse flow of information. Two ways of suppressing sneaks are to absorb them in a resistor as in the Wang and Woo shift register (this adversely affects the speed) and to use a blocking pulse. Since the sneaks resemble a differentiated clock pulse, this method requires a specially shaped blocking pulse, which can be obtained from another core that is saturated and driven by the clock pulse.

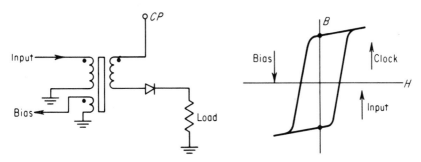

**Fig. 5.40.** Series magnetic amplifier.

The reverse flow of information may be prevented by diodes, as in Fig. 5.38. The resistor may be shorted out and the shunt diode eliminated if a blocking pulse is applied to the bottom of the input winding.

The basic circuit of the *series* magnetic amplifier is shown in Fig. 5.40. Typical waveforms are shown in Fig. 5.41.

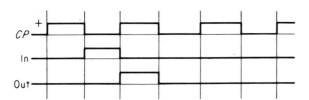

**Fig. 5.41.** Timing waveforms for series magnetic amplifier.

In the absence of an input, the clock and the bias drive the core up and down the loop so that the only current in the load is the "dynamic" coercive current. An input will prevent the bias from resetting the core so that a clock pulse will find the core saturated and at the top of the loop. The output winding will then resemble a short circuit allowing the clock pulse to pump power into the load.

As in the shunt magnetic amplifier, additional components are required to suppress sneaks (the dynamic coercive current $I$) and to prevent the backward transfer of information. Improved efficiency can also be obtained by applying the bias only during the time when the clock pulse is negative.

One circuit for suppressing sneaks is shown in Fig. 5.42. It operates by shunting away the dynamic coercive current (and d-c bias current referred to the output winding).

To prevent the reverse flow of information we may use, for example, the arrangement in Fig. 5.43. The blocking pulse is so adjusted as to prevent the diode from conducting if there is no input and if the bias is switching the core.

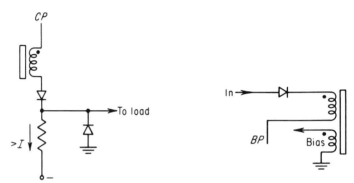

Fig. 5.42. Sneak suppressor for series magnetic amplifier.

Fig. 5.43. To prevent the reverse flow of information.

The series magnetic amplifier may be made to complement the input if connected as in Fig. 5.44. A shunt complementer can also be constructed. Either type of magnetic amplifier incorporates the functions of pulse forming and amplification. Logic may be performed with diodes or by interconnecting windings, the greatest efficiency being obtained with diodes.

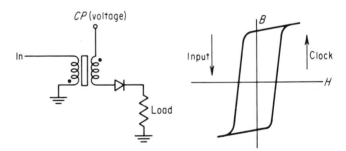

Fig. 5.44. Basic complementing connection.

Table 5.3 provides a convenient summary of the mode of operation of each type of amplifier.

**TABLE 5.3.** SUMMARY OF AMPLIFIER OPERATION

|         | Core switches | Core saturated |
|---------|---------------|----------------|
| Series  | no output     | output         |
| Shunt   | output        | no output      |

## 5.13  CORE LOGIC

M. Karnaugh has introduced a symbolism which is useful in schematically representing networks of magnetic cores (square-loop) connected to perform logic. This symbolism is illustrated in Fig. 5.45 by Karnaugh's example. The core is represented by a vertical line. Windings on a core are represented by horizontal lines crossing the vertical line. A current into a winding, as shown, produces a field $H$ in the core whose "sense" is obtained by reflecting the current in the winding mirror symbol. The induced emfs

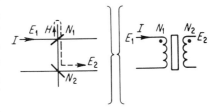

**Fig. 5.45.** Karnaugh mirror symbolism.

are obtained by reversing the $H$ arrow and reflecting it in each winding mirror symbol.

The series and shunt magnetic amplifiers represented in this symbolism are shown in Fig. 5.46 and should be compared with Figs. 5.39 and 5.40.

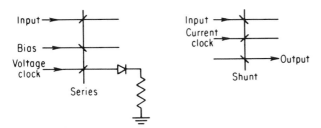

**Fig. 5.46.** Magnetic amplifier representation.

We will give two examples of core-logic circuits which illustrate some of the principles. The reader who wishes to pursue the subject further may consult the references.

A modification of Karnaugh's AF circuit is shown in Fig. 5.47 with output buffing using diodes. In this circuit, logic is done in the input windings and also with the output diodes. The operation also mixes

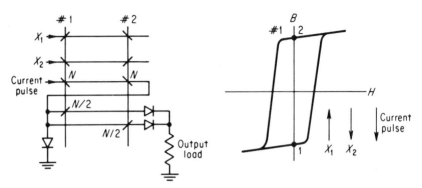

Fig. **5.47.** An AF circuit.

features of both the shunt and series magnetic amplifiers, besides illustrating current steering. The circuit also can provide power gain and does pulse forming.

Core 1 is set to 2 (see $B$-$H$ loop) if $X_1 X_2' = 1$ and core 2 is set to 2 if $X_1' X_2 = 1$. The current pulse is applied after the inputs have disappeared. If both cores are in state 1 (see $B$-$H$ loop), no voltage appears across any of the output windings and the current pulse passes through the left-hand diode to ground. If either core is set, however, the switching magnetomotive force for that core is $NI/2$, and as long as the voltage drop across the load is less than the voltage across the $N/2$ turn winding, the current pulse is *steered* to the output load. Hence, the circuit computes $X_1 X_2' + X_1' X_2$.

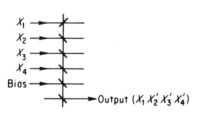

Fig. **5.48.** A magnetic switch.

A special case of core logic circuits is the Rajchmann switch, an example of which in the mirror symbol notation is given in Fig. 5.48. If the bias is properly selected, $X_1$ by itself will switch the core, yielding an output unless any of the other inputs are present. The bias will reset the core. There is no clocking provided or power gain obtainable from this arrangement. It is seen to be an illustration of how logic may be performed using input windings only.

## 5.14   TRANSISTOR-MAGNETIC CORE CIRCUITS

An example of such a circuit is given in Fig. 5.49. An input will turn the transistor on. Regeneration will continue the setting of the core until it saturates, at which time the transistor will cease to conduct. The reset

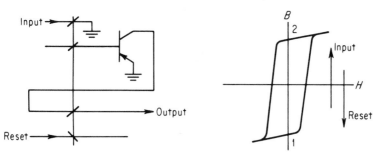

**Fig. 5.49.** A transistor-magnetic core circuit.

signal can then be used to return the core to point 1, where the circuit is prepared to receive another input.

## 5.15 MISCELLANEOUS MAGNETIC DEVICES

In the discussion of the shunt and series magnetic amplifiers, it has been shown how power gain may be obtained from magnetic cores. In these amplifiers, and the logic networks constructed from them, single-apertured cores have been used which could be made from metal tapes or from ferrites. Now we will discuss one of the kinds of *multi-apertured devices* (MAD) that have been proposed for logic. These devices depend for their operation on the divergenceless character of the magnetic flux density, **B**. Thus, flux may be switched from one leg to another of a multi-apertured magnetic circuit without changing the total flux. It is possible to also obtain power gain from these devices by using the magnetic amplifier principles, previously discussed. However, their efficiency is usually considerably below that of diode-transistor logic circuits because of their slow speed.

An example of MAD is shown in Fig. 5.50(a). Assume that the device is made from a ferrite having a rectangular hysteresis loop, that the four vertical legs have the same cross-sectional area, and that the two horizontal bars each have twice the cross-sectional area of a leg. Current pulses are applied to the windings in the sequences shown in Table 5.4, giving the flux directions shown in that table. Two sequences are shown corresponding to the transfer of a 0 and of a 1 from the set winding to the output winding. The blocking pulse must be of sufficient amplitude to achieve a standard flux condition. Application of the set pulse produces the flux condition shown in the second line of the table. The flux in leg 4 can be made to stay fixed by using either of the two techniques below:

1. If $l_{13} < l_{14}$ and if the set current is properly adjusted, we can make $H_3 > H_c > H_4$ so that the flux in leg 3 will switch, while that in leg 4 will

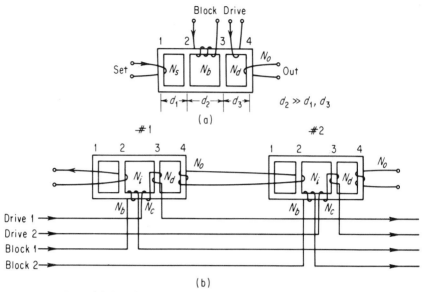

**Fig. 5.50.** (a) A multi-apertured magnetic device. (b) A MAD register.

not. If legs 1 and 3 have equal cross sections, then, since $\nabla \cdot \mathbf{B} = 0$, the change in flux in leg 1 will be the same as the change in flux in leg 3.

2. If the output winding is shorted, we have for leg 4 by Faraday's law,

$$\int e\, dt = 0 = N_o \Delta\phi$$

In this case, the set current can be anything greater than a threshold value related to the coercive force of the material.

In sequence (1), the drive current must change the direction of the fluxes in legs 3 and 4 but must not affect the flux in leg 2. This can be done by controlling the drive current, as was assumed to be done in setting the MAD, or by using a cancelling winding as in the shift register of Fig. 5.50(b). Since the flux in leg 4 changes in sequence (1), an output is

**TABLE 5.4.** Sequences of Flux Changes in Legs
of MAD of Fig. 5.50(a)

| Sequence (1) | Leg: | 1 | 2 | 3 | 4 | Comments |
|---|---|---|---|---|---|---|
| after block | | ↓ | ↓ | ↑ | ↑ | |
| after set (1) | | ↑ | ↓ | ↓ | ↑ | 4 stays fixed (see text) |
| after drive | | ↑ | ↓ | ↑ | ↓ | (output) |
| Sequence (0) | Leg: | 1 | 2 | 3 | 4 | Comments |
| after block | | ↓ | ↓ | ↑ | ↑ | |
| after set (0) | | ↓ | ↓ | ↑ | ↑ | |
| after drive | | ↓ | ↓ | ↑ | ↑ | (no output) |

obtained. The reader should have no difficulty in following through sequence (0).

Since a bit is transferred from input to output through the sequences, one may ask whether or not a shift register may be built using MAD. If this can be done together with the performance of combinational logic, a sequential system can be built. One such shift register is shown in Fig. 5.50(b); it is a double-rank shift register and only one stage is shown. The drive and block pulses do not overlap. The sequences of flux directions for shifting a zero and a one are given in Table 5.5.

**TABLE 5.5.** Sequences of Flux Changes in MAD Shift Register

| | Core 1 | | | | Core 2 | | | | |
|---|---|---|---|---|---|---|---|---|---|
| Sequence (1) | 1 | 2 | 3 | 4 | 1 | 2 | 3 | 4 | Comments |
| after block | ↓ | ↓ | ↑ | ↑ | ↓ | ↓ | ↑ | ↑ | |
| after drive 2 | ↓ | ↑ | ↓ | ↑ | ↓ | ↓ | ↑ | ↑ | ("1" in) |
| after block 2 | ↑ | ↓ | ↓ | ↑ | ↓ | ↓ | ↑ | ↑ | (Flux change caused by |
| after drive 1 | ↑ | ↓ | ↑ | ↓ | ↓ | ↑ | ↓ | ↑ | change in previous stage) |
| after block 1 | ↓ | ↓ | ↑ | ↑ | ↑ | ↓ | ↓ | ↑ | (no back transfer) |
| Sequence (0) | 1 | 2 | 3 | 4 | 1 | 2 | 3 | 4 | |
| after block | ↓ | ↓ | ↑ | ↑ | ↓ | ↓ | ↑ | ↑ | |
| after drive 2 | ↓ | ↓ | ↑ | ↑ | ↓ | ↓ | ↑ | ↑ | ("0" in) |
| after block 2 | ↓ | ↓ | ↑ | ↑ | ↓ | ↓ | ↑ | ↑ | |
| after drive 1 | ↓ | ↓ | ↑ | ↑ | ↓ | ↓ | ↑ | ↑ | |
| after block 1 | ↓ | ↓ | ↑ | ↑ | ↓ | ↓ | ↑ | ↑ | |

In the second line of sequence (1), the input current must be adjusted so as to switch the flux in leg 3 but not in leg 4. The input to core 1 takes place when drive 2 occurs. Because block 2 follows drive 2, the flux change in the stage which transferred the one to core 1 produces a further change in the flux in core 1 by a mechanism which will be understood when we consider the transfer of information from core 1 to core 2. When drive 1 occurs, the ·cancellation winding $N_c$ causes the magnetomotive force in legs 1 and 2 to be zero, if $N_c = N_d$, so that the upper limit on the magnitude of the drive current can be removed. Since shunt magnetic amplifier operation occurs here, greater power gain can be obtained if the winding $N_c$ is used. Drive 1 changes the flux in leg 4. The output winding $N_o$ coupled with the input winding to core 2, $N_i$, acts as a shorted turn around both legs, i.e., leg 4 of 1 and leg 2 of 2. Hence, if $\Delta\phi_{41}$ and $\Delta\phi_{22}$ are the changes in flux in legs 4 of core 1 and 2 of core 2 respectively, by Faraday's law,

$$\int e \, dt = N_o \, \Delta\phi_{41} + N_i \, \Delta\phi_{22} = 0$$

Thus,

$$\Delta\phi_{22} = -\frac{N_o}{N_i} \Delta\phi_{41}$$

If $N_o/N_i = 1$, then the change in flux in leg 4 of core 2 causes the flux in leg 2 of core 2 to reverse as in fourth line of the sequence. The amplitude of the drive pulse must be adjusted so that only the flux in legs 2 and 3 of core 2 is changed. Because of the losses in the windings $N_o$, $N_i$, it is necessary that $N_o/N_i$ be greater than unity. The application of the block 1 pulse now blocks core 1. It is seen from Table 5.5 that there is no flux change in leg 2 of core 1, thus causing no reverse transfer of information to the preceding stage. However, the flux in leg 4 of core 1 reverses, causing the fluxes in legs 1 and 2 of core 2 to reverse, provided that suitable conditions of the applied magnetomotive force are met. When drive 2 is applied, the information is transferred to the next stage in the same way it was transferred from core 1 to core 2. The reader should have no difficulty in following the sequence for transferring a zero.

A way of performing the AND and OR functions with MAD's is diagrammed in Fig. 5.50(c). Circular MAD's are shown and are electrically

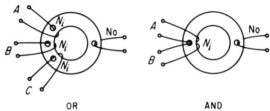

OR                    AND

**Fig. 5.50c.** MAD logic.

equivalent to those in Figs. 5.50(a) and (b) as far as the areas of cross section of the various legs are concerned. The block and drive windings are not shown. The left hand legs are labelled $A_1$, $A_2$, $B_1$, $C_1$, and $C_2$ while the output legs are 3 and 4 consistent with the previous numbering. Flux patterns for receiving a one at input $A$ are shown in Table 5.6. Note that

**TABLE 5.6.** MAD OR FLUX PATTERNS

| Leg: | $A_1$ | $A_2$ | $B_1$ | $B_2$ | $C_1$ | $C_2$ | 3 | 4 |
|---|---|---|---|---|---|---|---|---|
| After block | ↓ | ↓ | ↓ | ↓ | ↓ | ↓ | ↑ | ↑ |
| After input | ↓ | ↑ | ↑ | ↓ | ↑ | ↓ | ↓ | ↑ |

the flux in leg $A_2$ is changed by the input. The input windings receiving zeroes ($B$ and $C$) come from MAD's transmitting zeroes, hence link legs that are saturated. Because of the shorted-turn effect, the flux in legs $B_2$ and $C_2$ cannot change. However, the flux in legs $B_1$ and $C_1$ can change, making it possible for the flux in leg 3 to change.

For the MAD "AND" element shown, since a MAD which is transmitting a zero effectively shorts the input winding, the flux in leg 2 changes only if a one is received at inputs $A$ and $B$.

The analysis of a MAD cannot be accomplished with the aid of the assumptions made for single-aperture cores, such as assuming that $H = NI/l$. The analysis requires either a reliance on experimentally obtained threshold data and excitation curves or the numerical integration of the sets of nonlinear differential equations which describe the circuit properties. Problems of analysis of digital circuits will be considered in the next chapter.

Fully switched cores, by virtue of their single-bit storage capacity, have been used in magnetic memories. Cycle times less than 1.5 $\mu$sec have been achieved in memories of 8192 or more words capacity. Two techniques tried for achieving greater speed have been partial switching and thin films.

In partial switching, use is made of the fact that a core need not be fully switched. Traversing a minor loop requires less energy, so higher speeds can be achieved without excessive core heating. It is also sometimes possible to achieve nondestructive readout of information in a core by applying a short high-amplitude pulse which produces no irreversible flux changes. The reversible flux changes produced by such a pulse induce a voltage in an output winding. However, successful use of these techniques is very difficult.

In the fabrication of tape-wound cores, it was found that the use of tape thicknesses of less than $\frac{1}{8}$ mil yielded little improvement in performance. This led to the investigation of the magnetic properties of thin films of magnetic materials deposited on an inert substrate. The advantage of the thin film is that the reduced volume of magnetic material has a lower switching constant. One disadvantage is that a storage element may produce as little as 1 per cent (1 mv) of the output that can be achieved from a ferrite memory core with comparable drive currents at speeds of the order of ten or more times greater; this means that the crosstalk from drive to output lines can be of the order of 1000 times as great as with ferrite memory cores. The system problems caused by this fact are very difficult to overcome.

**Fig. 5.51.** A thin magnetic film spot.

If a thin magnetic film is deposited as a spot (Fig. 5.51) in a magnetic field, it will have a direction of preferred magnetization called the "easy axis." A field applied opposite to the direction of magnetization but parallel to the easy axis will cause a slow reversal of magnetization (in the microsecond range). However, if a small component of field is simultaneously applied perpendicular to the easy axis, the magnetization of the spot will reverse by coherent rotation in a few nanoseconds. Such a field-coincidence switching property makes it possible to use a spot as a memory element and as an amplifying device.

### 5.16  LOW-TEMPERATURE DEVICES

The resistance of metal decreases with decreasing temperature. Below a critical temperature, a material such as tantalum becomes superconductive because its resistance vanishes. However, its resistance may be restored by applying a magnetic field (see Fig. 5.52). Such control action suggests the construction of the switching device, the "cryotron" (named thus by its inventor, D. A. Buck). The early cryotrons were made by winding a control winding around a piece of wire (gate) that was superconducting in the

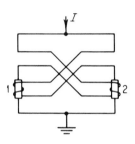

Fig. **5.52.**

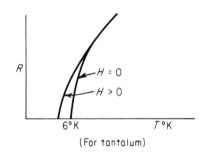

(For tantalum)

Fig. **5.53.** Bistable cryotron device.

absence of a magnetic field. The control winding and all other connections had to be superconducting at all times. Current in the control winding restored the resistance of the gate.

An example of how cryotrons can be used to perform switching is shown in Fig. 5.53. If the current $I$ divides so that most of it passes through the control winding of cryotron 2, then 2 will have more gate resistance than 1, which results in a further division of current until all of $I$ flows through the control winding of 2 and none flows through the control winding of 1; thus, the device shown has two stable states. It may also be switched by external sources if a cryotron is placed in series with each of the two already present to yield a flip-flop. Note that a cryotron is a relay-like device in its behavior in Fig. 5.53. With respect to speed, it is easily seen from Fig. 5.53 that a measure of switching speed is $L/R$ where $L$ is the inductance of a control winding and $R$ is the resistance of a nonsuperconducting gate. Development has resulted in the reduction of the time constant from the neighborhood of 100 $\mu$sec for the early units to submicrosecond values obtained using thin films. Because cryotrons can be used in an NRZ system and also can be used in contact logic, their effective speed is several times greater than that implied by their time constants.

In Fig. 5.54, a qualitative comparison is made of $V$-$I$ characteristics of several logic devices.

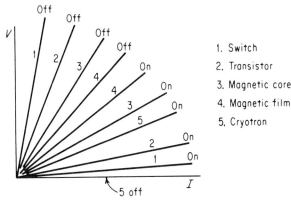

1. Switch
2. Transistor
3. Magnetic core
4. Magnetic film
5. Cryotron

**Fig. 5.54.** Comparison of switching devices.

### 5.17  PRINCIPLES OF PARAMETRIC AMPLIFICATION

Amplification via the variation of a parameter, such as an inductance or capacitance, has received some attention in connection with computer applications, especially in Japan where several computers were built using magnetic parametrons. Parametric amplification has been of theoretical interest for decades, and a considerable body of literature on it has accumulated. However, it was not until fairly recently that suitable capacitors and inductors became available which could be varied at radio frequencies.

If a capacitor $C$ is varied sinusoidally at a "pump" frequency $\omega_p$ such that

$$\frac{1}{C} = \frac{1}{C_o}(1 + K \cos \omega_p t)$$

the charge $q$ in a series LRC circuit can easily be shown to satisfy Mathieu's equation

$$\frac{d^2y}{d\tau^2} + \epsilon(1 + k \cos \tau)y = 0$$

where $q = ye^{-\alpha t}$, $\alpha = R/2L$,

$$\epsilon = \frac{1 - \dfrac{R^2C_o}{4L}}{\omega_p^2 L C_o}, \qquad k = \frac{K}{1 - \dfrac{R^2C_o}{4L}}$$

and $\tau = \omega_p t$. For certain sets of values of $\epsilon$ and $k$, the oscillations in $q$ will grow indefinitely. The energy required for this comes from the source which varies the capacitance. The differential equation that arises with nonsinusoidal capacitance or inductance variation is called Hill's equation; it differs from Mathieu's equation in that the coefficient of $y$ is a Fourier series instead of $\epsilon(1 + k \cos \tau)$. Solution of Hill's equation can be avoided in the special case where the inductance or capacitance is modulated by a square wave.

For example, consider a capacitor whose value is fixed at $C_1$ when an amount of energy $W_1$ is put into it. Then, $W_1 = \frac{1}{2}Q^2/C_1$ or $Q = \sqrt{2C_1W_1}$. If the pump changes the capacitance to $C_2$, then the energy stored, $W_2$, becomes

$$W_2 = \frac{\frac{1}{2}Q^2}{C_2} = \frac{C_1W_1}{C_2}$$

if $Q$ is kept constant. The energy gain is

$$\frac{W_2}{W_1} = \frac{C_1}{C_2} > 1 \qquad \text{if } C_2 < C_1$$

If the parameter is an inductance, the energy required to establish a current $I$ is

$$W_1 = \frac{1}{2}L_1I_1^2$$

The voltage produced by a change of flux linkages $\psi$ is, by Faraday's law,

$$e = \frac{d\psi}{dt} = \frac{d}{dt}(LI)$$

If the terminal voltage of the inductor is fixed at zero by external circuit elements when the inductance is changed in value, we have that $LI$ remains constant, or

$$L_1I_1 = L_2I_2$$

where $L_1$, $I_1$ and $L_2$, $I_2$ are respectively the inductance and current values before and after the parameter change. The final energy is

$$W_2 = \frac{1}{2}L_2I_2^2 = \frac{1}{2}\frac{(L_2I_2)^2}{L_2} = \frac{1}{2}\frac{(L_1I_1)^2}{L_2} = \frac{L_1}{L_2}W_1$$

or

$$\frac{W_2}{W_1} = \frac{L_1}{L_2} > 1 \qquad \text{if } L_1 > L_2$$

If a capacitor is used to maintain the voltage fixed at zero when the inductance is changed, the circuit of Fig. 5.55 results. The inductance $L$ is decreased to $L_2$ when the voltage $v$ is zero to increase the energy of the system. In one-quarter of a cycle of oscillation, this energy is transferred to the capacitor, i.e., $v_{max} = 2W_2/C$. At the instant $v = v_{max}$ or $i = 0$, the inductance is changed back to $L_1$; since $i = 0$, no change in stored energy occurs. One-quarter of a cycle of oscillation later, the pump cycle can be repeated (see Fig. 5.56). It is simple to show in the case of no losses that if the initial voltage across $C$ is $V_0$ it becomes, after $n$ cycles of oscillation,

$$v = V_0 \exp \left[ n \log \left( \frac{L_1}{L_2} \right) \right] \left\{ = V_0 \left( \frac{L_1}{L_2} \right)^n \right\}$$

an exponential increase. In practice, nonlinear effects will limit the amplitude as in the case of the vacuum-tube oscillator.

In Fig. 5.56 if $f_o$ is the oscillation frequency and $f_p$ is the pump frequency,

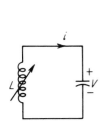

Fig. **5.55.** Parametric oscillator.

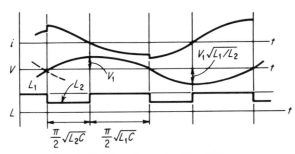

Fig. **5.56.** Waveforms for Fig. 5.55.

we have $f_o = \frac{1}{2}f_p$; the reader should attempt to see what other relationships can exist between $f_o$ and $f_p$ for this *linear* parametric amplifier.

In Goto's Parametron I, the variable inductance was obtained as in Fig. 5.57. The flux-current characteristic is shown in Fig. 5.58 for three values of $I_B$ assuming the single-core characteristic shown in the same figure (it is not necessary that square-loop cores be used, however). The principle of operation is essentially that the input flux $\phi_{in}$ arrives when $I_B$ is small and the output is delivered when $I_B$ is large. The gain in energy is proportional to the shaded area in the figure.

An arrangement, with characteristic curves, due to Prywes is shown

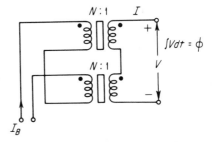

Fig. **5.57.** Parametron I connection.

in Fig. 5.59. In this arrangement, the exciting supply is separated into a d-c bias current, $I_b$, and an a-c pump current $i_p$. When used in a parametric oscillator circuit, it can operate such that $f_p = f_o$. Because of this, energy is added twice per pump cycle rather than once as in the arrangement of Figs. 5.57 and 5.58. Hence, greater gain is achieved. Also greater phase mismatch is possible with respect to a triggering input signal.

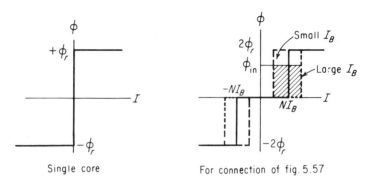

Single core          For connection of fig. 5.57

**Fig. 5.58.** Characteristics of Parametron I connection.

The Parametron I circuit is shown in Fig. 5.60 using the arrangement of Fig. 5.57. Two modes of operation are possible. These are:

1. "Soft" oscillation, where the bias is arranged so that a minimum of energy input is required to start oscillations when the pump is applied. When $f_o = \frac{1}{2}f_p$ and if the reader refers to Fig. 5.56, he will see that oscillation can occur either as shown or displaced 180° in phase. These two states of oscillation can represent the two values of a bit. Majority logic can be performed at the input windings so that the phase of the oscillation is determined by the majority of the applied inputs.

2. "Hard" oscillation, where the bias is arranged so that a threshold must be exceeded in order for oscillations to start. The binary states can be either of the two phases as above or "on" and "off" states.

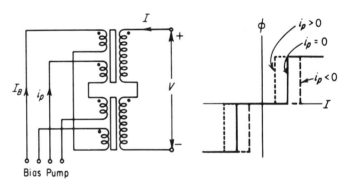

Bias Pump

**Fig. 5.59.** Another connection.

Since the parametric amplifier provides gain and majority logic can be performed with it, parametrons can be used to perform combinational logic. It is also, by its very nature, a single-bit storage device. To perform sequential logic, one needs to be able to build a shift register. It is necessary to use three or more clock phases in order to prevent back transfer of

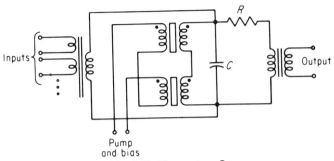

**Fig. 5.60.** Parametron I.

information. Three parametrons are connected to form a single shift register stage in Fig. 5.61.

In Fig. 5.60, the resistance $R$ serves to couple the power to the output and also to assist in the damping of the oscillations. Clock and signal

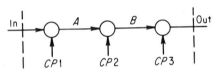

**Fig. 5.61.** Parametron shift register.

waveforms for transmitting a zero and a one in on-off operation are shown in Fig. 5.62. An input establishes a small oscillation in the resonant circuit. When $CP1$ (pump) arrives, the amplitude of oscillation is built up to a limiting amplitude. The circuit sends power in all directions, and the proper

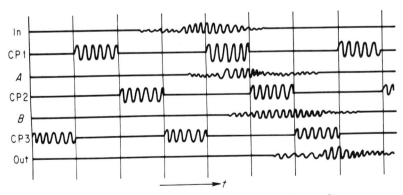

**Fig. 5.62.** Clock and signal waveforms for on-off operation.

choice of transformer turns ratios and the resistance $R$ must be made to limit the reverse transferred power even when a three-phase clock is used.

Since there is a three-phase clock, a time period exists in which oscillations can be further damped out.

It is also possible to prevent back transfer by using gated coupling networks.

### 5.18   TUNNEL DIODE CIRCUITS

The tunnel diode is only one of a large number of semiconductor devices that have been considered for digital circuit applications. The feature of its operation that has made it of great interest is its fast switching speed, which for some types is in the fractional nanosecond range. It is a junction diode which uses a semiconductor having a very high impurity density. A typical characteristic curve (germanium) is shown in Fig. 5.63. As shown,

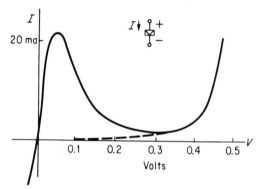

**Fig. 5.63.** Tunnel diode characteristic.

a negative resistance exists in the range from about 60 mv to 350 mv, which can be exploited to yield power gain. Tunnel diodes also can be fabricated to have the positive bump minimized (dotted curve in Fig. 5.63) to yield the "backward diode," which can be used as a diode at very low voltage levels.

The "Goto pair" is shown in Fig. 5.64. It is an RZ logical and amplifying element including clocking and pulse shaping so that sequential logic can be performed with the one circuit. However, carefully matched diodes must be used. Majority logic is performed with resistors prebiasing the point $A$ either positive or negative. When the clock pulses arrive, either the upper or lower diode will be put into a low-voltage state, while the other will be in the opposite state, producing a noninverted amplified output. It is necessary to use at least three clock phases to prevent back transfer of information when performing sequential logic.

A single tunnel diode may be used as a bistable device as in Fig. 5.65. If a current $I$ is established, a stable point at $A$ may be occupied. An input current making $V_J > V_p$ will cause the stable point to become $B$. To return to $A$, the input has to make $V_J < V_v$.

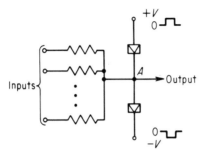

**Fig. 5.64.** Goto pair.

Tunnel diodes have also been used with transistors, yielding an improvement in performance above that obtained with either component alone.

An equivalent circuit for a tunnel diode is shown in Fig. 5.66. The function $i = f(v)$ is given in Fig. 5.63. $r$ and $l$ are linear elements, while $c$

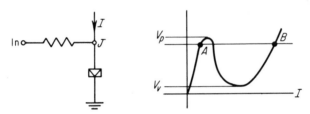

**Fig. 5.65.** Bistable device.

is the "junction transition capacitance," a nonlinear function of voltage which may be of the order of 5 $\mu$f/cm$^2$ of junction area in the range of tunnel-diode operating voltages.

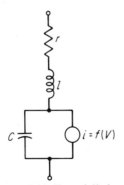

**Fig. 5.66.** Tunnel diode
equivalent circuit.

## REFERENCES

1. Buck, D. A., "The Cryotron–A Superconductive Computer Component," *Proc. I.R.E.*, **44** (April 1956), 482–493.

2. Caldwell, S. H., *Switching Circuits and Logical Design* (New York: John Wiley & Sons, 1958), chap. 9.

3. Chen, T. C., and A. Papoulis, "Terminal Properties of Magnetic Cores," *Proc. I.R.E.*, **46**:5 (May 1958), 839–849.

4. Crane, H. D., "A High-Speed Logic System Using Magnetic Elements and Connecting Wire Only," *Proc. I.R.E.*, **47**:1 (Jan. 1959), 63–73.

5. Dekker, A. J., *Electrical Engineering Materials* (Englewood Cliffs, N.J.: Prentice-Hall, Inc., 1959).

6. Goto, Eiichi, "The Parametron, A Digital Computing Element which Utilizes Parametric Oscillation," *Proc. I.R.E.*, **47**:8 (Aug. 1959), 1304–1316.

7. Gray, H. J. Jr., "Transistor Logical Element," U.S. Patent No. 2,853,632 (Sept. 23, 1958), filed Sept. 8, 1955. (RZ buffer-inverter.)

8. Guterman, S., and W. M. Cavey, "A Transistor-Magnetic Core Circuit; a New Device Applied to Digital Computing Techniques," *I.R.E. National Convention Record*, pt. 4, vol. 3 (March 1955), p. 84.

9. Haynes, M. K., "A Model for Nonlinear Flux Reversals of Square Loop Polycrystalline Magnetic Cores," A.I.E.E. Conference on Magnetism and Magnetic Materials, Washington, D.C. (Nov. 18–21, 1957).

10. *Investigation of Transistor and Transistor/Magnetic-Core Circuitry for High Speed Digital Computer Applications*, Scientific Report AFCRC-TN-56-184, 30 April 1956.

11. Karnaugh, M., "Pulse Switching Circuits Using Magnetic Cores," *Proc. I.R.E.*, **43**:5 (May 1955), 570–584.

12. Katz, H. W., *Solid State Magnetic and Dielectric Devices* (New York: John Wiley & Sons, 1959).

13. McLachlan, N. W., *Theory and Application of Mathieu Functions* (Fair Lawn, N.J.: Oxford University Press, 1947).

14. Minnick, Robert C., "Synthesis of Linear-Input Logic by the Simplex Method," 6th Annual Symposium on Computers and Data Processing, Denver Research Institute, 30 July 1959.

15. Prywes, Noah S., "Diodeless Magnetic Shift Registers Utilizing Transfluxors," *I.R.E. Transactions on Electronic Computers*, **EC-7** (Dec. 1958), 316–324.

16. Prywes, Noah S., "On Parametric Excitation with Current Saturable Inductances," *Journal of the Franklin Institute*, **270**:6 (Dec. 1960), 468–491.

17. Rajchmann, J. A., "Magnetics for Computers—A Survey of the State of the Art," *RCA Review*, **20**:1 (March 1959).

18. Rajchmann, J. A., "Static Magnetic Matrix Memory and Switching Circuits," *RCA Review*, **13** (June 1952), 183–201.

19. Rajchmann, J. A., and A. W. Lo, "The Transfluxor," *Proc. I.R.E.*, **44** (March 1956), 321–332.

20. Ramey, R. A., "The Single-Core Magnetic Amplifier as a Computer Element," *A.I.E.E. Trans. Part 1, Communications and Electronics*, **71** (1952), 442–446.

21. Richards, R. K., *Digital Computer Components and Circuits* (Princeton, N.J.: D. Van Nostrand Co., 1957).

22. Sims, R. C., E. R. Beck, Jr., and V. C. Kamm, "A Survey of Tunnel-Diode Digital Techniques," *Proc. I.R.E.*, **49**:1 (Jan. 1961), 136–146.

23. Smallman, C. R., A. E. Slade, and M. L. Cohen, "Thin-Film Cryotrons," *Proc. I.R.E.*, **48**:9 (Sept. 1960), 1562–1582.

24. Smith, W. R., and A. V. Pohm, "A New Approach to Resistor-Transistor-Tunnel-Diode Nanosecond Logic," *I.R.E. Transactions on Electronic Computers*, **EC-11**:5 (Oct. 1962), 658–664. Use of tunnel diode in collector-follower.

25. Sommers, H. S. Jr., "Tunnel Diodes as High-Frequency Devices," *Proc. I.R.E.*, **47**:7 (July 1959), 1201–1206.

26. Use of parametrons in digital systems is described in J. von Neumann, "Non-Linear Capacitance and Inductance Switching, Amplifying, and Memory Organs," U.S. Patent No. 2815488, issued Dec. 7, 1957.

27. Wang, An, and Way Dong Woo, "Magnetic Delay Storage," *Proc. I.R.E.*, **39** (1951), 401.

28. Wigington, R. L., "A New Concept in Computing," *Proc. I.R.E.*, **47**:4 (April 1959), 516–523. On parametric circuits.

## PROBLEMS

1. Prepare a table like that in Fig. 5.5 for connections of two transistors.

2. Investigate the relations that must exist among the various signal and supply voltages in Fig. 5.19 and a similar circuit using n-p-n transistors, in order that combinational logic networks may be constructed from them.

3. Show, where applicable, examples of how a flip-flop and a pulse former may be constructed from each of the NRZ logic circuits discussed.

4. In a clock system (Figs. 5.21, 5.22, and 5.23) the clock rate is 2 mc ± 0.01 per cent. The delay and tolerance of the pulse shaper is 20 ± 5 nsec and the delay and tolerance of the amplifier is 30 ± 10 nsec for both rising and falling

waveforms (steps). Given that $T_W = 100$ nsec and $T_\phi = 250$ nsec, compute the tolerances on $T_p$, $T_W$, and $T_\phi$ wherever applicable for the systems of Figs. 5.21, 5.22, and 5.23. In Fig. 5.23, compare the results when the tolerance on the delay of the delay element is taken to be zero and $\pm 10$ nsec.

**5.** Show how a flip-flop can be constructed using a SEAC type circuit and a delay line (dynamic flip-flop).

**6.** In the SEAC type circuit of Fig. 5.24, the delay from input to output for a transition is $60 \pm 40$ nsec. Neglecting delays of external wiring, determine the widths of CP and NCP and the maximum permissible number of phases for a 1-mc clock rate. The transformer cannot pass a pulse wider than 500 nsec. Assume (a) no clock timing tolerances (b) the clock timing tolerances of Prob. 4.

**7.** Show that Eq. (5.6) may be obtained from Eq. (5.5).

**8.** Discuss the following circuit from the point of view of what, if any, computer functions can be performed by it singly or in networks. (Carroll and Cooper, 1958 Solid State Circuits Conference—*modified*.)

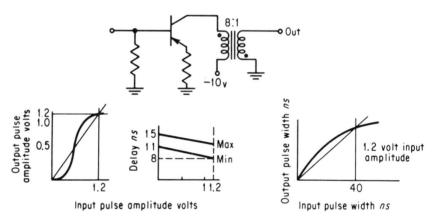

**Fig. P5.1.**

**9.** Can the AF circuit in Fig. 5.47 operate in a single-phase clocked system? With a two-phase clock? With an $n$-phase clock? If your answer to the last part is "Yes," show the timing.

**10.** Show how to connect an AF circuit as a stage of a shift register. [*Hint:* This requires a slight modification of the output circuit.]

**11.** Show what should be the sense of the windings, the timing of the reset, and any necessary clock signals so that the transistor-magnetic core circuit of Fig. 5.49 can be used as a stage of a shift register.

**12.** Explain the limitation on gain in circuitry using multi-aperture square-loop magnetic devices.

**13.** Calculate the energy required to switch the phase of a parametron circuit in terms of the volume of the cores and the maximum flux density. For simplification you can take cores having flux-current characteristics as indicated below and square-pulse alternating exciting current.

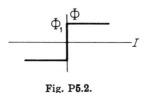

**Fig. P5.2.**

**14.** In the circuit below, sketch the output waveform, showing all times and voltages. Assume ideal diodes and also assume that the input signal switches the core completely.

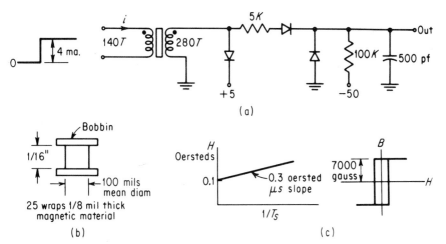

**Fig. P5.3.** (a) Circuit. (b) Core dimensions. (c) Core characteristics to be used.

# 6

# DIGITAL COMPUTER

# CIRCUIT ANALYSIS

Once the logical requirements that a circuit must meet are determined and once a circuit configuration is obtained that appears able to meet these requirements, it becomes necessary to analyze the circuit in order that it may later be designed. The purpose of circuit analysis is to obtain an understanding of the operation of the circuit in all details so that (a) the component characteristics that affect the operation of the circuit are known, and (b) the effects these component characteristics have on the circuit performance are known.

This information is necessary so that a circuit can be designed for a specified performance and so that the component characteristics required to achieve this performance may be specified. However, it is only rarely that theoretical analysis produces relations that are sufficiently accurate for the design of highly optimized circuits. It is usually necessary to augment the theoretical analysis with experimental work to determine accurate quantitative relationships. In other words, *the theoretical analysis serves to discover those component characteristics that significantly affect circuit operation and the form of the relationships between the component characteristics and circuit performance.*

## 6.1  STATEMENT OF THE PROBLEM

It is theoretically possible to determine the performance of a pulse circuit by solving the differential or other equations of the circuit. These equations are usually nonlinear, so that the problem is essentially one of the solution of sets of nonlinear differential, integral, algebraic, and/or difference equations. There are essentially four classes of approaches to this problem, and they are:

1. *Methods of nonlinear analysis* such as series solutions, phase-plane analysis, and other analytic and graphical approaches which attempt to solve the nonlinear problem as it stands without making simplifying assumptions.

2. *Numerical analysis, which is usually capable of giving an accurate numerical solution of the circuit equations.* However, a single solution for a given set of component values will not give the form of the relationships between the component characteristics and circuit performance. If many such solutions are obtained, one may be able to deduce the form of these relations and can then resort to experiment to adjust constants.

3. *Approximation methods, which attempt to arrive at a set of differential equations that are simpler to solve than the original set.* One such method that is widely used is piecewise linear analysis, wherein the simpler differential equations are linear. The danger here is that the linearizing assumptions will eliminate some essential feature of the circuit's performance that exists only because the system is nonlinear.

4. *Analog simulation techniques, wherein the system of equations is set up on an analog computer.* For example, an equivalent circuit of the complex system to be analyzed is set up on a breadboard with component values possibly scaled for operation at lower speeds. At lower speeds, parasitic capacitances or inductances that are suspected to exist in a high-speed circuit may be simulated by lumped capacitors or inductors, thus simplifying observational problems.

In order to be able to set up the differential (or other) equations that describe the circuit, it is necessary to have the differential equations describing the components. If these are available, it is a simple job to set up the mesh or node equations for the circuit, using well-known procedures. The components that have appeared in the circuits in Chap. 5 include:

| | |
|---|---|
| Resistors | Diodes (semiconductor) |
| Capacitors | Square-loop cores |
| Inductors (linear) | Transformers |
| Vacuum tubes | Tunnel diodes |
| Transistors | Delay lines |

Equivalent circuits that have been used for resistors, capacitors, and linear inductors are shown in Fig. 6.1. All elements in these equivalent circuits are usually linear and fairly independent of frequency, so that it is a routine matter to write the differential equations for these components. An equivalent circuit for the tunnel diode is given in Chap. 5. Equivalent circuits for vacuum tubes consist of the nonlinear characteristics together with the stray inductances and capacitances that are always present. We will develop approximate representations for transistors, semiconductor (logic) diodes, and pulse transformers, and we summarize the important principles of delay lines in Appendix III. In Chap. 5, equations describing the approximate properties of square-loop core materials were presented. The nature of the parasitic elements that must be included will be brought out in the discussion of pulse transformers. A small number of circuits will be analyzed showing the application of the various techniques.

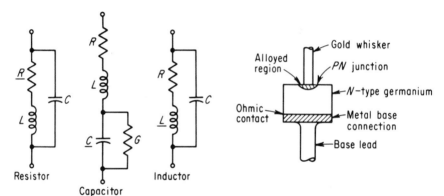

**Fig. 6.1.** Equivalent circuits for $R$, $C$, and $L$.

**Fig. 6.2.** Gold-bonded diode construction.

## 6.2 DIODE LOGIC CIRCUITS

The discussion of diodes will be confined to the gold-bonded types which have seen wide use in computer logic circuits. A typical structure is shown in Fig. 6.2.

A planar junction has a theoretical d-c characteristic given by

$$I = I_s \left( \exp \frac{qV}{kT} - 1 \right) \tag{6.1}$$

where  $T$ = absolute temperature,

$k$ = Boltzmann's constant,

$q$ = electronic charge,

$I_s$ = saturation current,

$\dfrac{kT}{q}$ = 0.026 volts at 300°K.

An actual is compared with a theoretical diode characteristic in Fig. 6.3. In that figure, the $V$-$I$ characteristic of an actual diode is drawn together

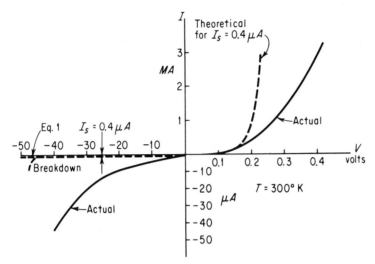

**Fig. 6.3.** Typical germanium diode characteristics.

with that computed from Eq. (6.1) assuming that $I_s = 0.4$ $\mu$amp, a value which yields the correct currents for $V \approx 0.1$–$0.2$ volts. The deviation in the forward direction occurs because the junction is not ideal and because of ohmic resistance arising from the ohmic contact resistance, the resistance of the bulk germanium, etc., which in the diode of Fig. 6.3 is about 65 ohms. The deviation of the reverse characteristic is caused by impurities at the surface of the semiconductor and is essentially ohmic in character (2 megohms in the diode of Fig. 6.3). The d-c equivalent circuit of the diode in

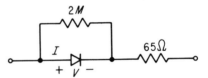

**Fig. 6.4.** Diode d-c equivalent circuit.

Fig. 6.3 is given in Fig. 6.4, where $I$ versus $V$ is given by Eq. (6.1). At large negative voltages certain breakdown phenomena occur, which can be of the following types:

1. Zener breakdown, a process similar to field emission.
2. Avalanche breakdown, caused by the generation of additional charge carriers through the collision of the existing carriers with the crystal lattice.
3. Punch-through effects occurring in thin-base diodes (see transistors).

Transient effects may be partially accounted for by including the junction capacitances, which are of the form

$$C = \frac{K_0}{(\phi - V)^n} + C_1, \qquad V < \phi \qquad (6.2)$$

where $n \leq 0.5$, and $K_0$, $\phi$, and $C_1$ are constants all of which can be determined experimentally. $C$ in Eq. (6.2) is defined such that $i = C \, dv/dt$ (see Prob. 20). In the case of logic diodes used in diode gating circuits, good results are obtained if an average value

$$C_{\text{eff}} = \frac{1}{\phi - V} \int_\phi^V C(V) \, dV \qquad (6.3)$$

is taken; in the case of logic diodes it is about 1 pf.

Because of minority-carrier storage effects, semiconductor diodes conduct an enhanced reverse current when one attempts to reverse the voltage across them. This is illustrated in Fig. 6.5. $T_s$ is the "storage time." $T_f$,

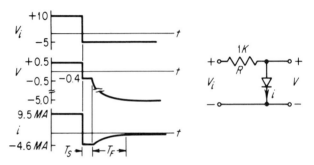

**Fig. 6.5.** Illustrating diode reverse recovery times.

the fall time, is measured to any suitably defined point on the current waveform. Because the storage effects are due to minority carriers in the base material, the maximum charge that can be extracted from the diode is essentially equal to the stored charge. The amount of stored charge increases with an increase in base volume, forward current, and junction area. Short minority-carrier lifetime will reduce the charge extracted, especially if the reverse bias is applied slowly, giving the minority carriers time to disappear through recombination. In the case of diode gating circuits, it is usually sufficient to assume that storage effects augment the diode capacitance by an amount that is simple to estimate (compare waveforms in Fig. 6.5 to those obtained if the diode is replaced by a storage-free diode shunted by a capacitor).

There is a similar storage effect which occurs when one attempts to turn a diode on, in that the diode behaves as if it contained a series inductance. This effect will be ignored in the analysis to follow.

We will consider the simple gate shown in Fig. 6.6. Of the $n$ inputs, $n - 1$ are biased at $V_i$ and the step is applied at input $A$. This is the input condition giving the slowest response. We will neglect diode reverse leakage currents. The initial value of $v$, which is $V_0$ may be obtained either by graphical means or by successive approximations. For a graphical solution, we may write

$$v_1 = E - RI$$

$$v_2 = f(I) \qquad \text{(the diode characteristic)}$$

$$V_0 = v_1 \qquad \text{when } v_1 = v_2$$

These two curves are plotted in Fig. 6.7, showing the solution. With the

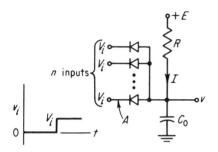

Fig. 6.6. Simple diode gate.

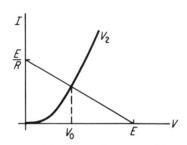

Fig. 6.7. Illustrating a graphical solution.

diode of Fig. 6.3, if $E = 10$ volts and $R = 10$ K, $V_0 \cong 0.27$ volts. Graphical solution becomes difficult in complex circuits, and successive approximation is then of value. If $E = 10$ volts and $R = 10$ K, the solution in the case above would proceed as follows:

1. Assume that the drop, $V_d$, across the diode is zero.
2. $I = E/R = 10/10 = 1$ ma.
3. From Fig. 6.3, $V_d = 0.27$ volts for 1 ma.
4. $I = (10 - 0.27)/10 = 0.973$ ma.
5. From Fig. 6.3, $V_d = 0.268$ volts.

Note that the convergence in this case is very rapid; a divergent iteration is:

1. Assume $I = 0.95$ ma.
2. $V_d = E - RI = 10 - 9.5 = 0.5$ volts.
3. From Fig. 6.3, $I = 5$ ma.
4. $V_d = 10 - 50 = -40$ volts.

In complex examples, the application of a little engineering judgment will enable one to develop a convergent iterative sequence of computations.

In piecewise linear analysis of the transient behavior of nonlinear circuits, the nonlinear elements are approximated by as few straight line segments as possible. The solution of the transient is then obtained by piecing together with appropriate initial conditions the solutions obtained by linear transient analysis of the circuit over the several linear segments of the approximated nonlinear components.

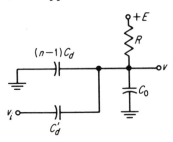

**Fig. 6.8.** Equivalent circuit.

In the case of the step response of the diode circuit, three regions of operation are of interest:

1. $v_i = 0.$
2. $v_i = V_i; v \leq V_i.$
3. $v_i = V_i; v > V_i.$

The first case has been solved by other means. Case 2 will be considered further.

If the diode reverse leakage is neglected, the equivalent circuit for Fig. 6.6 for $V_o < v < V_i, t > 0$ is shown in Fig. 6.8. $C'_d > C_d$ to account for the charge stored in the bottom diode of Fig. 6.6, which is the only diode switched.

The voltage, $v$, satisfies the differential equation

$$C \frac{dv}{dt} + \frac{v}{R} = \frac{E}{R} + C'_d \frac{dv_i}{dt}; \qquad t > 0, v < V_i$$

where $C = C_o(n - 1)C_d + C'_d$. Laplace transformation yields

$$sCV(s) - CV_o + \frac{V}{R} = \frac{E}{sR} + C'_d V_i \qquad (6.4)$$

Equation (6.4) may be rewritten,

$$V(s) = \frac{V_i \frac{C'_d}{C} + V_o}{s + \frac{1}{RC}} + \frac{E}{RC} \frac{1}{s\left(s + \frac{1}{RC}\right)} \qquad (6.5)$$

Inverse transformation of Eq. (6.5) yields

$$v(t) = E - \left[E - \frac{C'_d}{C} V_i - V_o\right] e^{-t/RC}; \qquad t > 0, v < V_i \qquad (6.6)$$

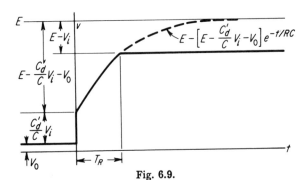

**Fig. 6.9.**

which is plotted in Fig. 6.9. $T_R$ is defined as the time at which $v = V_i$. From Eq. (6.6), we find

$$T_R = RC \log \frac{E - \frac{C'_d}{C} V_i - V_o}{E - V_i} \tag{6.7}$$

$$= RC \log \frac{\text{initial voltage across } R}{\text{final voltage across } R}$$

Noting that

$$\log x = 2 \left[ \frac{x-1}{x+1} + \frac{1}{3} \left( \frac{x-1}{x+1} \right)^3 + \frac{1}{5} \left( \frac{x-1}{x+1} \right)^5 + \cdots \right] \qquad \text{for } x > 1 \tag{6.8}$$

and using only the first term of Eq. (6.8) in Eq. (6.7), we obtain

$$T_R \cong \frac{[C] \left[ V_i \left( 1 - \frac{C'_d}{C} \right) - V_o \right]}{\left[ \dfrac{E - \frac{1}{2} V_i \left( 1 + \dfrac{C'_d}{C} \right) - \dfrac{V_o}{2}}{R} \right]}$$

or

$$T_R \cong C \frac{\Delta V}{I} \tag{6.9}$$

where $C$ is the capacitance to be charged, $\Delta V$ is the change of voltage across the capacitance during $T_R$, and $I$ is the arithmetic average of the capacitor charging currents at $t = 0$ and $t = T_R$. It is easy to show, from Eq. (6.8), that the error in the approximation is about 3 per cent when $x$—the ratio of initial and final voltages across $R$—is 2; and that the error decreases rapidly as this ratio approaches unity. The significance of the terms in Eq. (6.9) should be carefully studied, as Eq. (6.9) makes it possible to analyze in a simple manner some rather complex circuits whose analysis by conventional methods is very difficult. This will be illustrated for a three-level multiple-input OR-AND-OR diode logic circuit.

## 6.3 MULTILEVEL DIODE LOGIC CIRCUITS

The diode circuit of Fig. 6.10 will be considered. All diodes are assumed ideal for simplicity and have zero reverse leakage and zero forward voltage drop. A pulse is applied to node 4. All inputs are assumed to be biased in such a way as to allow the pulse to pass from node 4 to node 1 via nodes 2 and 3 without interference. The symbols $C_d$, $C'_d$, $C''_d$ serve only to distinguish the diode capacitances in the various paths.

The capacitances appearing at the various nodes are:
At node 1:

$$C_{1e} = C_1 + (n_1 - 1)C_d + C''_d$$

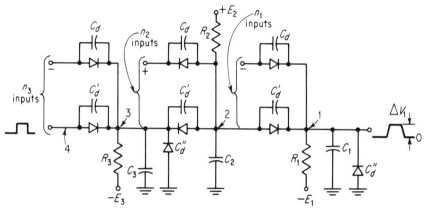

**Fig. 6.10.** Three-level diode logic circuit.

At node 2:

$$C_{2e} = C_2 + (n_2 - 1)C_d$$

At node 3:

$$C_{3e} = C_3 + (n_3 - 1)C_d + C_d''$$

The fall time at node 1 is:

$$T_{F1} = C_{1e} \frac{\Delta V_1}{I_1}, \qquad I_1 = \frac{E_1 + \dfrac{\Delta V_1}{2}}{R_1} \tag{6.10}$$

If the rise time at node 3 is faster than the rise time at node 1, then the latter is

$$T_{R1} = \frac{C_{1e} \Delta V_1 + C_{2e} \Delta V_2}{I_2 - I_1}, \qquad I_2 = \frac{E_2 - \dfrac{\Delta V_2}{2}}{R_2} \tag{6.11}$$

The reader should observe that $I_2 - I_1$ is the mean of the minimum and maximum currents available for charging the capacitances at nodes 1 and 2. The rise time of node 3 is determined from the capabilities of the circuit driving the diode circuit. Under some circumstances the nodes 2 and 3 may tend to limit the rate of fall of node 1. Under these circumstances, we must replace Eq. (6.10) by

$$T_{F1} = \frac{C_{1e} \Delta V_1 + C_{2e} \Delta V_2 + C_{3e} \Delta V_3}{I_3 - I_2 + I_1}, \qquad I_3 \frac{E_3 + \dfrac{\Delta V_3}{2}}{R_3} \tag{6.12}$$

Note that $I_3 - I_2 + I_1$ is the mean of the minimum and maximum currents available for charging the capacitances in the circuit. If diode leakages are present, it is a simple matter to incorporate their effect in these currents. If node 1 tends to fall slower than nodes 2 and 3, then

$$T_{F3} = \frac{C_3 \, \Delta V_3 + C_2 \, \Delta V_2}{I_3 - I_2} \tag{6.13}$$

When $T_{F3} = T_{F1}$ [as given by Eq. (6.10)] the algebraic theorem,

$$\text{if } \frac{a+b}{c+d} = \frac{e}{f} \text{ then } \frac{a+b+e}{c+d+f} = \frac{e}{f}$$

shows that Eqs. (6.10), (6.12), and (6.13) are consistent. In this analysis, we have omitted the effect of the $C_d'$ for simplicity's sake. To include their effects in a numerical example, examine carefully the time histories of the voltages at the various nodes to determine the changes of voltages across these capacitances and whether or not these diodes had been previously conducting. Depending on the circumstances, adjust the rise and fall times to correct for the amount of charge that the $C_d'$ account for. This process can also be carried out for the $C_d''$. In a numerical example it is also quite easy to correct for the voltage drops across the conducting diodes. Determine the quiescent potentials before and after the transitions. Corrected values of $\Delta V_1$, $\Delta V_2$, and $\Delta V_3$ can be determined for use in Eqs. (6.10) through (6.13).

## 6.4  NUMERICAL ANALYSIS OF THE SIMPLE GATE

The steps involved in the analysis of a transient situation can be summarized.

1. Determine all the relations controlling the node voltages or loop currents. These will be curves for some elements and differential equations for others. Some of the relations may be nonlinear.
2. Using a suitable quadrature formula and interval, integrate these equations numerically.

The process will be outlined for the simple diode gate shown in Fig. 6.6. For simplicity, we will assume that $C_d$ and $C_d'$ are constants, although the method allows the use of the actual values as functions of voltage or, more properly, as described by differential equations. The differential equation for $v$ is

$$C \frac{dv}{dt} + \frac{v}{R} + i_d = \frac{E}{R} + C_d' \frac{dv_i}{dt}$$

Assume $C_o = 28$ pf, $C_d = C_d' = 1$ pf, and $n = 2$. Hence $C = 30$ pf. If $R = 3$ K, $E = +10$ v, and the input signal has a 20-nsec rise time to a 5-v ramp, then

(a) $\dfrac{dv}{dt} = -\dfrac{1}{9} \times 10^8 v - \dfrac{v_d}{30} \times 10^{12} + \dfrac{1}{9} \times 10^9 + \dfrac{1}{30}\dfrac{dv_i}{dt}$

(b) $i_d = f(v - v_i)$    (see Fig. 6.3)

(c) $v_i = 0$,            $t < 0$          (6.14)

      $= \dfrac{t}{4} \times 10^{-9}$,    $0 \le t \le 20 \times 10^{-9}$

      $= 5$,           $t > 20 \times 10^{-9}$

The procedure for any given time instant is the calculation of $v_i$ from (c), the calculation of $i_d$ from (b), and then the calculation of $dv/dt$ from (a). These data can then be used together with a quadrature formula to obtain the value of $v$ at the next instant of time. Since $v$ is used in these calculations, its initial value is required, and we can obtain it by at least three methods: (a) successive approximations, (b) graphical analysis, and (c) assume a value. With $v_i = 0$, follow the procedure outlined above for the process of numerical quadrature until $v$ settles down to a steady value.

## 6.5 SOME TECHNIQUES FOR THE NUMERICAL SOLUTION OF DIFFERENTIAL EQUATIONS

The differential equation in Eq. (6.14) is of the form

$$\frac{dx}{dt} = g(x, t)$$

Let us replace $dx/dt$ by $\Delta x/\Delta t$, $\Delta t \equiv h$. Label values of $x$ and $t$ as follows $(n = 0, 1, 2, \ldots)$:

$$x(0) = x_0 \qquad t(0) = 0 = t_0$$
$$x(h) = x_1 \qquad t(h) = h = t_1$$
$$\vdots \qquad\qquad \vdots$$
$$x(nh) = x_n \qquad t(nh) = nh = t_n$$

Now $\Delta x = x_{n+1} - x_n$ and

$$\frac{x_{n+1} - x_n}{h} = g(x_n, t_n)$$

replaces the differential equation. Its solution is, under certain circumstances, close to the solution of the differential equation.

Rearranging,

$$x_{n+1} = x_n + hg(x_n, t_n)$$

or

$$x_{n+1} = x_n + h\left[\frac{dx}{dt}\right]_{t = t_n} \qquad \text{(Euler method)}$$

sometimes called $O_{11}$ (open, one ordinate, one derivative). If we set

$$\frac{x_{n+1} - x_n}{h} = g(x_{n+1}, t_{n+1})$$

we get

$$x_{n+1} = x_n + h\left[\frac{dx}{dt}\right]_{t=t_{n+1}}$$

sometimes called formula $C_{11}$ (closed, one ordinate, one derivative). As an example of the use of $O_{11}$ we will solve the differential equation, $dx/dt = -x$, for $x_0 = 1$ and $h = 0.1$.

$$x_0 = 1$$

$$\left[\frac{dx}{dt}\right]_{t=t_0} = -[x]_{x=x_0} = -1$$

$$x_1 = 1 + 0.1[-1] = 0.9$$

$$x_2 = 0.9 + 0.1[-0.9] = 0.81$$

$$\cdots$$

The solution is known to be $e^{-t}$ and is 0.819 at $t = 0.2$.

We can show how closed formulas are used by applying $C_{11}$ to the above problem.

$$x_0 = 1$$

$$x_1^0 = 0.9 \qquad\qquad\qquad\qquad \text{(by } O_{11})$$

$$\text{repeated}\atop\text{use of } C_{11} \left\{\begin{array}{l} x_1' = 1 + 0.1[-0.9] = 0.91 \\ x_1'' = 1 + 0.1[-0.91] = 0.909 \\ x_1''' = 1 + 0.1[-0.909] = 0.909 \end{array}\right\} \quad \text{no change}$$

$$x_2^0 = 0.909 + 0.1[-0.909] = 0.818 \qquad \text{(by } O_{11})$$

$$\text{repeated}\atop\text{use of } C_{11} \left\{\begin{array}{l} x_2' = 0.909 + 0.1[-0.818] = 0.827 \\ x_2'' = 0.909 + 0.1[-0.827] = 0.826 \\ x_2''' = 0.909 + 0.1[-0.826] = 0.826 \end{array}\right\} \quad \text{no change}$$

The solution obtained by using $O_{11}$ is 0.009 low, and that obtained by the repeated use of $C_{11}$ is 0.007 high. Note that $x_1^0$ and $x_2^0$ could have been obtained by methods other than $O_{11}$, as the final result obtained from repeated use of $C_{11}$ depends only on the error behavior of $C_{11}$.

We can estimate the propagated error when $O_{11}$ is used on linear differential equations by the following method. Consider the differential equation,

$$\frac{dx}{dt} = \lambda x \tag{6.15}$$

where $\lambda$ may be a complex number. Its solution is $x = x_0 e^{\lambda t}$. If integrated by $O_{11}$, we can find the form of the numerical solution without actually calculating it. Substitute $dx/dt = \lambda x$ into $O_{11}$.

$$x_{n+1} = x_n + h\lambda x_n = (1 + h\lambda)x_n \qquad (6.16)$$

is the recurrence relation by which we would obtain the numerical solution of $dx/dt = \lambda x$.

Assume $x_n = x_0 e^{\mu t}$. When substituted into Eq. (6.16), we get

$$x_0 e^{(n+1)\mu h} = (1 + h\lambda)x_0 e^{n\mu h}$$

or

$$e^{\mu h} = 1 + h\lambda \qquad (6.17)$$

Hence, $\mu = (1/h) \log (1 + h\lambda)$. ($\mu \cong \lambda$ for $h\lambda \ll 1$). For $h = 0.1$ and $\lambda = -1$ (previous example) $\mu = 10 \log (1 - 0.1) = -1.052$. At $t = 0.2$, $e^{\mu t} = 0.81$ which is the value obtained numerically. The error at any time when using $O_{11}$ on $dx/dt = \lambda x$ is

$$x_0 e^{\lambda t} - x_0 e^{(t/h) \log (1+\lambda h)}$$

To handle a second (or higher) order differential equation proceed as in the following example. Consider

$$A \frac{d^2x}{dt^2} + B \left(\frac{dx}{dt}\right)^2 + Cx^3 = D$$

where $A$, $B$, etc., may be functions of $x$ and/or $t$. Let $y = dx/dt$. Then

$$\frac{dx}{dt} = y$$

$$\frac{dy}{dt} = +\frac{1}{A} (D - By^2 - Cx^3)$$

These are equivalent to the more general forms:

$$\frac{dx}{dt} = f_1(x, y, t)$$

$$\frac{dy}{dt} = f_2(x, y, t) \qquad (6.18)$$

which may be integrated using $O_{11}$ in the forms:

$$x_{n+1} = x_n + h \left[\frac{dx}{dt}\right]_{x=x_n,\, y=y_n,\, t=t_n}$$

$$y_{n+1} = y_n + h \left[\frac{dy}{dt}\right]_{x=x_n,\, y=y_n,\, t=t_n}$$

The quantity, $\lambda$, appearing in Eq. (6.15) is the natural frequency (expressed as a complex number) of oscillation of the true solution of the differential equation. Its real part is the damping factor and its imaginary part is $2\pi$ times the frequency of oscillation of the true solution, which for Eq. (6.15) is

$$x = x_0 e^{\lambda t} = x_0 e^{\sigma t} \cos \omega t + j x_0 e^{\sigma t} \sin \omega t$$

where $\lambda = \sigma + j\omega$. If known, it can be used to estimate the size of the interval $h$ required to obtain accurate numerical solutions using Eq. (6.17). When the differential equations of the circuit are of second or higher order, more than one natural frequency exists in the solution. The one corresponding to the highest frequency has the strongest effect on the error. If

$$\frac{dx}{dt} = a_{11}x + a_{12}y$$

$$\frac{dy}{dt} = a_{21}x + a_{22}y$$

(6.19)

the $\lambda$'s used to estimate $\mu$ in Eq. (6.17) can be obtained from:

$$\begin{vmatrix} a_{11} - \lambda & a_{12} \\ a_{21} & a_{22} - \lambda \end{vmatrix} = 0$$

(6.20)

and used to estimate the interval required.

Equation (6.20) is just the characteristic equation for the system described by Eq. (6.19). Hence, the $\lambda$'s are also the roots of the characteristic equation and are the characteristic vibrations used in the Heaviside expansion theorem.

If the differential equations are nonlinear, as are Eqs. (6.18), we can use a linearized version of them to estimate the required interval by putting

$$a_{11} = \frac{\partial f_1}{\partial x}, \qquad a_{12} = \frac{\partial f_1}{\partial y}$$

$$a_{21} = \frac{\partial f_2}{\partial x}, \qquad a_{22} = \frac{\partial f_2}{\partial y}$$

obtained from Eqs. (6.18), in Eq. (6.20), evaluated at the point of interest.

An open quadrature formula developed for real-time digital control purposes is a modified $O_{33}$. It will give results about as good for $|\lambda h| < 0.3$ as will $O_{11}$ for $|\lambda h| < 0.1$. However, with $|\lambda h| > 0.53$, the solution obtained from the modified $O_{33}$ may diverge to infinity (see Fig. 6.12).

Modified $O_{33}$ (coefficients to four decimal places):

$$x_0 = 1.1462 x_{-1} - 0.2011 x_{-2} + 0.0549 x_{-3}$$

$$+ h[1.6416 \dot{x}_{-1} - 1.0080 \dot{x}_{-2} + 0.2751 \dot{x}_{-3}]$$

$$\dot{x}_n = \left[\frac{dx}{dt}\right]_{t_n}$$

$O_{11}$ is preferable to any other method for the numerical solution of small systems of differential equations by hand computation. This modified $O_{33}$ is suitable for large systems where as large an interval as possible is desired to avoid the recomputation of complicated derivatives. For systems where a digital computer is available, the reader should consult the literature and the practice.

Returning to the diode circuit problem, the $\lambda$'s can be estimated from the time constants.

When $i_d = 0$, the time constant is $RC = 3 \times 10^3 \times 30 \times 10^{-12} = 90$ nsec. Hence $\lambda \cong 1/RC = 11 \times 10^6$. For $|\lambda h| < 0.1$, we have $h < 9$ nsec (note that for this problem, $C\,\Delta V/I = 30$ nsec). However, when $i_d \neq 0$, the circuit resistance shunting $C$ falls to the order of 50 $\Omega$ (dynamic resistance of paralleled diodes at 1.66 ma). Hence $RC = 1.5 \times 10^{-9}$. For $\lambda h < 0.1$, $h < 0.15$ nsec. An interval as small as this may, however, not be needed. Usually, stability only must be maintained. We wish to find the region where the method is unstable ($Re\,\mu > 0$). From Eq. (6.17),

$$|e^{\mu h}| = |e^{hRe\mu}| = |1 + h\lambda|$$

$$|1 + h\lambda| > 1, \qquad Re\,\mu > 0$$

$$|1 + h\lambda| < 1, \qquad Re\,\mu < 0$$

Setting $|1 + h\lambda| = 1$ yields the contour in the $z = h\lambda = x + jy$ plane on which $Re\mu = 0$. It is the circle of radius unity with center at $z = -1 + j0$

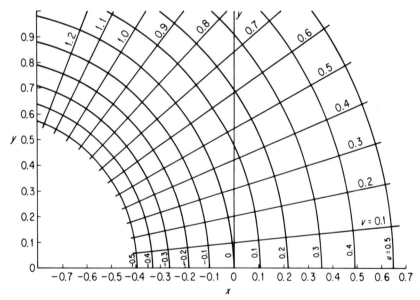

Fig. 6.11. $O_{11}$.

inside of which $Re\mu < 0$. This is shown in Fig. 6.11. If $u + jv = \mu h$ and $x + jy = \lambda h$, the relation Eq. (6.17) yields the plot in Fig. 6.11. A similar plot for the modified $O_{33}$ is shown in Fig. 6.12. However, the defining equation (see Prob. 9 at the end of this chapter) for the modified $O_{33}$ is satisfied by more than one value of $\mu$.

For $RC = 1.5 \times 10^{-9}$ sec, $h < 3$ nsec with $O_{11}$ will give a stable (but inaccurate) result, because for this value of $h$ we have $h\lambda > -2$, which gives $Re\mu < 0$ (stable). Figure 6.12 shows only the value of $\mu$ having the largest real part for a given $\lambda$. All the other values of $\mu$ would be expected to give rise to rapidly vanishing components of the computed solution.

To illustrate how Figs. 6.11 and 6.12 can be used to obtain the natural

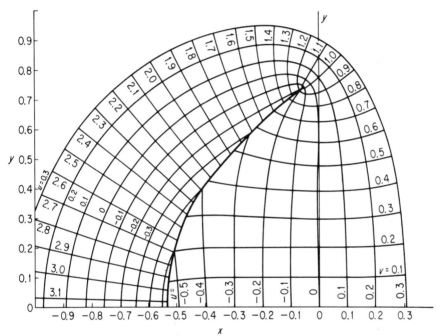

**Fig. 6.12.** Modified $O_{33}$.

frequencies in the computed solution from the frequencies in the true solution, assume that a differential equation is integrated numerically with $O_{11}$ with $h = 0.3$. Assume that the $\lambda$'s are

$$\lambda = 0, -1 \pm j3$$

Hence,

$$\lambda h = 0, -0.3 \pm j0.9$$

From Fig. 6.11,

$$\mu h = 0, +0.13 \pm j0.91$$

Hence,

$$\mu = 0, +0.43 \pm j3.03$$

Since $\mu$ and $\lambda$ differ greatly, $h$ would have to be reduced considerably to obtain an accurate solution.

The same conclusion could have been reached by using Eq. (6.17). However, no formula similar to Eq. (6.17) exists relating $\mu$ and $\lambda$ for the modified $O_{33}$, so that we must rely on Fig. 6.12. It is beyond the scope of this book to discuss the derivation of Fig. 6.12.

### 6.6 JUNCTION TRANSISTORS*

In this section we will develop a d-c equivalent circuit for a transistor. This will be obtained by building on the properties of the junction diode as obtained in Appendix I and in Sec. 6.2. The discussion is for p-n-p transistors and may be applied to n-p-n transistors by reversing the signs of all voltages and currents.

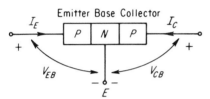

Fig. 6.13. Junction transistor.

Consider the p-n-p junction transistor shown in Fig. 6.13 having planar junctions and a homogeneous base.

One may solve the diffusion equation (Appendix I) and obtain the following results:

$$I_E = A_{11}(e^{qV_{EB}/kT} - 1) + A_{12}(e^{qV_{CB}/kT} - 1)$$

$$I_C = A_{21}(e^{qV_{EB}/kT} - 1) + A_{22}(e^{qV_{CB}/kT} - 1) \quad (6.21)$$

$$A_{12} = A_{21}$$

Equations (6.21) should also be conceptually evident from Fig. 6.13. For example, $I_C$ should contain a component of current (second term) which depends on $V_{CB}$ in the same manner as the current in a p-n junction depends on its bias voltage. Also, $I_C$ should contain a term that is proportional to the emitter diode current (first term); the reason is that holes injected at the emitter-base junction can diffuse to the collector junction. One might expect that $A_{12} = A_{21}$ if $A_{12}$ and $A_{21}$ have only to do with the diffusion process and if the base material is homogeneous.

If the collector is reverse biased, we have approximately from Eqs. (6.21)

$$I_E = A_{11}(e^{qV_{EB}/kT} - 1) - A_{12}$$

$$I_C = A_{21}(e^{qV_{EB}/kT} - 1) - A_{22} \quad (6.22)$$

* See Ref. 3.

Elimination of $(e^{qV_{EB}/kT} - 1)$ in Eqs. (6.22) yields

$$I_C = \frac{A_{21}}{A_{11}} I_E + \frac{A_{12}A_{21}}{A_{11}} - A_{22} \qquad (6.23)$$

If $\alpha_F$ is defined as $-A_{21}/A_{11}$ and $I_{CO}$ is defined as $(A_{12}A_{21}/A_{11}) - A_{22}$, then Eq. (6.23) becomes ($I_{CO} < 0$ in a p-n-p transistor)

$$I_C = -\alpha_F I_E + I_{CO} \qquad (6.24)$$

If the emitter is reverse biased, we obtain by a similar derivation,

$$I_E = -\alpha_R I_C + I_{EO} \qquad (6.25)$$

where ($I_{EO} < 0$ in a p-n-p transistor)

$$\alpha_R = -\frac{A_{12}}{A_{22}}$$

$$I_{EO} = \frac{A_{12}A_{21}}{A_{22}} - A_{11} \qquad (6.26)$$

Note that $I_{CO}$ and $I_{EO}$ are respectively the collector and emitter currents when $I_E = 0$ and $I_C = 0$. $\alpha_F$ and $\alpha_R$ are respectively the forward and reverse short-circuit current gains.

From the definition of $I_{CO}$ and $\alpha_F$ when the collector is reverse biased and from Eqs. (6.26) the following pair of equations is obtained.

$$\frac{A_{12}A_{21}}{A_{22}} - A_{11} = I_{EO} = A_{11}(\alpha_F\alpha_R - 1)$$

$$\frac{A_{12}A_{21}}{A_{11}} - A_{22} = I_{CO} = A_{22}(\alpha_F\alpha_R - 1) \qquad (6.27)$$

These equations are easily solved for $A_{11}$ and $A_{22}$ to yield

$$A_{11} = -\frac{I_{EO}}{1 - \alpha_F\alpha_R}$$

$$A_{22} = -\frac{I_{CO}}{1 - \alpha_F\alpha_R} \qquad (6.28)$$

From Eqs. (6.28) and the first of Eqs. (6.26) and its counterpart for $\alpha_F$, we obtain

$$A_{12} = \frac{\alpha_R I_{CO}}{1 - \alpha_F\alpha_R}$$

$$A_{21} = \frac{\alpha_F I_{EO}}{1 - \alpha_F\alpha_R} \qquad (6.29)$$

and from the third of Eqs. (6.21) and Eqs. (6.29),

$$\alpha_F I_{EO} = \alpha_R I_{CO} \qquad (6.30)$$

Equation (6.30) works in practice near zero volts for transistors having homogeneous bases.

We may write using Eqs. (6.21), (6.28), and (6.29),

$$I_E = -\frac{I_{EO}}{1 - \alpha_F\alpha_R}(e^{qV_{EB}/kT} - 1) + \frac{\alpha_R I_{CO}}{1 - \alpha_F\alpha_R}(e^{qV_{CB}/kT} - 1)$$

$$I_C = \frac{\alpha_F I_{EO}}{1 - \alpha_F\alpha_R}(e^{qV_{EB}/kT} - 1) - \frac{I_{CO}}{1 - \alpha_F\alpha_R}(e^{qV_{CB}/kT} - 1)$$

(6.31)

Equations (6.31) describe the d-c characteristics of homogeneous-base junction transistors neglecting the resistances of the emitter, collector, and base regions, and any leakage currents that may exist due to surface contamination. An equivalent circuit into which these effects may be incorporated may be obtained by noting that the current in a p-n junction is given by an expression of the form

$$I = I_s(e^{qV/kT} - 1)$$

so that Eqs. (6.31) become

$$I_E = I_{SE}(e^{qV_{EB}/kT} - 1) - \alpha_R I_{SC}(e^{qV_{CB}/kT} - 1)$$

$$I_C = -\alpha_F I_{SE}(e^{qV_{EB}/kT} - 1) + I_{SC}(e^{qV_{CB}/kT} - 1)$$

(6.32)

where

$$I_{SE} = -\frac{I_{EO}}{1 - \alpha_F\alpha_R}, \qquad I_{SC} = -\frac{I_{CO}}{1 - \alpha_F\alpha_R}$$

(6.33)

If we let

$$I_1 = I_{SE}(e^{qV_{EB}/kT} - 1)$$

$$I_2 = I_{SC}(e^{qV_{CB}/kT} - 1)$$

(6.34)

then Eqs. (6.32) become

$$I_E = I_1 - \alpha_R I_2$$

$$I_C = -\alpha_F I_1 + I_2$$

(6.35)

An equivalent circuit deduced from Eqs. (6.34) and (6.35) is shown in Fig. 6.14. In order to account for the resistances of the emitter, collector, and

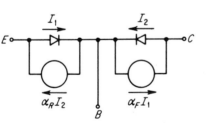

Fig. 6.14. D-c equivalent circuit of a p-n-p transistor.

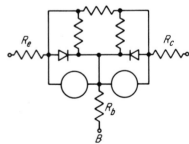

Fig. 6.15. Augmented d-c equivalent circuit.

base regions, resistances can be inserted in the equivalent circuit in series with the emitter, base, and collector. Ohmic leakage currents can be represented by the appropriately inserted shunt resistances (see Fig. 6.15). Equations (6.35) and the equivalent circuits of Fig. 6.14 and 6.15 are of wide application.

The d-c collector characteristics are shown in Fig. 6.16 for the four quadrants. Note that the third quadrant contains the negatively biased collector characteristics of a p-n-p transistor. The first and fourth quadrants show the collector saturation characteristics as given by Eq. (6.32). The emitter characteristics in normal operation (biased collector) have a shape similar to the collector characteristics in the first quadrant of Fig. 6.16.

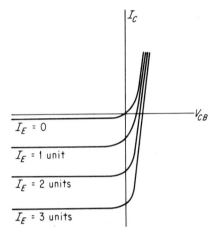

Fig. **6.16.** D-c characteristics of p-n-p transistor for $V_{EB} > 0$.

In an actual transistor, quantities such as $\alpha_F$ and $\alpha_R$ are not independent of voltage and current. However, the results developed so far can often be used if interpreted with care.

## 6.7 BREAKDOWN PHENOMENA

Since the collector and emitter junctions are both p-n junctions, avalanche or Zener breakdown effects may occur to limit the amount of reverse bias that may be applied to the device. Such a breakdown does not ordinarily damage a transistor if the maximum junction-temperature limit is not exceeded. However, those having much surface contamination may exhibit a change of properties in the reverse direction after having been subjected to high reverse voltages. This is really a reliability question, which will be dealt with in Chap. 7.

The width of the transition region (Appendix I) may be found by solving Poisson's equation. For step junctions (homogeneous collectors, emitters, and bases), it can be shown that the width of the transition region (depletion layer) is

$$d = \sqrt{\frac{2\epsilon}{q}\,(\phi - V)\left(\frac{1}{N_d} + \frac{1}{N_a}\right)} \qquad \text{(MKS)} \qquad (6.36)$$

where $\epsilon$ is the dielectric constant ($8.85 \times 10^{-12}k_e$ farads/meter), and $N_a$ and $N_d$ are, respectively, the densities of the acceptor and donor ions in the p- and n-type materials. In most transistors except grown-junction and some mesa types, $N_a \gg N_d$ such that the transition region (depletion layer) lies almost entirely in the base region to a distance (p-n-p transistor)

$$d = \sqrt{\frac{2\epsilon}{qN_d}} (\phi - V) \qquad (6.37)$$

When $d$ from Eq. (6.37) equals the base width, the transition region (depletion layer) extends to the emitter. Transistor action no longer takes place, and the transistor is said to have *punched through*. Large collector currents can then be drawn such that punch-through breakdown occurs. However, as with avalanche and Zener breakdown, no permanent damage usually results unless temperature limits are exceeded.

Since $N_d$ is proportional to the conductivity of the base material, the punch-through voltage may be increased by increasing the conductivity of the base material, keeping all dimensions constant. However, this lowers the avalanche breakdown voltage such that the product of the two breakdown voltages is approximately a constant. Resort must be made to graded-base techniques to circumvent this limitation.

### 6.8  TRANSIENT RESPONSE OF JUNCTION TRANSISTORS

We will consider in this section only those effects caused by the time lag of the diffusion currents. This means that the analysis applies to transistors such as the alloy-junction and surface-barrier types which exhibit small charge storage effects in the emitter and collector regions. This excludes grown junctions and some mesa transistors which are characterized by having large high-resistivity collector regions, and which are, incidentally, unsuitable for switching purposes for this same reason.

We will first assume that the collector of a p-n-p transistor is connected to the base and to ground (common-base connection—collector short-circuited). There is no collector load resistance, only a narrow transition region, and there are no changes in collector-to-base voltage (Fig. 6.17). Note the convention taken for the current directions in Fig. 6.17.

Solution of the diffusion equation (Appendix I) for this case gives the collector current as a function of the emitter current and the Laplacian variable $s$, neglecting $I_{CO}$ which is a constant

$$I_c(s) = \alpha_F(s)I_E(s) = I_E(s) \operatorname{sech} a\sqrt{1 + sT_p} \qquad (6.38)$$

where $a = W/L_p$ $(a \ll 1)$, $W$ is the base width, $L_p = \sqrt{D_pT_p}$ is the diffusion length for holes in the base, $T_p$ is the hole lifetime, and $D_p$ is the diffusion constant for holes. By the inversion integral, the collector current for a step of emitter current of amplitude $I_E$ is

$$i_c(t) = \frac{I_E}{2\pi j} \int_B \frac{e^{st}}{s \cosh a\sqrt{1 + sT_p}} \, ds \qquad (6.39)$$

where the contour $B$ is shown in Fig. 6.18. This contour integral will be rigorously evaluated to provide a sound mathematical basis for some of the approximate formulas to be developed. This evaluation serves also to show how far one may have to go if one is not willing to accept approximations that are obtained more easily but are less rigorous.

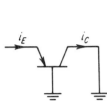

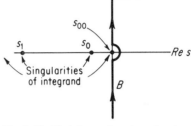

Fig. 6.17.   Short-cir- | Fig. 6.18.   Undeformed contour for step
cuited transistor. | response calculation by contour inte-
| gration.

The singularities of the integrand are found by setting

$$s \cosh a\sqrt{1 + sT_p} = 0 \qquad (6.40)$$

Since $\cosh z = 0$ at $z = (n + \tfrac{1}{2})\pi j$, we have from Eq. (6.40) that the singularities are located at $s = 0 = s_{00}$, and at the zeroes of $\cosh a\sqrt{1 + sT_p}$

$$s = -\frac{1}{T_p} - \frac{(n + \tfrac{1}{2})^2\pi^2}{a^2 T_p} = s_n, \qquad n = \ldots, -2, -1, 0, 1, 2, \ldots \quad (6.41)$$

Calculation of a few values of $s_n$ yields

$$s_0 = s_{-1}$$

$$s_1 = s_{-2}$$

$$s_2 = s_{-3}$$

$$\cdots$$

Hence, it is necessary only that $n$ have the values $0, 1, 2, \ldots$ to yield all of the zeroes of $\cosh a\sqrt{1 + sT_p}$.

The method of calculating the residues shows that all of the singularities of the integrand are simple poles. The residue at $s_{00}$ is

$$\mathcal{R}_{00} = \lim_{s \to 0} \frac{e^{st}}{\cosh a\sqrt{1 + sT_p}} = \operatorname{sech} a$$

But $\operatorname{sech} a$ is the short-circuit d-c current gain $\alpha_F$. The residues at $s = s_n$ are

$$\Re_n = \lim_{s \to s_n} \frac{(s - s_n)e^{st}}{s \cosh a\sqrt{1 + sT_p}}$$

By L'Hospital's rule,

$$\Re_n = \lim_{s \to s_n} \frac{(s - s_n)te^{st} + e^{st}}{(s \sinh a\sqrt{1 + sT_p})\dfrac{aT_p}{2}(1 + sT_p)^{-1/2} + \cosh a\sqrt{1 + sT_p}}$$

or

$$\Re_n = \frac{2\sqrt{1 + s_nT_p}\,e^{s_nt}}{aT_p s_n \sinh a\sqrt{1 + sT_p}}$$

Now

$$\sinh a\sqrt{1 + s_nT_p} = j \sin (n + \tfrac{1}{2})\pi = j(-1)^n$$

Hence

$$\Re_n = \frac{2j(n + \tfrac{1}{2})\pi e^{s_nt}}{a^2T_p j(-1)^n[-1/T_p - (n + \tfrac{1}{2})^2\pi^2/a^2T_p]}$$

or

$$\Re_n = 2(-1)^{n+1}\frac{(n + \tfrac{1}{2})\pi}{[a^2 + (n + \tfrac{1}{2})^2\pi^2]}e^{s_nt} \tag{6.42}$$

Since $\cosh z = 1 + \dfrac{z^2}{2!} + \dfrac{z^4}{4!} + \cdots$, we have

$$\cosh a\sqrt{1 + sT_p} = 1 + \frac{a^2(1 + sT_p)}{2!} + \frac{a^4(1 + sT_p)^2}{4!} + \cdots$$

such that the integrand is a single-valued function of the complex variable $s$.

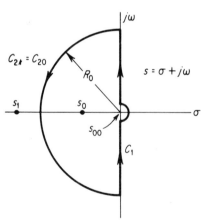

**Fig. 6.19.** Illustrating closure of the contour for $K = 0$.

We now attempt to close the contour in such a way as to be able to evaluate the contour integral by the residue theorem. The presence of the term $e^{st}$ in the integrand suggests that if the contour is closed by a semicircle in the left half-plane, the integral along the semicircle, if of sufficient radius, may be negligible if $t > 0$. If this is the case, the integral becomes equal to $2\pi j$ times the sum of the residues. The semicircle chosen is shown in Fig. 6.19 to lie between two adjacent poles $s_K$ and $s_{K+1}$ and has a radius of $R_K$ ($K = 0$ in Fig. 6.19).

We clearly have that

$$\int_B = \lim_{K \to \infty} \int_{C_1}$$

Also from Fig. 6.19 and from the residue theorem, we have for any $K$

$$\int_{C_1} + \int_{C_{2K}} = 2\pi j \left( \mathcal{R}_{00} + \sum_{n=0}^{K} \mathcal{R}_n \right)$$

such that if $\lim_{K \to \infty} \int_{C_{2K}} = 0$, for $t > 0$, then

$$\int_B = 2\pi j \left( \mathcal{R}_{00} + \sum_{n=0}^{\infty} \mathcal{R}_n \right), \qquad t > 0 \qquad (6.43)$$

From Eqs. (6.39), (6.41), (6.42), and (6.43) we would have

$$i_c(t) = I_E \left[ \alpha_F - 2 \sum_{n=0}^{\infty} (-1)^n \frac{(n + \tfrac{1}{2})\pi}{[a^2 + (n + \tfrac{1}{2})^2 \pi^2]} \right.$$

$$e^{-(t/a^2 T_p)\{a^2 + [n + (1/2)]^2 \pi^2\}}, \qquad t > 0 \quad (6.44)$$

which is the desired result. It remains to prove that

$$\lim_{K \to \infty} \int_{C_{2K}} = 0 \qquad (6.45)$$

If $R_K$ is chosen to be

$$R_K = \frac{1}{T_p} + \frac{(K + 1)^2 \pi^2}{a^2 T_p}$$

then the contour $C_{2K}$ intersects the negative $\sigma$ axis between $s_K$ and $s_{K+1}$. On the negative $\sigma$ axis, we have $(s = -R_K)$

$$|\cosh a\sqrt{1 + sT_p}| = |\cosh j(k + 1)\pi| = 1$$

Since

$$\cosh z = \prod_{n=0}^{\infty} \left[ 1 + \frac{z^2}{(n + \tfrac{1}{2})^2 \pi^2} \right]$$

then we have on $C_{2K}$ where $s = R_K e^{j\theta}$ that

$$|\cosh a\sqrt{1 + sT_p}| = \prod_{n=0}^{\infty} \left| 1 + \frac{a^2 + [a^2 + (K + 1)^2 \pi^2]e^{j\theta}}{(n + \tfrac{1}{2})^2 \pi^2} \right|$$

The infinite product clearly is minimum at $\theta = \pi$, giving

$$|\cosh a\sqrt{1 + sT_p}| \geq \prod_{n=0}^{\infty} \left| 1 + \frac{[j(K + 1)\pi]^2}{(n + \tfrac{1}{2})^2 \pi^2} \right| = |\cos (K + 1)\pi| = 1$$

It is now clear that

$$|\cosh a\sqrt{1 + sT_p}| \geq 1$$

for $s$ on contour $C_{2K}$ where $s = R_K e^{j\theta}$, $\pi/2 \leq \theta \leq 3\pi/2$, and $R_K = 1/T_p + (K + 1)^2 \pi^2 / a^2 T_p$. Hence,

$$I_K = \int_{C_{2K}} = \int_{\pi/2}^{3\pi/2} \frac{e^{R_K t(\cos \theta + j \sin \theta)}}{R_K e^{j\theta} \cosh a\sqrt{1 + sT}} j R e^{j\theta} \, d\theta$$

and

$$|I_K| \leq \int_{\pi/2}^{3\pi/2} e^{R_K t \cos \theta} \, d\theta = 2 \int_0^{\pi/2} e^{-R_K t \sin \theta} \, d\theta$$

But $\sin \theta \geq (2/\pi)\theta$ for $0 \leq \theta \leq \pi/2$, so that

$$I_K \leq 2 \int_0^{\pi/2} e^{-(2R_K t/\pi)\theta} \, d\theta = \frac{\pi}{R_K t} (1 - e^{-R_K t})$$

such that for $t > 0$,

$$\lim_{K \to \infty} |I_K| \leq \lim_{K \to \infty} \frac{\pi}{R_K t} (1 - e^{-R_K t}) = 0$$

proving Eq. (6.45).

## 6.9  AN APPROXIMATION TO THE RESPONSE

The alpha cutoff frequency, $f_\alpha$, is a parameter that is often available for a transistor. It is defined as the frequency at which the small-signal forward short-circuit current gain is 0.707 of the low-frequency value. If we assume that the small-signal gain is given as a function of frequency by

$$\alpha_f = \operatorname{sech} a\sqrt{1 + j\omega T_p}$$

then

$$|\operatorname{sech} a\sqrt{1 + j\omega_\alpha T_p}| = 0.707 \operatorname{sech} a \qquad (6.46)$$

Letting $a\sqrt{1 + j\omega_\alpha T_p} = x + jy$ yields

$$a^2 = x^2 - y^2, \qquad \omega_\alpha T_p a^2 = 2xy \qquad (6.47)$$

For the case where the low-frequency value of $\alpha_f$ is unity, we have $a = 0$. Thus from Eqs. (6.47), we have $x = \pm y$. Equation (6.46) becomes

$$|\cosh (x \pm jx)| = 1.414 \qquad (6.48)$$

A numerical solution of Eq. (6.48) yields the result that $x = 1.105$. From the second of Eqs. (6.47) when $a$ is small but nonzero, we have the approximation

$$\omega_\alpha = (1.105)^2 \frac{2}{a^2 T_p} = \frac{2.44}{a^2 T_p}$$

If we now define a quantity $\omega_F$ such that

$$a^2 T_p = \frac{2.44}{\omega_F}$$

Eq. (6.44) becomes

$$\frac{i_c(t)}{I_E} = \alpha_F - 2 \sum_{n=0}^{\infty} (-1)^n \frac{(n + \tfrac{1}{2})\pi}{[a^2 + (n + \tfrac{1}{2})^2\pi^2]} e^{-[\omega_F t/2.44\{a^2 + [n + (1/2)]^2\pi^2\}}},$$

$$t > 0 \qquad (6.49)$$

Equation (6.49) versus $\omega_F t$ for $a = 0$ is plotted in Fig. 6.20; it is the curve labeled "from series."

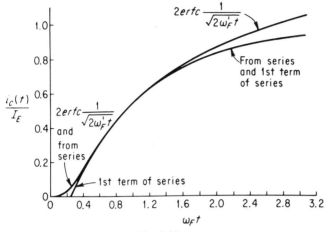

**Fig. 6.20.**

Retaining only the first term of the series of Eq. (6.49) yields for $a = 0$

$$\frac{i_c(t)}{I_E} = 1 - \frac{4}{\pi} e^{-1.01\omega_F t} \tag{6.50}$$

Equation (6.50) versus $\omega_F t$ is plotted in Fig. 6.20 and is labeled "first term of series." Note that this curve lies on the curve plotted from Eq. (6.49) for all values of $\omega_F t$ except for very small values of $\omega_F t$.

From Eq. (6.50) $i_c = 0$ at $t = 0.238/\omega_F t$. Hence Eq. (6.50) may be written

$$\frac{i_c(t)}{I_E} = 0, \qquad\qquad t < D_F$$

$$\frac{i_c(t)}{I_E} = 1 - e^{-1.01\omega_F(t - D_F)}, \qquad t \geq D_F \tag{6.51}$$

$$D = \frac{0.238}{\omega_F}$$

Equation (6.51) states that to a good approximation the response to a step in emitter current is an exponential waveform delayed an amount $D = 0.238/\omega_F$ and with a time constant of approximately $1/\omega_F$ where $\omega_F$ is $2\pi f_a$. It follows from Eq. (6.51) that the transistor behaves as if $\alpha_F(s)$ were given by the approximation,

$$\alpha_F(s) = \frac{\alpha_F e^{-sD_F}}{1 + s/\omega_F} \tag{6.52}$$

which is good when $\alpha_F$ is close to unity.

Equation (6.52) may be applied to the case of an arbitrary emitter waveform to yield

$$\left(1 + \frac{s}{\omega_F}\right) I_c(s) = \alpha_F I_E(s) e^{-sD_F} \tag{6.53}$$

If Eq. (6.53) is inverse transformed, there results the differential equation below, which is of fundamental importance.

$$\frac{1}{\omega_F} \frac{di_c}{dt} + i_c = \alpha_F i_E(t - D_F) \tag{6.54}$$

### 6.10  APPROXIMATION TECHNIQUES

To obtain Eqs. (6.52) and (6.54) we had to evaluate a certain contour integral, which in this case, fortunately, was suitable for exact evaluation. For other connections of this transistor or for other devices we may not be so lucky. In this and succeeding sections we will consider and apply several approximation techniques to this device.

A careful review of the preceding section will show that the behavior of the time function for moderate and large values of $t$ is clear from the behavior of $\alpha_F(s)$ in the vicinity of $s = 0$ and the behavior of the time function for small values of $t$ is determined by the behavior of $\alpha_F(s)$ for $s$ far from the origin.

We will now apply this principle to obtain an approximate expression for $\alpha_F(s)$ when given

$$\alpha_F(s) = \frac{1}{\cosh a\sqrt{1 + sT_p}} \equiv \frac{1}{f(s)}$$

Expansion of $f(s)$ in a McLaurin series yields, approximately,

$$f(0) = \cosh a$$

$$f'(0) \cong \frac{a^2 T_p}{2} \cong \frac{a^2 T_p}{2} \cosh a \qquad (\sinh a \cong a, \cosh a \cong 1)$$

$$f''(0) = 0$$

$$f'''(0) = \tfrac{1}{4} a^2 T_c^3 \cosh a$$

Therefore,

$$\alpha_F(s) \cong \frac{1}{(\cosh a)\left(1 + \dfrac{a^2 T_p}{2} s + \dfrac{a^2 T_p^3}{24} s^3 + \cdots\right)}$$

and for small $s$,

$$\alpha_F(s) \cong \frac{\alpha_F}{1 + s/\omega_F'} \tag{6.55}$$

where $\omega_F' = 2/a^2 T_p$. For large $s = j\omega$, for $I_E(s) = I_E/s$,

$$I_c(s) \cong \frac{2I_E}{s} e^{-a\sqrt{sT_p}}$$

Hence, for $t$ small,

$$i_c(t) \cong 2I_E \, \mathrm{erfc}\left(\frac{a\sqrt{T_p}}{2\sqrt{t}}\right) \tag{6.56}$$

Equation (6.56) versus $\omega_F t$ is plotted in Fig. 6.20 and versus $\omega_F' t$ in Fig. 6.21. Note how it compares in Fig. 6.20 with the other curves. Extrapolation of the curve in Fig. 6.21 back to zero current suggests the presence of an

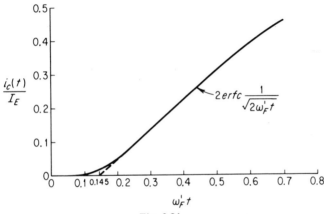

Fig. 6.21.

equivalent delay of the order of $D_F' = 0.145/\omega_F'$. This suggests that for $s$ large,

$$I_C(s) \cong \frac{I_E(s)e^{-sD_F'}}{s} \tag{6.57}$$

Connecting together the approximate expressions given by Eqs. (6.55) and (6.67) yields

$$\alpha_F(s) \cong \frac{\alpha_F e^{-sD_F'}}{1 + s/\omega_F'} \tag{6.58}$$

Note that Eqs. (6.58) and (6.52) have the same form. However, note that they contain different values of the important numerical constants. This illustrates the principle that approximations may yield expressions that show the functional dependence but contain constants that must be obtained experimentally.

### 6.11 COMMON-BASE CONNECTION—COLLECTOR BIASED

When the collector is biased in the normal direction, the depletion layer at the collector junction widens. The remainder of the base region is field free, and the diffusion equation and results derived from it can be expected to be valid. However, carriers in the depletion layer exists in an electric field and their motion would be expected to be affected by the electric field. It would be expected that $\omega_F$ would increase, but it would take careful analysis to determine the effect on $D$.

One would expect, however, that the result

$$\alpha_F(s) = \frac{\alpha_F e^{-sD}}{1 + s/\omega_F} \tag{6.59}$$

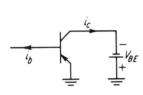

would still be satisfactory if the appropriate values of $\omega_F$ and $D$ were used.

**Fig. 6.22.** Common emitter connection—collector short-circuited.

### 6.12 COMMON EMITTER CONNECTION— COLLECTOR SHORT-CIRCUITED

This connection is shown in Fig. 6.22 for a p-n-p transistor.

We have

$$\alpha_{FE}(s) = \frac{\alpha_F(s)}{1 - \alpha_F(s)} = \frac{1}{\cosh a \sqrt{1 + sT_p} - 1} \tag{6.60}$$

For large $t$ (small $s$) the response to a unit step in base current may be obtained from Eq. (6.60) by the same procedure used to obtain Eq. (6.55). The result is

$$I_c(s) \cong \frac{1}{s(\cosh a - 1)(1 + sT_p + (a^2T_p^2/8)s^2 + \cdots)}$$

Since $a \ll 1$ and $(\cosh a - 1)^{-1} = \alpha_{FE}$, the static common-emitter current gain, we have

$$I_c(s) \cong \frac{\alpha_{FE}}{s(1 + sT_p)} \qquad (s \text{ small}) \tag{6.61}$$

For small $t$ (large $s$), we have

$$I_c(s) \cong \frac{2}{s} e^{-a\sqrt{sT_p}} \tag{6.62}$$

Equation (6.62) is the same as previously obtained for the same conditions with the common-base connected transistor. Combining Eq. (6.61) and the consequence of Eq. (6.62) yields the approximation

$$\alpha_{FE}(s) = \frac{\alpha_{FE} e^{-sD}}{1 + sT_p} \tag{6.63}$$

This result can be derived a different way. Using Eq. (6.59) and the fact that

$$\alpha_{FE}(s) = \frac{\alpha_F(s)}{1 - \alpha_F(s)}$$

we have approximately

$$\alpha_{FE}(s) = \frac{\alpha_F e^{-sD}}{1 + s/\omega_F - \alpha_F e^{-sD}} \qquad (6.64)$$

For small $s$, this becomes

$$\alpha_{FE}(s) \cong \frac{\alpha_F e^{-sD}}{1 + s/\omega_F - \alpha_F + sD\alpha_F} \qquad (s \text{ small}) \qquad (6.65)$$

For large $s = j\omega$, the term $\alpha_F e^{-sD}$ in the denominator of Eq. (6.64) is of the order of unity and can be neglected in comparison to the term $s/\omega_F$ if $\omega \gg \omega_F$. Then

$$\alpha_{FE}(s) = \frac{\alpha_F e^{-sD}}{s/\omega_F} \qquad (s \text{ large}) \qquad (6.66)$$

Combining Eqs. (6.65) and (6.66) yields the approximation

$$\alpha_{FE}(s) = \frac{\alpha_{FE} e^{-sD}}{1 + \dfrac{s\alpha_F D + 1/\omega_F}{1 - \alpha_F}} \qquad (6.67)$$

If $\alpha_F D$ can be neglected compared to $1/\omega_F$, we have

$$\omega_F(1 - \alpha_F) \cong \frac{1}{T_p} = \omega_\beta$$

$2\pi$ times the "beta cutoff frequency."

## 6.13  COMMON-EMITTER CONNECTION—COLLECTOR BIASED

The remarks made in Sec. 6.11 apply here. Hence we may use Eq. (6.67) as the basis of further investigation. For a unit step of base current,

$$I_C(s) = \frac{\alpha_{FE} e^{-sD}}{s(1 + sT_\epsilon)} \qquad (6.68)$$

where

$$T_\epsilon = \frac{\alpha_F D + 1/\omega_F}{1 - \alpha_F} \quad \text{and} \quad i_C(t) = \alpha_{FE}(1 - e^{-(t-D)/T_\epsilon})$$

For small values of $t$,

$$i_C(t) \cong \frac{\alpha_F(t - D)}{\alpha_F D + 1/\omega_F}$$

For most useful transistors, $\alpha_F \approx 1$; hence for $t$ small,

$$i_C(t) \cong \frac{\omega_F}{1 + \omega_F D}(t - D) \qquad (6.69)$$

Equation (6.69) is an extremely useful equation. It states that the collector current starts to increase after a delay $D$ and that it increases linearly with time for a while with a slope of $\omega_F \div (1 + \omega_F d)$ if the base current is a unit step. Equation (6.68) suggests

$$T_\epsilon \frac{di_C}{dt} + i_C = \alpha_{FE} i_b(t - D) \tag{6.70}$$

For $i_C$ (and $t$) small, Eq. (6.70) yields for $\alpha_F \cong 1$

$$i_C \cong \frac{\omega_F}{1 + \omega_F D} \int_0^t i_b(t - D)\, dt \tag{6.71}$$

useful for $i_b$ arbitrary.

The gain-bandwidth product, $f_T$, of a common-emitter connected transistor is defined as the frequency at which the small-signal current gain becomes unity. If we assume that Eq. (6.68) also approximates the small-signal current gain as a function of frequency, at large frequencies

$$|\alpha_{FE}(\omega)| \cong \frac{\alpha_{FE}}{\omega T_\epsilon}$$

Hence,

$$|\alpha_{FE}(\omega_T)| = 1 = \frac{\alpha_{FE}}{\omega_T T_\epsilon} \qquad (\omega_T = 2\pi f_T)$$

Thus

$$\frac{\alpha_{FE}}{T_\epsilon} = \omega_T$$

Equation (6.71) becomes

$$i_C \cong \omega_T \int_0^t i_b(t - D)\, dt$$

and Eq. (6.68) becomes

$$\alpha_{FE}(s) = \frac{\alpha_{FE} e^{-sD}}{1 + s(\alpha_{FE}/\omega_T)} \tag{6.72}$$

That Eq. (6.72) has the correct form has been verified in many experiments. In one instance the turn-on waveform was determined by experiment, computed by numerical solution of the differential equations of the unsimplified equivalent circuit, and determined by these approximate methods. The three sets of curves were in suprisingly close agreement.

### 6.14  CHARGE ANALYSIS

Another procedure for obtaining essentially the results that we have obtained above is that of charge analysis. From Appendix I, the equation satisfied by the hole *charge* density in the base material, neglecting thermally generated carriers, is, at an arbitrary point,

$$-\nabla \cdot \mathbf{J}_p = \frac{\rho_p}{T_p} + \frac{\partial \rho_p}{\partial t} \tag{6.73}$$

where $\mathbf{J}_p$ is the hole current density at the point, and $T_p$ is the hole lifetime. Integration of Eq. (6.73) throughout the base material yields

$$- \int \nabla \cdot \mathbf{J}_p \, dv = \frac{Q}{T_p} + \frac{dQ}{dt} \tag{6.74}$$

where $Q$ is the total charge due to holes in the base. The left-hand side may be transformed by Gauss' theorem to yield (current directions as in Fig. 6.17)

$$- \int \mathbf{J}_p \cdot d\mathbf{S} = \frac{Q}{T_p} + \frac{dQ}{dt}$$

When a p-n-p transistor is in the active region, the base current is due to electrons. Neglecting the electron component of emitter current, we obtain

$$i_E - i_C = \frac{Q}{T_p} + \frac{dQ}{dt}$$

but

$$i_E - i_C = i_B$$

Hence,

$$i_B = \frac{Q}{T_p} + \frac{dQ}{dt} \tag{6.75}$$

The solution of Eq. (6.75) for a step $I_B$ in base current yields

$$Q(t) = T_p I_B [1 - e^{-t/T_p}] \tag{6.76}$$

From Eq. (6.72) neglecting $D$ for a step $I_B$ in base current

$$i_c(t) = \alpha_{FE} I_B [1 - e^{(\omega_T / \alpha_{FE}) t}] \tag{6.77}$$

Comparison of Eqs. (6.76) and (6.77) shows that

$$T_p = \frac{\alpha_{FE}}{\omega_T} \tag{6.78}$$

and

$$i_c = \omega_T Q \tag{6.79}$$

Using Eq. (6.78), we may rewrite Eq. (6.75) as

$$i_B = \frac{\omega_T}{\alpha_{FE}} Q + \frac{dQ}{dt} \tag{6.80}$$

Equations (6.79) and (6.80) form the basis of the charge-analysis technique and reduce to Eq. (6.70) with $D$ neglected and with $\omega_T$ assumed independent of time.

The results so far have stated implicitly, in their derivation, the assumption that the quantities $\alpha_F$, $\alpha_R$, $\omega_F$, $\omega_R$, etc., are independent of voltages and currents and, hence, of time. In actual devices this assumption is usually not valid. Nonetheless, the approximations developed retain their value, provided they are interpreted as approximations to the true relationships between the component characteristics and their performance. If the component characteristics do not change radically in the operating range of the device, good results can often be obtained by using average values of the characteristic parameters.

However, the differential equations, Eqs. (6.70) and (6.80), could be the starting point of a more careful analysis. Equation (6.80) may be rewritten, using Eqs. (6.79) and (6.70), as

$$\alpha_{FE} \frac{d}{dt}\left(\frac{i_c}{\omega_T}\right) + i_c = \alpha_{FE} i_b(t - D) \tag{6.81}$$

Equation (6.81) differs from Eq. (6.70) when $\omega_T$ is not a constant.

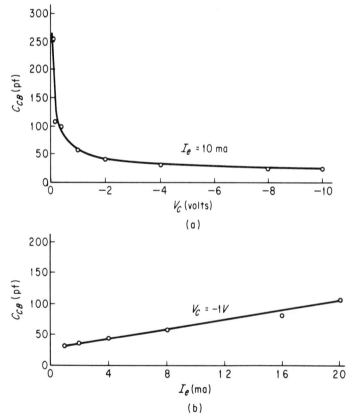

**Fig. 6.23.** Collector capacitance versus collector voltage (a) and emitter current (b). Common-base connection is used.

## 6.15 TRANSITION AND DIFFUSION CAPACITANCES

The depletion layer acts as the dielectric of a capacitor which can be shown to have a capacitance $C_T$,

$$C_T = \frac{dQ}{dV} = \frac{K_0}{\sqrt{\phi - V}} \tag{6.82}$$

where $K_0$ is a constant. Equation (6.82) holds for a homogeneous-base transistor. In general,

$$C_T = K_0(\phi - V)^n, \qquad n < 0$$

where $K_0$, $\phi$, and $n$ can be obtained by experiment. When current flows in a junction, the capacitance is modified by the diffusion capacitance arising from carrier storage in the base. This capacitance $C_D$ depends linearly on current. Figure 6.23 shows the dependence of collector capacitance on bias and current for an alloy junction transistor.

For example, the junction capacitance of a certain semiconductor element is found, from an r-f bridge measurement, to be

| $v$ | $C$(pf) |
|-----|---------|
| 0   | 22      |
| −3  | 12      |
| −6  | 9.6     |
| −12 | 7.6     |
| −24 | 6       |

Adjustment of constants yields

$$C = 20(1 - v)^{-1/2} + 2 \text{ pf}$$

Switching from zero volts to $-10$ volts requires a charge $Q$

$$Q = \int_0^{-10} C \, dv = \int_0^{-10} [20(1 - v)^{-1/2} + 2] \, dv = 112.5 \times 10^{-12} \text{ coulombs}$$

The effective linear capacitance is $112.5/10 = 11.25$ pf.

## 6.16 COMMON-EMITTER CONNECTION— EFFECT OF COLLECTOR CAPACITANCE

Assume that the transistor is connected to a resistive load as in Fig. 6.24. The approximate differential equations for the change in $v_c$ for Fig. 6.24 are clearly nonlinear:

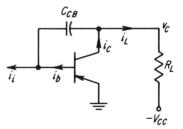

Fig. 6.24.

$$i_b + C_{CB}(v_c)\frac{dv_c}{dt} = i_i \qquad (6.83a)$$

$$T_\epsilon \frac{di_c}{dt} + i_c = \alpha_{FE}i_b(t - D) \qquad (6.83b)$$

$$\frac{v_c}{R_L} + C_{CB}(v_c)\frac{dv_c}{dt} = i_c \qquad (6.83c)$$

The change of base-to-emitter voltage has been neglected in writing the above equations. A useful approximate solution can be obtained for the initial part of the collector waveform by neglecting $i_c$ in Eq. (6.83b), neglecting $C_{CB}(v_c)(dv_c/dt)$ in Eq. (6.83c), and assuming $C_{CB}(v_c)$ is a constant. The first assumption is equivalent to assuming that we are interested only in the first initial part of the waveform; the second assumption neglects the feedback current in comparison to the collector current; the third assumption is good if the collector is biased in the region where $C_{CB}$ is almost constant. All Eqs. (6.83) become for a step input of magnitude $I_i$

$$i_b + C_{CB}\frac{dv_c}{dt} = I_i \qquad (6.84a)$$

$$\frac{T_\epsilon}{R_L}\frac{dv_c}{dt} = \alpha_{FE}i_b(t - D) \qquad (6.84b)$$

$$v_c = R_L i_c \qquad (6.84c)$$

If $dv_c/dt$ is eliminated between Eqs. (6.84a) and (6.84b) and $D$ is assumed to be negligible, we obtain

$$i_b = \frac{\alpha_F D + \dfrac{1}{\omega_F}}{\alpha_F D + \dfrac{1}{\omega_F} + R_L C_{CB}} I_i$$

Substitution in Eq. (6.84a) and solution of the resultant differential equation yields

$$i_c = \frac{\omega_F I_i}{1 + \omega_F(\alpha_F D + R_L C_{CB})} (t - D)$$

in terms of the gain-bandwidth product

$$i_c = \frac{\omega_T I_i}{1 + \omega_T R_L C_{CB}} (t - D)$$

and for arbitrary input current, we have the approximation

$$i_c \cong \frac{\omega_T}{1 + \omega_T R_L C_c} \int_0^t i_i(t - D)\, dt \qquad (6.85)$$

which should be compared to the next to last equation of Sec. 6.13 and also to Prob. 24 at the end of this chapter.

### 6.17  COMMON-EMITTER CONNECTION—EFFECT OF LOAD CAPACITANCE

Such an arrangement is shown in Fig. 6.25.

An accurate solution requires that the nonlinear differential equations for this circuit be solved. An approximate solution may be obtained if the approximation

$$i_c = \omega_T \int_0^t i_b(t)\, dt$$

is good enough for the transistor, the collector voltage rise waveform is approximately linear, and $C_{CB}$ is the effective collector capacitance as defined in Sec. 6.15. With these assumptions, a charge-balance equation in the collector circuit is

$$\frac{\omega_T}{2}\, T_r[I_i T_r - C_{CB}\, \Delta v_c] = (C + C_{CB})\, \Delta v_c + \frac{\Delta v_c T_r}{2 R_L}$$

where $I_i$ is the amplitude of the input step. Solution for $T_r$, the time it takes $v_c$ to change by $\Delta v_c$, yields

$$T_r = \frac{\Delta v_c}{2 I_i}\left\{\frac{1}{\omega_T R_L} + C_{CB} + \sqrt{\left[\frac{1}{\omega_T R_L} + C_{CB}\right]^2 + \frac{8(C + C_{CB})}{\omega_T}}\right\} \quad (6.86)$$

This equation shows a dependence on the various parameters that one might expect from comparison of Eq. (6.86) with Fig. 6.25.

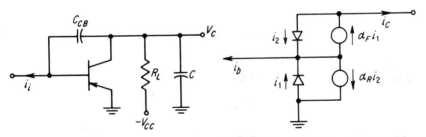

Fig. 6.25.                 Fig. 6.26. Equivalent circuit of a transistor
in saturation.

### 6.18  CALCULATION OF STORAGE TIME—COMMON-EMITTER CONNECTION

The calculation is based on the use of the equivalent circuit in Fig. 6.26. We have

$$i_b = (1 - \alpha_F)i_1 + (1 - \alpha_R)i_2$$

$$i_c = \alpha_F i_1 - i_2$$

If we eliminate $i_1$, we obtain

$$i_2 = \frac{\alpha_F i_b - (1 - \alpha_F) i_c}{1 - \alpha_F \alpha_R} \tag{6.87}$$

We will say that the transistor is in saturation if $i_2 > 0$ and it will be out of saturation if $i_2 = 0$ (leakage currents are neglected).

In order for $i_2 > 0$, we must have

$$\alpha_F i_b > (1 - \alpha_F) i_c \quad \text{or} \quad \alpha_{FE} i_b > i_c$$

That is, the collector current must be less than the current that the transistor is capable of furnishing.

If the transistor has been on for some time with a base current $I_{b1}$, and is turned off by a reverse base current of magnitude $I_{b2}$, the current $i_2$ must decrease by an amount [from Eq. (6.87)]

$$\Delta i_2 = \frac{\alpha_F I_{b1} - (1 - \alpha_F) I_c}{1 - \alpha_F \alpha_R} \tag{6.88}$$

before the transistor comes out of saturation. The time that this takes will be called the storage time $T_s$. The change in $i_2$ due to a change in $i_b$ can be obtained from the transformed equation

$$I_2(s) = \frac{\alpha_F(s) I_b(s) - (1 - \alpha_F(s)) I_c(s)}{1 - \alpha_F(s) \alpha_R(s)} \tag{6.89}$$

where we write

$$\alpha_F(s) = \frac{\alpha_F e^{-sD_F}}{1 + s/\omega_F} \tag{6.90a}$$

$$\alpha_R(s) = \frac{\alpha_R \, e^{-sD_R}}{1 + s/\omega_R} \tag{6.90b}$$

Equation (6.90b) is not always a good approximation to $\alpha_R(s)$. In some cases, the following expression yields better results:

$$\alpha_R(s) = \frac{\alpha_R e^{-sD_R}}{1 + a_1 s + a_2 s^2} \tag{6.91}$$

where $a_1$, $a_2$, $\alpha_R$, and $D_R$ can be obtained experimentally (see Prob. 22 at the end of this chapter).

Substitution of Eqs. (6.90a) and (6.90b) in Eq. (6.89) yields

$$I_2(s) =$$

$$\frac{\alpha_F I_b(s) \left(1 + \dfrac{s}{\omega_R}\right) e^{-sD_F} - \left[\left(1 + \dfrac{s}{\omega_F}\right)\left(1 + \dfrac{s}{\omega_R}\right) - \alpha_F \left(1 + \dfrac{s}{\omega_R}\right) e^{-sD_F}\right] I_c(s)}{\left(1 + \dfrac{s}{\omega_F}\right)\left(1 + \dfrac{s}{\omega_R}\right) - \alpha_F \alpha_R e^{-s(D_F + D_R)}} \tag{6.92}$$

A power series in $t$ for the change in $i_2(t)$ can be obtained by expanding

Eq. (6.92) as a power series in $1/s$ and by transforming inversely. The first term of this series is obtained by taking $s = j\omega$ large in Eq. (6.32) to obtain the transformation for the *change* in $i_2$

$$I_2(s) \cong \frac{\alpha_F \omega_F e^{-sD_F}}{s} I_b(s)$$

If

$$I_b(s) = -\frac{I_{b1} + I_{b2}}{s} = -\frac{\Delta i_b}{s},$$

we have

$$I_2(s) \cong -\frac{\alpha_F \omega_F e^{-sD_F}}{s^2} (I_{b1} + I_{b2})$$

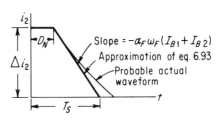

Fig. 6.27.

and

$$i_2(t) \cong -\alpha_F \omega_F (I_{b1} + I_{b2})(t - D_N), \qquad t \geq D_N \qquad (6.93)$$

for small values of $t$. The relationships are shown in Fig. 6.27.

From Fig. 6.27 and Eq. (6.93)

$$T_S \cong D_F + \frac{\Delta i_2}{\alpha_F \omega_F (I_{b1} + I_{b2})} \qquad (6.94)$$

Using Eqs. (6.88) and (6.94), we obtain

$$T_S \cong D_F + \frac{\alpha_F I_{b1} - (1 - \alpha_F) I_c}{\alpha_F \omega_F (1 - \alpha_F \alpha_R)(I_{b1} + I_{b2})}, \qquad \alpha_{FE} I_{b1} > I_c \qquad (6.95)$$

Equation (6.95) predicts a value of $T_S$ which is somewhat smaller than that obtained experimentally. This is what one would expect from Fig. 6.27. However, the dependence of $T_S$ on the quantities appearing in Eq. (6.95) as determined by experiment indicates that the form of the relationship is approximately correct.[*]

## 6.19  CALCULATION OF FALL TIME—COMMON-EMITTER CONNECTION

The transistor is in the active region and Eq. (6.70) can be expected to hold. The solution of the problem is obtained by writing the differential equations for the circuit including the effect of all loads and capacitances and then solving them. For the case in which the collector is short-circuited, an approximation can be obtained which gives a lower bound on the fall time. To do this, assume that the transistor has been on with a collector current of $I_c(0)$ and is turned off with a reverse base current, step $I_{b2}$. Eq. (6.70) transformed yields

---

[*] See Ref. 3 for an expression useful when $T_S$ is large.

$$sT_\epsilon I_c(s) - T_\epsilon I_c(0) + I_c(s) = -\alpha_{FE}\frac{I_{b2}}{s}e^{-sD}, \qquad T_\epsilon = \frac{\alpha_{FE}}{\omega_T}$$

Solving for $I_c(s)$, we get

$$I_c(s) = \frac{I_c(0)}{s + 1/T_\epsilon} - \frac{\alpha_{FE}I_{b2}}{s(sT_\epsilon + 1)}e^{-sD}$$

Inverse transformation yields

$$i_c(t) = I_c(0)e^{-t/T_\epsilon} - \alpha_{FE}I_{b2}(1 - e^{-(t-D)/T_\epsilon}) \qquad t > D \quad (6.96)$$

Now $i_c = 0$ at $t = T_f$. Solving for $Tf$ in Eq. (6.96) yields

$$T_f = D + T_\epsilon \log\left[1 + \frac{I_c(0)e^{-D/T_\epsilon}}{\alpha_{FE}I_{b2}}\right]$$

### 6.20  GRADED-BASE TRANSISTORS

In a graded-base transistor with its collector biased beyond the "starting voltage," the collector depletion layer extends an appreciable distance into the base. Thus, there exists an appreciable drift time causing the delay $D$ to be significant. Hence,

$$\alpha_F(s) \cong \frac{\alpha_F e^{-sD}}{1 + s/\omega_F}$$

for such a transistor.

In a step-junction transistor, the delay $D$ is usually negligible, such that $T_\epsilon \cong 1/[\omega_F(1 - \alpha_F)]$. However, in the graded-base transistor, $1 + \omega_F D$ is not close to unity. Values that have been observed are of the order of two or three. However, the expression connecting the gain-bandwidth product of the common-emitter connected transistor with $T_\epsilon$ enables us to use the previously derived results.

### 6.21  ASYNCHRONOUS RACE-RESOLVING FLIP-FLOP

As an example of the application of probability theory to circuit analysis, we will consider the case of the asynchronous race-resolving flip-flop shown in Fig. 6.28.

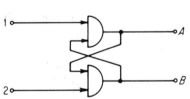

Inputs 1 and 2 are normally positive. If at some time 1 goes negative followed by 2 going negative, output $A$ goes positive and remains so. If at some time 2 goes negative, however, followed later by 1 going negative, output $B$ goes positive and remains so. If the time interval between the transitions of 1 and 2 is at least two circuit delays after either input changes, the flip-flop

**Fig. 6.28.** Race-resolving flip-flop.

will settle to its final state ($A$ or $B$ positive), thus resolving the race after a known time interval. However, 1 and 2 can go negative so close together in time that the flip-flop can hang up with both $A$ and $B$ negative with only random noise available to trigger it to one of the two stable states.

In a certain instance, the designer of a system needed to know what the practical maximum settling time would be. The final answer was obtained experimentally, but some initial theoretical considerations were found necessary in order to determine (a) what experiments should be made and (b) what should be expected from these experiments.

Because random noise and input signals are present, the problem is one of determining the distribution of settling times. A rigorous solution could be very difficult to obtain. However, through the application of general principles, answers to questions (a) and (b) can be found.

In the intermediate state, the flip-flop is a regenerative amplifier having a loop gain $A(s)$. Hence, its output $E_o$ is related to some input disturbance $E_i$ by the well-known expression

$$E_o(s) = \frac{A(s)E_i(s)}{1 - A(s)}, \qquad A(0) > 1$$

By the Heaviside expansion theorem, $e_o(t)$ can be written as a sum of exponential functions of time. Since $A(s) > 1$, at least one of these has a positive growth factor. Hence, asymptotically,

$$e_o(t) \xrightarrow[t \to \infty]{} k e_i e^{\alpha t} \tag{6.97}$$

represents the response to an impulse of area $e_i$ where $k$ is a constant depending on the circuit components in the logical elements making up the flip-flop. For example, if

$$A(s) = \frac{A_0}{(1 + s/\omega_0)^2}$$

then the asymptotic response to an impulse of area $e_i$ is

$$e_o \xrightarrow[t \to \infty]{} e_i \frac{\omega_0 \sqrt{A_0}}{2} e^{\omega_0 t (\sqrt{A_0} - 1)}$$

The input signal $e_i$ is the sum of a component which exists because of the distribution of the relative times of arrival of inputs 1 and 2 and a component which exists because of random noise. Let us assume that the frequency function for the distribution of $e_i$ is $f_{e_i}(x)$. Then

$$P(x < e_i \le x + dx) = f_{e_i}(x)\, dx \tag{6.98}$$

From Eq. (6.97), we will assume that the flip-flop has settled down when $e_o = E$. Hence $e_i$ treated as a random variable becomes

$$e_i = \frac{E}{K} e^{-\alpha T}$$

where $T$ is the settling time. Since $de_i = -(\alpha E/K)e^{-\alpha T}\, dT$, the frequency function for the distribution of settling times, $f_T(x)$, is

$$P(x < T \le x + dx) = \left| \left[ f_{e_i}\left(\frac{E}{K} e^{-\alpha x}\right)\right]\left[ -\frac{\alpha E}{k} e^{-\alpha x}\, dx \right]\right| \tag{6.99}$$

$$= f_T(x)\, dx$$

For large settling times,

$$f_T(x) \cong \frac{\alpha E}{K} f_{e_i}(0)e^{-\alpha T} \tag{6.100}$$

The probability that the settling time exceeds some value $T_0$ is obtained from Eq. (6.100) as

$$P(T > T_0) = \int_{T_0}^{\infty} f_T(x)\, dx \cong \frac{E}{K} f_{e_i}(0)e^{-\alpha T_0} \tag{6.101}$$

Equation (6.101) indicates that the probability that the settling time is greater than some value $T_0$ is an exponentially decreasing function of $T_0$. In the instance cited above, this probability was measured by electronically counting the number of times the settling time exceeded $T_0$ in a given period of time for several values of $T_0$. The results agreed perfectly, within the experimental error, with the mathematical form predicted by Eq. (6.101). This established the asymptotic form of the settling-time distribution on a sound theoretical and experimental basis, enabling the aforementioned designer to predict the settling-time distribution for values of $T_0$ so large that actual measurement was out of the question.

For the special case when the flip-flop is perfectly balanced and the inputs 1 and 2 go negative simultaneously, presumably random noise provides the triggering. Hence

$$f_{e_i}(x) = \frac{1}{\sigma\sqrt{2\pi}} e^{-x^2/2\sigma^2}$$

and $f_T(x)$ becomes

$$f_T(x)dx = \frac{E}{\sigma k\sqrt{2\pi}} e^{-\alpha x} \exp\left[ -\frac{E^2}{2k^2\sigma^2} e^{-2\alpha x}\right] d(\alpha x) \tag{6.102}$$

This is plotted vs. $\alpha x$ for $E/k\sigma = 10^5$ in Fig. 6.29. The curve is essentially exponential for $\alpha x > 13$.

The distribution of rise times of a regenerative amplifier triggered by a signal $m$ in addition to random noise can be obtained by using in Eq. (6.99)

$$f_{e_i}(x) = \frac{1}{\sigma\sqrt{2\pi}} e^{-(x-m)^2/2\sigma^2}$$

If $\sigma^2/m^2 \ll 1$, the resulting distribution is sharply peaked at about

$$T = \frac{1}{\alpha} \log \frac{E}{mk}$$

which is the settling time our simplified model would have in the absence

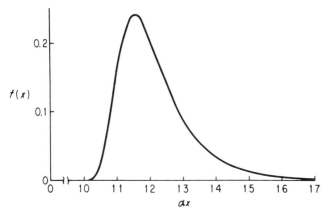

**Fig. 6.29.** Distribution of flip-flop settling times for $E/k\sigma = 10^5$ and normally distributed disturbance.

of noise. This illustrates the existence of the commonly observed rise-time jitter of triggered regenerative amplifiers such as blocking oscillators.

### 6.22  PULSE TRANSFORMERS

A number of equivalent circuits have been developed for transformers. However, modern computer-type pulse transformers using, for example, ferrite cup cores have tight coupling between windings, low losses, and small capacitances. Also, the requirements on the shape of the waveforms passed through these devices, although not loose, are usually such that the performance requirements of the transformers are less stringent than in communications applications. For these reasons it is often possible to make successful use of simplified approaches such as the one below.

A schematic drawing of a loaded transformer is shown in Fig. 6.30. The mesh equations are

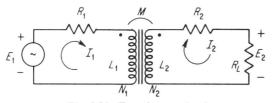

**Fig. 6.30.** Transformer circuit.

$$E_1 = R_1 I_1 + sL_1 I_1 - sMI_2$$
$$0 = (R_2 + R_L)I_2 + sL_2 I_2 - sMI_1, \qquad E_2 = R_L I_2 \tag{6.103}$$

We assume the equivalent circuit of Fig. 6.31; the mesh equations for this circuit are

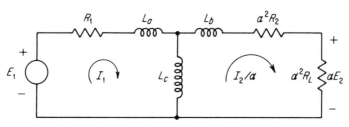

**Fig. 6.31.** Equivalent circuit.

$$E_1 = R_1 I_1 + s(L_a + L_c)I_1 - sL_c I_2 \tag{6.104}$$
$$0 = \alpha^2 (R_2 + R_L)\frac{I_2}{\alpha} + s(L_b + L_c)\frac{I_2}{\alpha} - sL_c I_1, \qquad E_2 = R_L I_2$$

For Eqs. (6.103) and (6.104) to be identical, we must have

$$L_a + L_c = L_1$$
$$L_b + L_c = \alpha^2 L_2 \tag{6.105}$$
$$L_c = \alpha M$$

From magnetic-field considerations it can be shown that

$$L_1 = N_1^2 f_1$$
$$L_2 = N_2^2 f_2 \tag{6.106}$$
$$M = N_1 N_2 f_{12}$$

where $f_1$, $f_2$, and $f_{12}$ are functions of geometry and the core material. It also can be shown that

$$f_1 < f_{12}, \qquad f_2 < f_{12}$$

and in tightly coupled transformers or in transformers with similarly constructed primary and secondary windings

$$f_1 \cong f_2$$

From Eqs. (6.106) it can be shown that

$$M = \frac{f_{12}}{\sqrt{f_1 f_2}} \sqrt{L_1 L_2}, \qquad \frac{f_{12}}{\sqrt{f_1 f_2}} \equiv k < 1 \tag{6.107}$$

where $k$ is the *coefficient of coupling* and is usually very close to unity. From Eqs. (6.105), (6.106), and (6.107) (if $f_1 = f_2$) it can be shown that

$$L_a = L_1(1 - k) \qquad L_c = kL_1$$

$$N^2 L_b = L_2(1 - k) \qquad \alpha = \frac{1}{N}$$

where $N \equiv N_2/N_1 \cong L_2/L_1$ is the *turns ratio*.

Hence, the equivalent circuit for the transformer becomes as in Fig. 6.32. The ideal transformer merely multiplies the current by $1/N$ and the

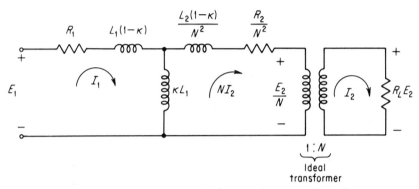

Fig. 6.32. Equivalent circuit neglecting capacitances and core losses.

voltage by $N$. The inductance $kL_1$ should be shunted by a resistance representing the core losses, but in well-designed pulse transformers the core-loss resistance has negligible effect on the accuracy of the measurements of $L_1$, $L_2$, $k$, and $N$.

These quantities can be determined by measuring certain inductances on a bridge. For example the primary inductance measured with the secondary open is $L_1$. The secondary inductance measured with the primary open is $L_2$. The primary inductance measured with the secondary shorted is approximately

$$\left(L_1 + \frac{L_2}{N^2}\right)(1 - k) \tag{6.108}$$

All of these results can be verified from Fig. 6.32. The measurements should be made at low enough frequencies so that the capacitances and core losses will have negligible effect on the results. This can be guaranteed by making sure that the measurements do not change when the frequency is varied around the measuring frequency. From $L_1$ and $L_2$, we can calculate $N$ as $N = \sqrt{L_2/L_1}$. Knowing $N$, Eq. (6.108) can be used to find $k$.

The capacitances as well as the inductances of a pulse transformer are distributed quantities. However, it is rarely necessary to consider the windings as distributed (if necessary they can be treated as transmission lines). We are interested in the equivalent lumped capacitances $C_1$ and $C_2$ when shunting the primary and secondary windings, and in $C_{12}$, the capacitance between these windings. If the transformer is physically large, there may be additional equivalent capacitances, especially if the core is grounded. These capacitances are quite complicated functions of geometry and sometimes can be calculated by formulas in the literature. Their effect can usually be satisfactorily taken into account by shunting the inductance $kL_1$ in Fig. 6.32 by an equivalent capacitance.

If the transformer is open-circuited on the secondary, the equivalent circuit of Fig. 6.32 becomes approximately that shown in Fig. 6.33, where $C$ is the equivalent shunt capacitance referred to the primary. Hence, $C$ can be determined knowing $L_1$, $R_1$, and the resonant frequency of this $L$-$R$-$C$ resonant circuit. This frequency can be measured either by r-f methods or by shock-exciting the circuit and allowing it to ring with its windings grounded in the way it is to be used.

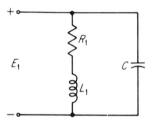

**Fig. 6.33.** Equivalent circuit, primary side, secondary open.

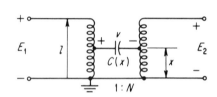

**Fig. 6.34.**

This capacitance is often small compared to the other capacitances existing in the circuit where the pulse transformer is used. However, it is helpful to know what construction features affect it. It is equal to $C_1 + N^2 C_2$ plus some factor times $C_{12}$. This factor is a function of how the windings are connected. To determine this factor approximately in a given case consider the connection shown in Fig. 6.34. We will assume the capacitance arises from the energy stored in the electric field between the windings considered as the plates of a capacitor having a capacitance $C(x)$ per unit length. Hence

$$C_{12} = \int_0^l C(x)\, dx \tag{6.109}$$

The voltage across $C(x)$, neglecting the effect of the winding resistance and leakage inductance and assuming a linear voltage distribution on the windings, is

$$v = \frac{E_1}{l} x - \frac{E_2}{l} x = \frac{E_1}{l} (1 - N)x$$

The energy stored is

$$w = \frac{1}{2} \int_0^l C(x) \left[ \frac{E_1}{l}(1 - N)x \right]^2 dx \qquad (6.110)$$

If $C(x)$ is a constant, $C_0$, Eq. (6.110) becomes

$$w = \frac{C_0 l}{6} E_1^2 (1 - N)^2 = \frac{1}{2} C_{12}' E_1^2$$

where $C_{12}'$ is the effective interwinding capacitance referred to the primary winding. From Eq. (6.109), $C_{12} = C_0 l$ so that

$$C_{12}' = \frac{C_{12}}{3}(1 - N)^2$$

The aforementioned factor is seen to be $(1 - N)^2$ for the connection of Fig. 6.34. Note that $C_{12}' = 0$ if $N = 1$. This can be understood physically by noting that if $N = 1$ in the connection of Fig. 6.34, no voltage appears between the windings so that no energy is stored in the interwinding capacitance.

The primary and secondary winding capacitances $C_1$ and $C_2$ result chiefly from the series connection of the turn-to-turn capacitances in the case of scramble-wound windings, the layer-to-layer capacitances in layer-wound windings, etc. The capacitance is less in the first case because the voltages and hence the energy storage are less. The capacitances $C_1$ and $C_2$ tend to *decrease* as the number of turns increases, since they result from the series connection of capacitances.

The leakage inductances are reduced by interleaving primary and secondary windings and are often a minimum when the windings are bifilar. The total winding capacitance tends to increase as the windings are placed closer together so that a compromise is necessary. It is a principle that when a compromise is necessary an optimum exists. This optimum is sometimes achieved by assuring that the windings are as closely matched as possible to the external circuit impedances when the windings are treated as transmission lines having the leakage inductances and stray capacitances as parameters. Each case must be considered in detail.

The required amount of core material is determined by the material characteristics and by the power-handling requirements. The size of the transformer tends to increase as the power-handling requirements increase. One usually tries to minimize the size of the transformer still meeting the requirements.

For the analysis of rise-time behavior of circuits, the equivalent circuit of Fig. 6.35 can be used.

The winding resistances can often be neglected, and the two leakage inductances can usually be lumped together with the capacitor $C$ moved

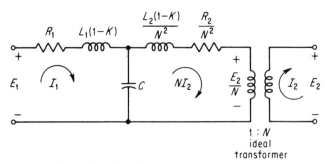

**Fig. 6.35.** High-frequency equivalent circuit.

either to the left of $L_1(1 - k)$ or to the right of $L_2(1 - k)/N^2$. An equivalent circuit valid for the duration of a pulse (provided the core is unsaturated) is shown in Fig. 6.36.

If $R_1$ and $R_2/N^2$ are negligible, a constant voltage $E_1$ will maintain a constant voltage $E_2 = NE_1$, until the core saturates. This happens because the magnetizing current $i_m$ builds up in $L_1$ which for constant $E_1$ is

$$i_m = \frac{E_1 t}{L_1}$$

and for varying $E_1$ is (from Faraday's law)

$$i_m = \frac{1}{L_1} \int_0^t E_1(t) \, dt$$

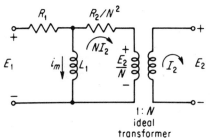

**Fig. 6.36.** Approximate low-frequency equivalent circuit ($k \sim 1$).

The magnetizing current $i_m$ represents an amount of reactive energy $\frac{1}{2} L_1 i_m^2$ absorbed by the transformer which must be largely dissipated before a second pulse is applied. If this is not done, the magnetizing current might build up until the core saturates and transformer action ceases. This cumulative build-up can be understood by the following approximate analysis.

Assume that a periodic pulse train is applied and that the magnetizing current builds up from zero to $I_{m0}$ at the end of the first pulse. This will decay to some fraction $\gamma$ of $I_{m0}$ at the time the second pulse ends, at which time the magnetizing current will be (if linearity is assumed)

$$i_m = I_{m0} + \gamma I_{m0}$$

At the end of the third pulse

$$i_m = I_{m0} + \gamma I_{m0} + \gamma^2 I_{m0}$$

and if the train of pulses persists for a long time,

$$i_m = I_{m0}(1 + \gamma + \gamma^2 + \cdots)$$

$$= \frac{I_{m0}}{1 - \gamma} \tag{6.111}$$

which represents the value of magnetizing current approached at the end of any pulse. This is of interest not only because of saturation effects but primarily because the circuits driving the transformer must furnish this current in addition to the load current.

An approximate equivalent circuit for the transformer which is often valid during the recovery period (when $i_m$ is decaying) is shown in Fig. 6.37.

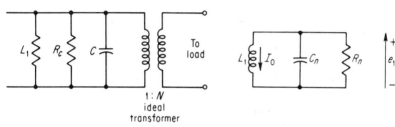

Fig. 6.37.                    Fig. 6.38.

All the quantities have been previously defined. The load and driving circuits will result in additional resistance and capacitance being shunted across the transformer windings so that the equivalent circuit for the transformer in the actual circuit will be as shown in Fig. 6.38. $C_n$ and $R_n$ are the total effective capacitance and resistance shunting $L_1$. When the circuit driving the transformer shuts off, the voltage $e_1$ falls to zero and then reverses correspondingly to the "ringback" of the transformer. $I_0$ *is the mag-*

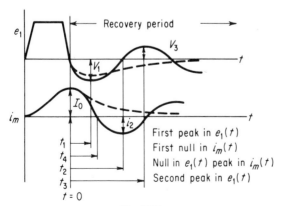

Fig. 6.39.

*netizing current when $e_1$ passes through zero at the trailing edge of the pulse.*
The situation is summarized in Fig. 6.39. The circuit of Fig. 6.38 may
ring after $t = 0$, as shown in Fig. 6.39, or exhibit the behavior shown
by the dotted lines in Fig. 6.39, depending on how heavily it is damped
by the core losses and the external circuit. The transformer generally
recovers more quickly if it is slightly underdamped. We will investigate
this case further.

Transient analysis of the circuit of Fig. 6.38 yields in the underdamped
case for $t > 0$,

$$e_1(t) = -\frac{I_0}{C_n \sqrt{\frac{1}{L_n C_n} - \left(\frac{1}{2R_n C_n}\right)^2}} e^{-t/2R_n C_n} \sin t \sqrt{\frac{1}{L_1 C_n} - \left(\frac{1}{2R_n C_n}\right)^2}$$

$$i_m(t) = \frac{1}{L_1} \int e_1 \, dt \tag{6.112}$$

We let

$$\omega_0 = \frac{1}{\sqrt{L_n C_n}} = \frac{1}{2R_{\text{crit}} C_n}$$

$$R_{\text{crit}} = \frac{1}{2} \sqrt{\frac{L_n}{C_n}}$$

$$v_m = I_0 \sqrt{\frac{L_n}{C_n}} = \frac{I_0}{\omega_0 C_n}$$

$$\rho = \frac{R_{\text{crit}}}{R_n}$$

$$\tau = \omega_0 t$$

$$T = \pi \sqrt{L_1 C_n} \qquad \text{(duration of undamped half-cycle)}$$

$\omega_0$ is the natural frequency of oscillation in the absence of damping. $R_{\text{crit}}$
is the value $R_n$ should have for critical damping, and $v_m$ is the value that $v_1$
would ring back to if there was no damping. In terms of these quantities,
the first of Eqs. (6.112) becomes

$$-\frac{e_1(t)}{v_m} = \frac{1}{\sqrt{1 - \rho^2}} e^{-\rho\tau} \sin \tau \sqrt{1 - \rho^2}, \qquad \rho < 1$$

The times $t_1$——$t_4$, voltages $v_1$ and $v_3$, and the current $i_2$ are of interest for
design purposes. Because $e_1 = L_1 \, di_m/dt$, the peaks in $i_m$ and the nulls in $e_1$
coincide; the converse is not true.

(a) Null in $e_1(t)$, peak in $i_m(t)$ after null

$$\tau_2\sqrt{1 - \rho^2} = \pi$$

$$\therefore \delta_2 = \frac{t_2}{T} = \frac{\tau_2}{\pi} = \frac{1}{\sqrt{1 - \rho^2}}; \quad T = \pi\sqrt{L_1 C_n}$$

From $i_m = -C_n\, dv/dt - v/R_n$ we have

$$\left|\frac{i_2}{I_0}\right| = \exp\left[-\frac{\rho\pi}{\sqrt{1 - \rho^2}}\right]$$

(b) First peak in $e_1(t)$
Setting $de_1/dt = 0$ yields

$$\delta_1 = \frac{t_1}{T} = \frac{\tau_1}{\pi} = \frac{1}{\pi\sqrt{1 - \rho^2}} \arctan \frac{\sqrt{1 - \rho^2}}{\rho}$$

$$\left|\frac{v_1}{v_m}\right| = \exp\left[-\frac{\rho}{\sqrt{1 - \rho^2}} \arctan \frac{\sqrt{1 - \rho^2}}{\rho}\right]$$

(c) Second peak in $e_1(t)$

$$\delta_3 = \frac{t_3}{T} = \frac{\tau_3}{\pi} = \delta_1 + \delta_2$$

$$\left|\frac{v_3}{v_m}\right| = |v_1| \exp\left[-\frac{\rho\pi}{\sqrt{1 - \rho^2}}\right]$$

(d) Null in $i_m(t)$

From the differential equation with $i_m = 0$: $R_n \dfrac{de_1}{dt} + e_1 = 0$, substitution yields

$$\delta_4 = \frac{t_4}{T} = \frac{1}{\sqrt{1 - \rho^2}} - \delta_1$$

These equations when plotted yield the curves in Figs. 6.40 and 6.41.

To use the curves in analysis, compute $T = \pi\sqrt{L_1 C_n}$, $\rho$, and $v_m = I_0\sqrt{L_1/C_n}$. Read off the various normalized quantities. To obtain the times $t_1$——$t_4$, multiply $\delta_1$——$\delta_4$ by $T$. To obtain the currents and voltages, multiply the quantities read off of Fig. 6.41 by $I_0$ or $v_m$ where appropriate.

In the gross design of a pulse transformer, we have to determine the value of $L_1$ and the turns ratio. The value of $L_1$ is usually dependent on the requirements on the recovery of the transformer. This is where the curves of Figs. 6.40 and 6.41 can be of assistance. One such design procedure is as follows. Since the times $t_2$——$t_4$ and hence the recovery time tend to increase rapidly as $\rho$ approaches unity, select a trial value of $\rho$ of the order of 0.7 or

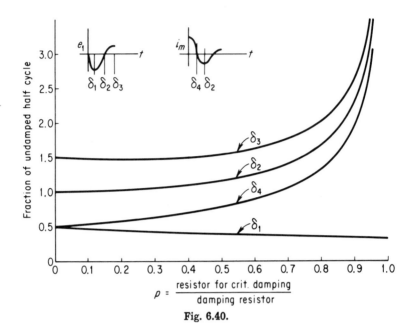

$$p = \frac{\text{resistor for crit. damping}}{\text{damping resistor}}$$

Fig. 6.40.

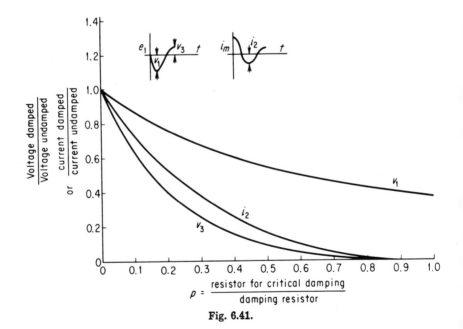

$$p = \frac{\text{resistor for critical damping}}{\text{damping resistor}}$$

Fig. 6.41.

0.8. From Fig. 6.40, read off $\delta_4$. This is the normalized time at which the magnetizing current first vanishes, and it is about the earliest time that the transformer can be considered to have recovered. From $\delta_4$ and the specifications the undamped half-cycle, $T = \pi\sqrt{L_1 C_n}$, can be computed. With the circuit capacitances as a first approximation to $C_n$, the primary inductance can be computed. This enables the current $I_0$ to be computed from

$$I_0 = \frac{\text{primary pulse volt-second area}}{L_1}$$

From this value, $v_m$ is computed. Figure 6.41 can then be used to estimate the currents and voltages during recovery. A core is then selected and the primary turns are determined to achieve the required primary inductance. There should now be sufficient information available to arrive at an estimate of the turns ratio on the basis of the circuit requirements. A model is constructed and the capacitances and leakage inductances are measured. With these data this initial design can be modified to take account of the transformer capacitances. If the losses and heating when tested in a circuit are excessive, a larger core and/or a different material must be selected and the design process repeated. When a design based on a chosen value of $\rho$ is obtained, it is much easier to repeat the design procedure trying different values of $\rho$ and different values of recovery time. Although the process appears lengthy it converges rapidly in practice if transformer models can be fabricated quickly in the laboratory.

It usually turns out that the optimum damping resistance is not equal to the load resistance. Many circuit configurations can be constructed which meet the damping resistor

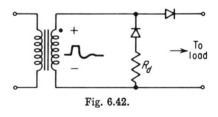

Fig. 6.42.

and load switching requirements; an example is shown in Fig. 6.42. The damping resistor is connected across the transformer winding only during the backswing when the load is disconnected. An additional feature is present in that the load capacitance is disconnected from the transformer during ringback, making faster recovery possible than if it were not.

### REFERENCES

1. Baker, A. N., "Charge Analysis of Transistor Operation," *Proc. I.R.E.*, **48:**1 (May 1960), 949–950.

2. Beaufoy and Sparkes, "The Junction Transistor as a Charge Controlled Device," *A.T.E. Journal*, **13** (March 1957), 310–327.

3. Ebers and Moll, "Large-Signal Behavior of Junction Transistors," *Proc. I.R.E.*, **42**:12 (Dec. 1954), 1761–1772.

4. Ekiss, J. A., "Applications of the Charge Control Theory," *I.R.E. Transactions on Electronic Computers*, **EC-11**:3 (June 1962), 374–381.

5. Goldman, S., *Transformation Calculus and Electrical Transients* (Englewood Cliffs, N.J.: Prentice-Hall, Inc., 1949). Excellent book on the solution of electrical transients.

6. Gray, H. J., "Digital Computer Solution of Differential Equations in Real Time," *Proceedings of the Western Joint Computer Conference*, 1958, pp. 87–91. Supplements section 6.5.

7. Ku, Y. H., *Analysis and Control of Non-Linear Systems* (New York: The Ronald Press Co., 1958). Classical analysis of nonlinear systems with up-to-date additions and developments included.

8. Le Can, C., *The Junction Transistor as a Switching Device* (New York: Reinhold Publishing Co., 1962). Presents a third approach to the analysis of transistors as switching devices.

9. Lo, Arthur W., and others, *Transistor Electronics* (Englewood Cliffs, N.J.: Prentice-Hall, Inc., 1955). Basic reference on transistors.

10. Middlebrook, R. D., *An Introduction to Junction Transistor Theory* (New York: John Wiley & Sons, Inc., 1957). Readable and systematic development of equivalent circuits for transistors.

11. Millman, J., and H. Taub, *Pulse and Digital Circuits* (New York: McGraw-Hill Book Co., 1956). Basic reference on the simplified analysis of pulse and digital circuits.

12. Stanton, R. G., *Numerical Methods for Science and Engineering* (Englewood Cliffs, N.J.: Prentice-Hall, Inc., 1955). Very readable book on numerical analysis directed to engineers.

13. Strauss, L., *Wave Generation and Shaping* (New York: McGraw-Hill Book Co., 1960). Supplements Millman and Taub, covering additional topics.

## PROBLEMS

1. Neglecting diode leakages and drops (ideal diodes) and neglecting component and voltage tolerances, determine the quiescent voltages at all points in the circuit shown below when (a) the input (IN) is at $-11$ volts and (b) the input (IN) is at $+5$ volts.

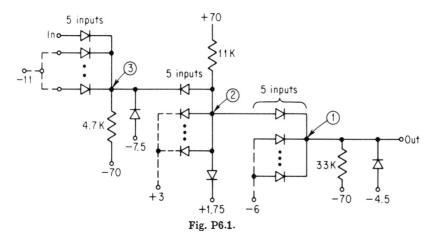

**Fig. P6.1.**

**2.** In the circuit of Prob. 1, each diode has a capacitance of 1 pf. The capacitances at points ①, ②, and ③ are 21 pf, 9 pf, and 9 pf, respectively, not including the diode capacitances.

(a) Determine the effective capacitances at points ①, ②, and ③ which affect the response of the circuit to pulses applied at IN.

(b) Determine the shapes, amplitudes, and important times for the waveforms at points ①, ②, and ③ if the input signal has the following shape (use the methods of Sec. 6.3).

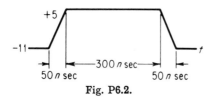

**Fig. P6.2.**

**3.** Extend the diode-characteristics curve in Fig. 6.3 to forward currents of 20 ma or so.

**4.** Repeat Prob. 1 assuming that all diodes have the forward characteristics obtained in Prob. 3 and the reverse characteristics in Fig. 6.3.

**5.** Repeat Prob. 2(b) assuming that all diodes have the forward characteristics obtained in Prob. 3 and the reverse characteristics in Fig. 6.3.

**6.** Show that when the differential equation

$$a\frac{d^2x}{dt^2} + b\frac{dx}{dt} + cx = 0$$

is integrated with $O_{11}$, the computed solution is of the form

$$k_1 e^{\mu_1 t} + k_2 e^{\mu_2 t}$$

where

$$\mu_j = \frac{1}{h} \log (1 + \lambda_j h), \qquad j = 1, 2$$

and

$$(\lambda_1, \lambda_2) = \frac{-b \pm \sqrt{b^2 - 4ac}}{2a}$$

**7.** Derive Eq. (6.20) and prove the statement made about it.

**\*8.** Extend the results of Sec. 6.5 to any number of simultaneous linear differential equations solved by $O_{11}$.

**\*9.** For the general operation, $O_{NM}$,

$$x_n = \sum_{j=1}^{N} a_{j_0} x_{n-j} + h \sum_{j=1}^{M} b_{j_0} \left[ \frac{dx}{dt} \right]_{n-j}$$

when applied to $x = \lambda x$, determine the defining equation for $\mu$.

**\*10.** For the general closed formula $C_{RQ}$ determine the conditions that must be satisfied for the convergence of iterations within an interval, $h$, for $dx/dt = \lambda x$.

$$C_{RQ}: \quad x_n = \sum_{j=1}^{R} a_{jc} x_{n-j} + h \sum_{j=0}^{Q-1} b_{jc} \left[ \frac{dx}{dt} \right]_{n-j}$$

**\*11.** For the closed formula, $C_{RQ}$, obtain the defining equation for $\mu$.

**12.** Write the differential equations for the circuit of Prob. 1 including the nonlinear diode characteristics used in Probs. 4 and 5 above.

**13.** Write the differential equation(s) for the circuit shown below, determine a suitable interval, and by numerical integration obtain the output waveform.

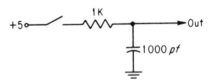

Fig. P6.3.

**14.** Compare your results obtained in Prob. 13 with the actual results obtained by transient analysis and with those predicted by the methods described in Sec. 6.5.

**15.** A certain ferrite toroid has an outer diameter of 1 cm, an inner diameter of 0.7 cm, and a thickness of 0.2 cm. The material has a coercive force of 0.4 amp/cm, a remanent induction of $2 \times 10^{-5}$ webers/cm², and a switching

* Problems marked with an asterisk are of exceptional difficulty.

constant of 0.64 amp $\mu$sec/cm. A current step of 200 ma is applied to a 10-turn winding when the core is at negative remanence causing the core to switch. Neglecting leakage inductances, stray capacitances, etc., and the variation of $H$ radially in the core material, determine the voltage waveform that would be detected across a second 10-turn (open-circuited) winding wound on the toroid by (a) integration of the Haynes equation in closed form, and (b) numerical integration of the Haynes equation. Compare your results with those predicted by the simplified switching equation.

16. In many practical problems, straightforward numerical integration fails because of the presence of extremely short time constants. These produce instability in the numerical method when reasonable intervals are chosen from the point of view of accuracy. The reason is that small changes in a variable produce large changes in the derivative. This instability is qualitatively analogous to that which can occur in a closed-loop servomechanism and which can be eliminated by opening the loop. Develop a technique for handling such problems by practicing on the circuit below. Choose an interval which gives good accuracy but makes the numerical method unstable (use $O_{11}$).

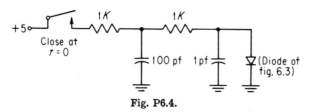

**Fig. P6.4.**

17. Show that

(a) $h_{FE} = -\dfrac{\alpha_F}{1 - \alpha_F} = -\dfrac{I_C}{I_B}$  (common-emitter-connection)

(b) $h_{FC} = -\dfrac{1}{1 - \alpha_F} = -\dfrac{I_E}{I_B}$  (common-collector-connection)

18. For a p-n-p common-emitter-connected transistor with $V_{CE} \ll 0$, and using Eqs. (6.32) and (6.33),
   (a) Obtain $I_C$ when $I_B = 0$. $(I_{CEO})$
   (b) Obtain $I_C$ when $V_{BE} = 0$. $(I_{CES})$
   (c) Obtain $I_C$ when the base is returned to the emitter through a resistance $R$. Plot $I_C$ versus $\log R$ for $\alpha_F = 0.98$, $\alpha_R = 0.7$, $|I_{co}| = 1$ $\mu$a, and $|I_{EO}| = 0.7$ $\mu$a. $(I_{CER})$

19. For the feedback circuit below when triggered by an impulse, and with $I_0 = 0$, show that the current $I_C$ grows approximately as $e^{s_0 t}$ where (a) $s_0 \cong \omega_F(\alpha_F K_f - 1)$ if $D$ is neglected and (b) $s_0 \cong \dfrac{\log \alpha_F K_f}{D + 1/\omega_F}$ if $D$ is not insignificant. Compute both values of $s_0$ if $\omega_F = 10^8$, $\alpha_F = 1$, $K_f = 10$, and $D = 3 \times 10^{-8}$. Can you improve on approximation (b)?

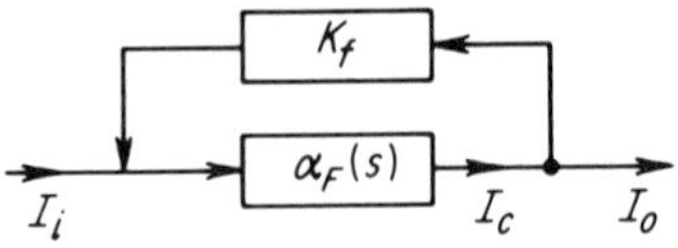

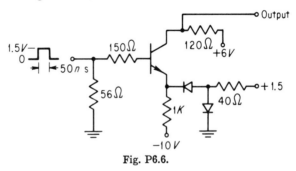

Fig. P6.5.

**20.** Show that a capacitance as measured by small-signal techniques is

$$C = \frac{dQ}{dV}$$

such that $i = C\, dv/dt$ and not $i = d(CV)/dt$.

**21.** Show that if

$$\alpha_{FE}(s) = \frac{\alpha_{FE}e^{-sD}}{1 + sT_\epsilon}$$

and if a charge $q_b = \int_{-\infty}^{\infty} i_b\, dt$ is extracted from the base of the transistor, then

$$q_c = \int_{-\infty}^{\infty} i_c\, dt = \alpha_{FE}q_b$$

**22.** In Eq. (6.91), try to express the constants $a_1$, $a_2$, $\alpha_R$, and $D_R$ in terms of measurements of the step response of the inverted transistor.

**23.** A certain n-p-n silicon diffused-base transistor has a small-signal current gain of 7.5 at 20 mcps, a delay of 0.6 $\mu$sec, and a common-emitter current gain of 20, and $C_{CB} = 8$ pf at $V_{CB} = +6$ volts. Obtain (a) the gain-bandwidth product, (b) the alpha cutoff frequency and (c) the output-voltage waveform in the following circuit. (Neglect base-emitter drop; assume ideal diodes.)

Fig. P6.6.

**24.** In the configuration shown below,[*] prove that the rise time $T_R$ from $v_c = V_{cc}$ to $v_c = 0$ is given by

$$\frac{T_R}{T_p} = \log \frac{1}{1 - \dfrac{I_c}{\alpha_{FE}I_B}} + \frac{2K_0R_L\omega_T}{\sqrt{\phi + V_{cc}}} \times \frac{1}{\sqrt{\dfrac{\alpha_{FE}I_B}{I_c} - 1}} \tan^{-1} \frac{1}{\sqrt{\dfrac{\alpha_{FE}I_B}{I_c} - 1}}$$

[*] From Ekiss and Simmons, *Proc. IRE*, **48**, 8.

where $I_c = V_{cc}/R_L$ and $i_B$ is a step of height $I_B$.

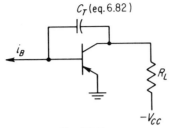

Fig. P6.7.

**25.** The input to the circuit shown below is a step going from $-3$ to $0$ volts. Compute the storage time for the transistor assuming that the diode drop is zero.

$$\alpha_F = 0.95, \quad \alpha_R = 0.6, \quad f_F = 30 \text{ mcps}, \quad f_R = 10 \text{ mcps}$$

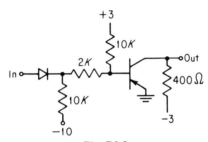

Fig. P6.8.

**26.** By expanding Eq. (6.92) in powers of $1/s$ develop an improved approximation to the storage time which reduces to Eq. (6.95) when the storage time is small.

**27.** Design a tester to determine the distribution of settling times of an asynchronous race-resolving flip-flop.

**28.** A pulse transformer is used in the following circuit:

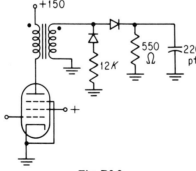

Fig. P6.9.

The capacitances in the primary circuit are:

| | |
|---|---|
| tube (plate to all electrodes) | 2.9 pf |
| transformer as connected | 1.0 pf |
| tube socket (plate pin to all others) | 1.2 pf |
| wiring (tube to transformer) | 1.0 pf |

The transformer has a primary inductance of 2 mh and a secondary inductance of 41 $\mu$h measured with the other winding open. The primary inductance measured with the secondary short-circuited is 12 $\mu$h.

(a) Determine the turns ratio, the leakage and magnetizing inductances, and the coefficient of coupling for the transformer.

(b) Determine the response of the circuit to a single pulse applied to the grid of the tube. The applied pulse is

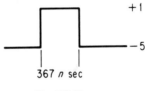

367 $n$ sec

**Fig. P6.10.**

Assume that the diodes are ideal, that the transformer is lossless, and that the tube characteristic is as below.

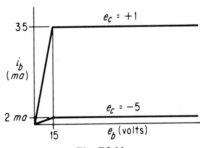

**Fig. P6.11.**

**29.** Approximate the response of the circuit of Prob. 28 to a continuous train of applied pulses each having the characteristics of the pulse given in that problem. The pulse rate is 1 mcps.

# 7

# RELIABILITY AND COMPONENTS

During World War II there occurred a great increase in the amount of electronic equipment used by the armed services. It cannot be said that the operating history of the equipment used indicated anything even approaching reliable operation. As a result of what was considered in some quarters a failure of the military electronics program, contracts were assigned to various study groups in order to arrive at recommendations for improvement of the reliability of electronic equipment. One report, that by R. R. Carhart, is considered to be a classic in its field because of its concise statement of the problems involved. Some of the findings reported therein include the following.

It was found that half of the failures in the field were caused by tubes. Tube failures occurred randomly with operating time (exponential law—see the next section). The mean lifetime for tubes in most military equipment was estimated to be from 2000 to 20,000 hours. More tube failures occurred in airborne equipment, and the airborne tube failures were more of a mechanical than an electrical nature. As a result of these findings, the airlines instigated the formation of a corporation (ARINC) to provide them with ruggedized tubes. Also some tube manufacturers developed a line of ruggedized or "reliable" tubes. These two tube categories exhibited a failure rate of about half that found in the military JAN types.

It was also found that 80 to 90 per cent of the down time was due to component failures. The reason was that it took longer to find a defective component than to find a defective tube. Since there were about ten times as many components as tubes, the failure history on components was about ten times better than on tubes, as tubes and components contributed about equally to the failures.

Some annual failure rates for components as reported by Vitro Corp. in 1952 were (Navy ship and shore electronic equipment):*

| Component | Per cent failures |
|---|---|
| Resistors | 3.3 |
| Capacitors | 3.2 |
| Connectors | 16.3 |
| Switches | 5.2 |
| Transformers, chokes, coils | 2.5 |
| Relays | 5.8 |
| Meters | 6.0 |
| 42 others | 10.1 |

These data are of little value today because component improvement programs have substantially decreased the failure rates. However, it is sometimes valuable to review the history of a program occasionally so that we may avoid continuing an unnecessary investigation. For example, some diodeless circuits were investigated because they did not have diodes. This was probably because the investigators unconsciously thought of the diodes as having the unreliability that they had when first introduced.

As another example, Vitro Corp. reported that the annual failure rates for those component types having the most failures were:†

| Component | Per cent failures |
|---|---|
| Composition resistors (fixed) | 2.6 |
| Connectors | 16.3 |
| Paper capacitors | 3.2 |
| Mica capacitors | 2.0 |
| Wire-wound resistors (fixed) | 7.6 |

One might conclude from these figures that it would be unwise to use large numbers of connectors or wire-wound resistors in a computing system. However, component improvement programs that have been applied in the past have shown that it is possible to achieve extremely low failure rates from properly designed and used connectors and wire-wound resistors. One computer which uses very large numbers of both is Remington Rand's LARC, which exhibits highly reliable operation.

* See Ref. 2, p. 42.
† *Ibid.*, p. 43.

Bell Laboratories and the Western Electric Company reported in 1953 the following data as a result of an investigation of the major sources of trouble involving components in U.S. Navy radio and radar equipment.*

| Source | Per cent | |
|---|---|---|
| *Engineering* | 43 | |
| electrical | | 33 |
| mechanical | | 10 |
| *Operations* | 30 | |
| conditions | | 12 |
| manhandling | | 10 |
| maintenance | | 8 |
| *Manufacturing* | 20 | |
| Work, inspection, control | | 18 |
| Defective raw material | | 2 |
| *Other causes* | 7 | |

Because the electrical behavior of a circuit or component is strongly affected by the mechanical aspects of its design, it is not reasonable to proceed with mechanical designs independent of electrical requirements. Consequently, it follows that all aspects of engineering are or should be under the technical control of the designers. Furthermore, it is necessary that the designers of a computing system have technical control over those manufacturing operations that affect reliability. Proper design also takes into account the nature of the environmental conditions and can ease maintenance. Hence, engineering has strong control and responsibility for the production of reliable equipment.

### 7.1 SYSTEM RELIABILITY

Carhart considers two types of failures: (a) chance failures and (b) wear-out failures.

Chance failures are found to satisfy the exponential law of failure

$$R = e^{-rt} \qquad (7.1)$$

where $t$ is the operating time, $r$ is the failure rate, and $R$ is the "reliability." The reliability is defined by Carhart: "Reliability of a given component or system is the probability that it will perform its required function under given conditions for a specified operating time."

If $p_1, p_2, \ldots, p_m$ are the reliabilities of the $m$ individual parts of a system and are independent and are in "series" as in a computer, where failure of a single part means system failure, the system reliability becomes

* Ref. 2, p. 47.

$$R = \prod_{i=1}^{m} p_i \qquad (7.2)$$

If the unreliability, $q$, is defined as

$$q = 1 - p$$

and if we assume $p_1 = p_2 = \cdots = p_m = p$, Eq. (7.2) becomes

$$R = p^m = (1 - q)^m$$

$$= 1 - \frac{mq}{1!} + \frac{m(m-1)}{2!} q^2 - \cdots$$

$$\cong 1 - mq \qquad \text{if } mq \ll 1$$

For example, if a system uses components with each having a failure rate of 0.1 per cent per 1000 hours, we have

$$r = 10^{-6} \text{ per hour}$$

The reliability for an eight-hour period for such a component is

$$R = e^{-rt} = \exp (8 \times 10^{-6}) \cong 1 - 8 \times 10^{-6}$$

If the system uses 100,000 such components in "series," the system reliability is

$$R \cong (1 - 8 \times 10^{-6})^{100,000}$$

$$= 0.45$$

That is, the probability that the system will be failure-free for an eight-hour period is 0.45, under the assumption that no replacements are made. If replacements occur, then failures occur randomly with a mean time $T$, where, using the statistical definition of the mean,

$$T = E(t) = \frac{\int_0^\infty t e^{-rt} \, dt}{\int_0^\infty e^{-rt} \, dt} = \frac{1}{r}$$

In the above example, the failure rate for the system is obtained from Eq. (7.1).

$$0.45 = e^{-8r}$$

Hence, $r = 0.1$ per hour such that the mean time to failure for the system in the example is ten hours.

If we have $m$ parts whose individual failure rates are $r_1, r_2, \ldots, r_m$ such that the part reliabilities are

$$p_i = e^{-r_i t}$$

Eq. (7.2) becomes

$$R = e^{-t(\Sigma r_i)} = e^{-rt}$$

where $r = \Sigma r_i$.

Since failure rates and mean time to failure are essentially statistical quantities, some measure of the trustworthiness of these quantities is desirable. The student, if interested, may pursue this subject further under the determination of confidence limits, tests of significance, etc., which are discussed in books on systems engineering and statistics.

## 7.2  PHYSICAL BASIS FOR THE EXPONENTIAL LAW

We will now attempt to support the viewpoint that chance failures frequently can be explained as the effect of uncontrolled environmental stresses on the components; they are wear-out failures of a special kind. Because of this, it has been possible to institute component improvement programs in which the nature of the stresses has been discovered and the resistance of the components to these stresses improved so that extremely low failure rates have been achieved. A similar point of view was first suggested by Robert M. Lusser, when he was Reliability Coordinator at the Redstone Arsenal: that chance failures could be explained as the effect of random environmental stresses on the components. An analysis of Lusser's proposed mechanism will be made, and will be followed by an analysis of the effect of uncontrolled stresses. The latter analysis rises out of a logical extension required to correct defects existing in the mechanism he proposed.

A stress distribution existing in a system and a component failure distribution existing as a result of that type of stress are shown in Fig. 7.1.

Let the probability that the stress $X_1$ lies between $x$ and $x + dx$ be $f_{X_1}(x)\, dx$ and let the fraction of the total number of components failing at stress $X_2$ be $F_{X_2}(x)$ where

$$F_{X_2}(x) = \int_{-\infty}^{x} f_{X_2}(x)\, dx$$

(continuous distributions are assumed for simplicity).

The probability of a component failing under stress distribution $f_{X_1}(x)$ is (strictly, $P$ is fraction of components failing)

$$P = \int_{-\infty}^{\infty} f_{X_1}(x) F_{X_2}(x)\, dx$$

Now

$$F_{X_2}(x) = \int_{-\infty}^{x} f_{X_2}(y)\, dy$$

so that

$$P = \int_{-\infty}^{\infty} \int_{-\infty}^{x} f_{X_1}(x) f_{X_2}(y)\, dy\, dx \tag{7.3}$$

Equation (7.3) provides a means by which $P$ could be evaluated by numerical integration. Now let $y = x - z$. Then Eq. (7.3) becomes

$$P = \int_{-\infty}^{\infty} \int_{0}^{\infty} f_{X_1}(x) f_{X_2}(x - z)\, dz\, dx$$

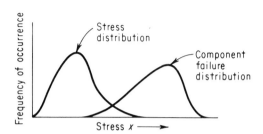

**Fig. 7.1.** Example of stress and component failure distributions.

which may be written

$$P = \int_0^\infty f(z) \, dz \qquad (7.4)$$

where

$$f(z) = \int_{-\infty}^\infty f_{X_1}(x) f_{X_2}(x - z) \, dx \qquad (7.5)$$

If $f_{X_1}(x)$ and $f_{X_2}(x)$ are normal distributions, $f(z)$ will be normal (see Ref. 3, p. 113). Thus, if we know the mean and standard distribution of $z$ and if $z$ is normally distributed, $P$ can be read from tables of the probability integral. To determine these quantities, we proceed as follows:

Let $m_{X_1}$, $\sigma_{X_1}$, and $m_{X_2}$, $\sigma_{X_2}$ be respectively the means and standard deviations of the distributions of $x$ given by $f_{X_1}(x)$ and $f_{X_2}(x)$. The mean of $f(z)$ is

$$m = \int_{-\infty}^\infty z f(z) \, dz \qquad (7.6)$$

Substitution of Eq. (7.5) into Eq. (7.6) yields

$$m = \int_{-\infty}^\infty \int_{-\infty}^\infty z f_{X_1}(x) f_{X_2}(x - z) \, dz \, dx$$

If we make the change of variable, $y = x - z$, we get

$$m = \int_{-\infty}^\infty \int_{-\infty}^\infty (x - y) f_{X_1}(x) f_{X_2}(y) \, dx \, dy \qquad (7.7)$$

Now

$$m_{X_1} = \int_{-\infty}^\infty x f_{X_1}(x) \, dx$$
$$\qquad (7.8)$$
$$m_{X_2} = \int_{-\infty}^\infty x f_{X_2}(x) \, dx$$

Evaluation of Eq. (7.7), making use of Eqs. (7.8), yields

$$m = m_{X_1} - m_{X_2} \qquad (7.9)$$

Since

$$\sigma^2 = \int_{-\infty}^\infty (z - m)^2 \, dz \qquad (7.10)$$

Eq. (7.10) becomes

$$\sigma^2 = \int_{-\infty}^{\infty} z^2 f(z) \, dz - m^2 = \alpha_2 - m^2 \qquad (7.11)$$

By analogy with Eq. (7.7)

$$\alpha_2 = \int_{-\infty}^{\infty} z^2 f(z) \, dz = \int_{-\infty}^{\infty} \int_{-\infty}^{\infty} (x - y)^2 f_{X_1}(x) f_{X_2}(y) \, dx \, dy \qquad (7.12)$$

Making use of

$$(\alpha_2)_{X_1} = \int_{-\infty}^{\infty} x^2 f_{X_1}(x) \, dx$$

$$(\alpha_2)_{X_2} = \int_{-\infty}^{\infty} x^2 f_{X_2}(x) \, dx$$

Eq. (7.12) becomes

$$\alpha_2 = (\alpha_2)_{X_1} - 2m_{X_1}m_{X_2} + (\alpha_2)_{X_2} \qquad (7.13)$$

Since by analogy to Eq. (7.11) we have

$$\sigma_{X_1}^2 = (\alpha_2)_{X_1} - m_{X_1}^2$$
$$\sigma_{X_2}^2 = (\alpha_2)_{X_2} - m_{X_2}^2$$

Eq. (7.13) becomes

$$\alpha_2 = \sigma_{X_1}^2 + m_{X_1}^2 - 2m_{X_1}m_{X_2} + \sigma_{X_2}^2 + m_{X_2}^2$$

which, after use of Eq. (7.11), reduces to

$$\sigma_2 = \sigma_{X_1}^2 + \sigma_{X_2}^2 \qquad (7.14)$$

(These results could also have been derived by recognizing that $f(z)$ by Eq. (7.5) is the frequency function for the distribution of the sum of two random variables, the applied stress $x_1$ and the negative of the component failure stress $-x_2$. Hence $m = m_{X_1} - m_{X_2}$ and $\sigma^2 = \sigma_{X_1}^2 + \sigma_{X_2}^2$.) Figure 7.2 shows how $f(z)$ might look.

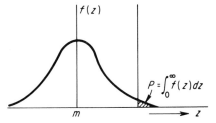

Fig. 7.2. Typical distribution function $f(z)$.

$P$ could be considered to be the probability of failure of a component in the array and ordinarily would be quite small. If such a set of events (failures) is distributed randomly in time at a rate $r$, the average frequency of failures is $rt$. The distribution that is defined by the probabilities $\pi_n$, where $\pi_n$ is the probability that $n$ events occur in an experiment at an average frequency $\lambda$, is the Poisson distribution,

$$\pi_n = \frac{\lambda^n}{n!} e^{-\lambda}$$

Hence the probability that no failures occur up to time $t$ is obtained by setting $\lambda = rt$ and $n = 0$ in the above to obtain

$$\pi_0 = e^{-rt} = R, \qquad t > 0 \tag{7.15}$$

The frequency function $f(t)$ for the distribution of single failures in time can be obtained from the fact that the probability of no failures up to time $t$ is one minus the probability of a single failure up to time $t$, or

$$R = 1 - \int_0^t f(t)\,dt = e^{-rt} \tag{7.16}$$

Solution of Eq. (7.16) subject to the condition that

$$\int_0^\infty f(t)\,dt = 1$$

yields

$$f(t) = re^{-rt}$$

The mean time to failure is

$$T = \int_0^\infty tf(t)\,dt = \frac{1}{r}$$

as determined in the first section.

$\pi_n$ evaluated with $\lambda = rt$ and $n \neq 0$ can be used to obtain expressions for the distributions of multiple failures. Furthermore, we have assumed that there is no replacement of failed components. Detailed consideration of these questions is beyond the scope of this book; however, it should be noted that in many cases it is sufficient to consider the distribution of single failures (see Sec. 2.4). Note also that for a multiple failure to occur, a single failure must have occurred.

The preceding demonstration is artificial in that it assumes that a component fails instantly if the applied stress exceeds a critical stress, and that it lasts forever if the applied stress is less than the critical stress. In actuality, an applied stress which is excessive will weaken a component so that it may fail at a later time, perhaps at a lower stress. This weakening may not show up immediately as a detectable electrical degradation.

Let us now consider a stress $x$ such as acceleration, which varies with time as in Fig. 7.3. The probability that the stress $X$ lies in an interval $dx$

Fig. 7.3.

is clearly equal to the fraction of time spent in that interval. Hence, if the stress is observed for a time $T$, and the frequency function of the stress is $f_X(x)$, then

$$f_X(x) \, dx = \frac{dt}{T} \tag{7.17}$$

Equation (7.17) can be used to find the distributions of many time-varying functions. For example, let a voltage $v$, considered as a random variable, vary sinusoidally with time such that

$$v = V_m \sin \omega t$$

We have by differentiation

$$dv = \omega V_m \cos \omega t \, dt$$

Hence

$$dt = \frac{dv}{\omega V_m \cos \omega t} = \frac{dv}{\omega V_m \sqrt{1 - (v/V_m)^2}}$$

is the amount of time spent in the interval $dv$ in the interval $T = \pi/\omega$. Hence

$$\frac{dt}{T} = \frac{dv}{\pi \sqrt{1 - (v/V_m)^2}}, \qquad -V_m \leq v \leq V_m$$

Thus, the frequency function for the distribution of a sinusoidally varying voltage is

$$f_V(x) = \frac{1}{\pi \sqrt{1 - (x/V_m)^2}}, \qquad -V_m \leq x \leq V_m$$

$$= 0, \qquad\qquad\qquad x < -V_m, x > V_m$$

The integral of this function from $x = -\infty$ to $x = +\infty$ is easily verified to be unity.

Now, assume that a large number of components are subjected to a random stress whose frequency function is $F_X(x)$. A given component has a parameter $p$ which degrades under stress such that the velocity of degradation is

$$\frac{dP}{dt} = h(X) \tag{7.18}$$

This parameter might be, for example, the strength of the bond between the whisker and semiconductor in a diode. By Eq. (7.18) we have assumed that the degradation rate depends only on the stress and not on the state of the parameter $p$. This may not always be a realistic assumption but in many cases is not too far from reality.

In a time $T$ the change in the parameter $p$ is, by integration of Eq. (7.18),

$$\Delta p = \int_0^T h(X) \, dt \tag{7.19}$$

and represents the sum of the amounts of degradation incurred in intervals $dt$. The substitution of Eq. (7.17) into Eq. (7.19) yields

$$\Delta p = T \int_{-\infty}^{\infty} h(x)f_X(x) \, dx = kT$$

where $k$ is a constant. Therefore, the total degradation is directly proportional to time of observation, a not too surprising result since most monotonic increasing functions have, as their simplest approximating function, the equation of a straight line. (Note that if $x$ is a constant stress $S$, $f_X(x) = \delta(x - S)$ and $p = Th(S)$ enabling the function $h(x)$ to be determined experimentally, the classical stress-failure relationship.)

It is now assumed that when the component has degraded a certain amount, $p_f$, it fails catastrophically, as a diode does when the whisker breaks loose from the semiconductor as a result of mechanical fatigue. However, we must assume that $p_f$ and $k$ are distributed, as no two components are likely to have the same sets of values.

Let the frequency functions for the distributions of $k$ and $p_f$ be $f_k(x)$ and $f_{p_f}(x)$ respectively. We would like to find $P \, (kT > p_f)$ which will give the fraction of components failing in a given observation time. Thus,

$$P(x < kT \leq x + dx) = \frac{1}{T} f_k\left(\frac{x}{T}\right) dx$$

If $k$ and $p_f$ are independent, their joint distribution is given by

$$P(x < kT \leq x + dx, y < p_f \leq y + dy) = \frac{1}{T} f_k\left(\frac{x}{T}\right) f_{p_f}(y) \, dx \, dy$$

Hence,

$$P(\Delta p > p_f) = \frac{1}{T} \int_{x=y}^{x=\infty} \int_{y=-\infty}^{\infty} f_k\left(\frac{x}{T}\right) f_{p_f}(y) \, dy \, dx \qquad (7.20)$$

Let $z = x - y$ so that Eq. (7.20) becomes

$$P(\Delta p > p_f) = \frac{1}{T} \int_{0}^{\infty} \int_{-\infty}^{\infty} f_k\left(\frac{x}{T}\right) f_{p_f}(x - z) \, dx \, dz \qquad (7.21)$$

(Note that Eq. (7.5), which has the same form as Eq. (7.21), could have been derived via the joint distribution as above.)

We will now approximately evaluate Eq. (7.21) for $T$ small. We have

$$\frac{1}{T} f_k\left(\frac{x}{T}\right) \cong \delta(x - \bar{k}T)$$

where $\delta(x)$ is the Dirac delta function, and $\bar{k}$ is the mean value of $k$, and

$$\delta(x) = 0, \quad x \neq 0; \qquad \int_{-\infty}^{\infty} \delta(x) \, dx = 1$$

Hence, Eq. (7.21) becomes

$$P(\Delta p > p_f) \cong \int_{0}^{\infty} f_{p_f}(\bar{k}T - z) \, dz$$

Letting $u = \bar{k}T - z$ yields

$$P(\Delta p > p_f) \cong \int_{-\infty}^{\bar{k}T} f_{p_f}(u) \, du \qquad (7.22)$$

which is the area under $f_{p_f}(u)$ up to the point $u = \bar{k}T$. Distributions of a component parameter illustrate the form shown in Fig. 7.4, when no attempt is made to eliminate weak components. That is, the values of the parameter (such as leakage current, resistance to shock, etc.) are clustered around a central value, as in Fig. 7.4, but the frequency function also

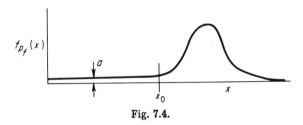

Fig. 7.4.

exhibits a tail stretching down almost uniformly to very low values of the parameter. Hence, Eq. (7.22) evaluated for $\bar{k}T < x_0$ would be

$$P(\Delta p > p_f) \cong a\bar{k}T$$

exhibiting a constant failure rate, $r = dP/dT = a\bar{k}$ up to about $T = x_0/\bar{k}$. A constant failure rate is characteristic of chance failures. From Eq. (7.22) it follows that the failure rate $r$ is given by

$$\frac{dP}{dT} \cong \bar{k}f_{p_f}(\bar{k}T) = r \qquad (7.23)$$

Thus, the failure rate as a function of time would be expected to have approximately the same shape as the curve in Fig. 7.4. The failure rate using such components often has the form shown in Fig. 7.5.

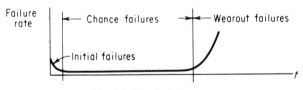

Fig. 7.5. Single failures.

When the equipment is turned on, the failure rate is high and then decreases rapidly to a constant value. It stays at this constant value for the design life of the equipment, at which time the parts start to wear out and cause an increase in the failure rate.

We have shown a possible mechanism for the presence of chance failures. However, we have assumed in the demonstration (see Fig. 7.4) that no components are so weak that because of stresses other than the one considered they could fail the moment the system is put into operation. These components would account for the high initial failures often observed.

A little reflection should now make it clear that the failure mechanism discussed in the first part of this section really applies to these initial failures rather than to the random failures.

This demonstration points the way for avoiding all but a few initial and chance failures. One should consider the following:

1. Determine all stresses that affect component life.
2. Weed out all components that could fail quickly at the maximum stress; i.e., eliminate all tails on component stress-failure distributions.

In systems where this has been done to some extent, chance failure rates have been reduced to very low values.

## 7.3  WEAR-OUT FAILURES

The previous discussion was concerned primarily with the chance or catastrophic failures, that is, failures that occur rather quickly when a stress limit is exceeded and which have been shown to be special instances of wear-out failures. This stress-failure mechanism provides one with a means for improving component reliability:

1. Determine the stress that causes the component failure.
2. Determine the mechanism by means of which the stress causes the component failure.
3. Modify the component manufacturing process and/or the component selection method and/or the environmental conditions in which the component is used so that the desired reliability is achieved. For example, 100 per cent testing may be required.

The classical wear-out failures are caused by *gradual* changes in component characteristics with time, such as drift in resistance value, etc. The question of these wear-out failures is better handled by designing for reliability and will be considered in Chap. 8. We will also discuss in the same chapter two methods of design techniques for reliability:

1. *Worst-case design*, in which the probability of failure due to wear-out is made to be at zero over the design life.
2. *Statistical design*, in which the probability of failure due to wear-out is allowed to be at an acceptable nonzero level at the end of the design life.

Worst-case design is usually safer, because sufficient margins exist in the system so that small errors occurring in design do not produce an inoperative system. The execution of a successful statistical design, on the other hand, requires engineering of the highest quality—and is therefore expensive—because a slight error, that would escape notice in a worst-case designed system, may increase to an unacceptable level the probability of failure.

For a worst-case or statistical design it is necessary to have data on the expected behavior of components during the lifetime of the system. However, a system may have a designed life of, say, ten years, and it is clearly impractical in most (but not all) cases to conduct life-tests for that period of time. As another example, to accumulate data that will justify stating that the catastrophic failure rate of a component is 0.01 per cent per 1000 hours (better than this was required in LARC for some components) requires at least 10 million component hours (component hours = number of components $\times$ hours on test). Such a life-test is difficult, if not impossible, to carry out; and for several reasons the results would have dubious value. One reason is that a component manufacturer must frequently modify his process to maintain a high yield, since he himself may be unable to control all the parameters in the process and in the raw materials. The components used in the system are often different from those that are life-tested. Another reason is the fact that the periodic examination of the components during the life-test can, and usually does, affect the measured results. To determine the effect of such periodic examinations requires much the same effort as required to determine the component life characteristics. Thus, such examinations might as well be used in the first place, thereby dispensing with a long, expensive life-test.

The question of predicting the life behavior of components can and has been successfully handled by

1. Determining the mechanism by which the environment causes the component to fail or change value.
2. Determining theoretical or empirical expressions for the component characteristics that change as a function of time and of the stress (such as temperature and humidity).
3. Conducting accelerated life-tests to obtain data so that these expressions can have their unknown constants determined and then can be used to predict life behavior.

## 7.4 COMPONENTS AND TESTING

Less error is made in design if the component characteristics that are measured are those that directly affect circuit performance. For example, in the case of semiconductor diodes used for logic circuits these characteristics are:

(a) The static forward drop at the current at which it will be used.
(b) The reverse leakage at the reverse voltage at which it will be used.
(c) The forward transient turn-on behavior at the operating conditions.
(d) The turn-off behavior at the operating conditions.

A simple tester for static forward drop is shown in Fig. 7.6. $V_2$ and $R$ provide the current $I$. Diode $D$ returned to $-V_1$ safeguards the operator and the vacuum-tube volt meter from high voltages and also avoids the possibility that the test diode will be damaged when inserted by having to discharge stray capacitances charged to high voltages. Such a tester is quickly and easily used, allowing several hundred diodes to be tested in an hour. It is suitable for both laboratory and production testing.

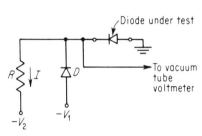

**Fig. 7.6.** Static forward drop tester.

Several kinds of tests, in the order of increasing complexity and expense of operation, are:

(a) "Go-no go" tests.
(b) Tests requiring that a meter reading be recorded.
(c) Tests requiring that a dial be adjusted for a specific meter reading, after which the dial reading is recorded.
(d) Tests requiring several readings.
(e) Tests requiring several readings after a dial adjustment.
(f) Tests requiring the reading of an oscilloscope trace.

Tests (a) through (c) are usually acceptable as production tests. However, tests (d) through (f) are usually confined to laboratory tests. It is sometimes acceptable, however, to use an oscilloscope as a null-indicating instrument in a production test.

The tester shown in Fig. 7.6 is satisfactory for both laboratory or production testing. A similar tester for diode leakages is shown in Fig. 7.7. $R$, $V_2$, and $D$ serve to limit the current through the meter if the diode under test is shorted or put in backwards. The switch can make it difficult for the operator to have his hands on electrified portions of the circuit.

An example of how a laboratory tester can be modified for production testing occurs in the case of diode reverse recovery. The laboratory tester and waveforms obtained are shown in Figs. 7.8 and 7.9. The resistors in the tester must be carefully selected high-frequency resistors, and the wiring must be very carefully laid out to minimize parasitic reactances. Disadvantages of such a tester for production use include the following.
(1) Oscilloscope presentation requires the measurement of a time at a given

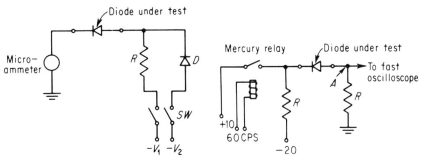

Fig. 7.7. Reverse leakage tester.    **Fig. 7.8.** Laboratory diode-recovery test circuit.

voltage (two quantities). (2) Bandwidth requirements are extremely severe, requiring an expensive oscilloscope.

A preferable scheme would consist of converting the time measurement to a voltage pulse measurement which could be made on a peak-reading VTVM or an oscilloscope. In the case of fast diodes, we may assume that the actual recovery curve is approximately an exponential. We then can measure the area which would be proportional to $T_R$. With high-speed diodes, measurement of the area amounts to measuring the charge extracted. A circuit for making such a measurement is shown in Fig. 7.10. Typical waveforms at various points are shown in Fig. 7.11.

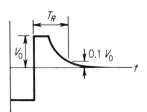

Fig. **7.9.** Ideal waveforms at point $A$ in Fig. 7.8.

Since the area under a pulse is multiplied by the low-frequency gain $A(0)$ of the amplifier, the waveform at $B$ will have the same area as the waveform at $A$. The diode $D$ in the clipper is a fast diode selected from the kind being tested. The clipper clips off the waveform $C$ and sends it to the integrator. Since it is the area under the total waveform that is preserved and not the area under the clipped waveform, the area under waveform $C$ differs from the stored charge by approximately the shaded area. The integrator produces a pulse whose amplitude is proportional to the area under pulse $C$.

Such a tester must be calibrated by measuring $T_R$ for a group of diodes on the laboratory tester, measuring $V$ on the production tester, and plotting a scatter diagram as shown in Fig. 7.12.

In a particular case of a tester of diodes whose recovery times were of the order of 7 nsec, the spread in the scatter diagram was found to be of the order of 1 nsec, as shown in Fig. 7.12.

In the case of transistor testing, one is interested in knowing, for switching applications, the following:

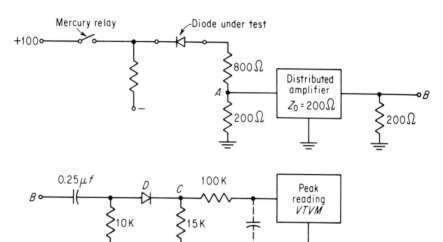

Fig. 7.10. Production diode-storage tester.

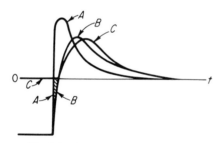

Fig. 7.11. Waveforms $[A(0) = 1]$.

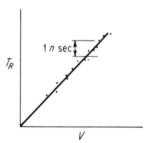

Fig. 7.12. Typical scatter diagram for diode reverse recovery.

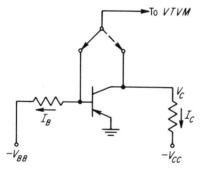

Fig. 7.13. Basic circuit for measuring ON characteristics.

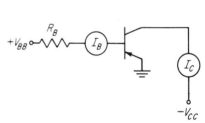

Fig. 7.14. Basic circuit for measuring OFF characteristics.

1. *ON characteristics.* Collector voltage and base-to-emitter voltage at a given base and collector current.

2. *OFF characteristics.* Collector and base currents at given base and collector voltages.

3. *Turn-on characteristics.* Rise time to a specified collector current or voltage for a given base-current step.

4. *Turn-off characteristics.* Storage time as a result of a given base-current change with a given collector and initial base current. The fall time can often be deduced from the turn-on characteristics.

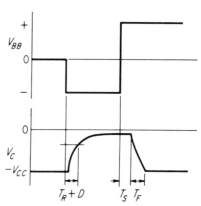

**Fig. 7.15.** Nature of turn-on and turn-off measurements.

Basic circuits for measurements 1 and 2 are shown in Figs. 7.13 and 7.14. Operator, meter, and device protective circuits are not shown.

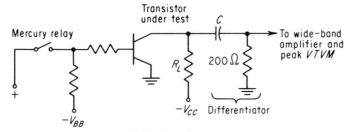

**Fig. 7.16.** Rise-time tester.

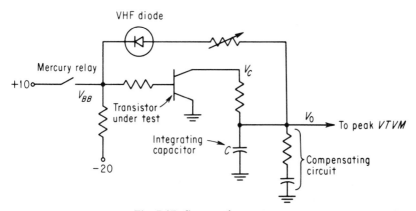

**Fig. 7.17.** Storage-time tester.

The circuit of Fig. 7.13 can be used to make laboratory measurements of the turn-on and turn-off characteristics if $V_{BB}$ is replaced by suitable pulsed sources. This requires oscilloscope measurements of the sort shown in Fig. 7.15.

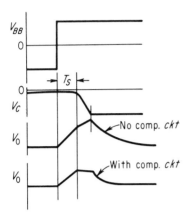

**Fig. 7.18.** Waveforms for storage-time tester.

When $D$ is small compared to $T_R$, we may measure $T_R$ and $D$ by differentiating the leading edge of the collector waveform and by reading the amplitude of the resultant pulse on a peak-reading VTVM. A test circuit using this principle which gave measurements to an accuracy of better than five per cent for $T_R + D$ in the vicinity of 10 nsec is shown in Fig. 7.16. Calibration by a scatter diagram was required periodically.

A storage-time tester which operates on the principle of integration of a pulse of constant amplitude whose width is proportional to the storage time $T_s$ is shown in Fig. 7.17.

## 7.5 THE ACCUMULATION OF COMPONENT DATA FOR DESIGN

Testers of the type previously shown can be used for the accumulation of data on components for circuit-design purposes. As an example of the considerations involved, consider the results of the measurement of $T_R$ (storage time) for a batch of diodes. These results may conveniently and quickly be presented in the form of distributions (not frequency functions since they are not normalized) of the form shown in Fig. 7.19. The ad-

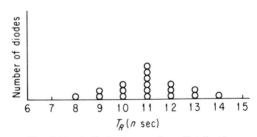

**Fig. 7.19.** A diode storage-time distribution.

vantage of such a data presentation is that no calculation is required and it can be plotted directly from the data or as the data are taken.

We may ask whether or not we may assume that $T_R < 15$ nsec for all diodes on the basis of the above data. The answer is generally no, because such distributions vary from batch to batch and to improve the data we should collect the data over a period of time. Suppose now that the cumulative distribution of many batches appears as in Fig. 7.20.

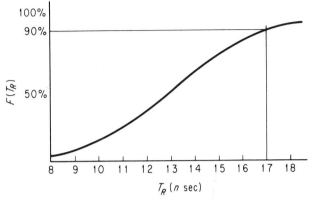

**Fig. 7.20.** Cumulative distribution over many batches.

We may ask if 17 nsec is adequate for design if we throw away 10 per cent (AQL). The answer is still no, as this figure does not include aging. If the effect of aging is as shown in Fig. 7.21, we may use 17 nsec for a design value.

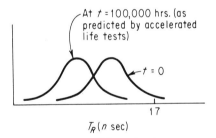

**Fig. 7.21.** Effect of aging.

## 7.6 CHECKLIST FOR STRESSES

The following stresses have been found to significantly affect the characteristics of solid-state components.

1. Heat
2. Voltage
3. Current
4. Temperature

5. Temperature cycles
6. Shock and vibration
7. Mechanical stresses such as tension
8. Humidity
9. Nuclear radiation
10. Electric fields
11. Magnetic fields
12. Light and electromagnetic radiation
13. Chemical vapors

## REFERENCES

1. Blanton, H. E., and R. M. Jacobs, "A Survey of Techniques for Analysis and Prediction of Equipment Reliability," *I.R.E. Transactions on Reliability and Quality Control,* **RQC-11**:2 (July 1962), 18–35.

2. Carhart, R. R., "A Survey of the Current Status of the Electronic Reliability Problem," The RAND Corporation, RM-1131, 14 Aug. 1953.

3. Cramér, H., *The Elements of Probability Theory and Some of Its Applications* (New York: John Wiley & Sons, 1955).

4. Goode, H. H., and R. E. Machol, *System Engineering* (New York: McGraw-Hill Book Co., 1957).

5. Gray, H. J., "On a Random Failure Mechanism," *Proceedings of the I.R.E.,* **50**:8 (August 1962), 1836.

6. Henney, K., and C. Walsh, *Electronic Components Handbook* (New York: McGraw-Hill Book Co., 1957).

7. Lusser, Robert M., 22 pamphlets on the Reliability of Missiles, Army Rocket and Guided Missile Agency, Redstone Arsenal, Alabama.

## PROBLEMS

1. A system has the following components, with quantities, and failure rates:

| Component | Number in system | Failure rate (Per cent per 1000 hr) |
| --- | --- | --- |
| Resistors | 40,000 | 0.008 |
| Capacitors | 10,000 | 0.01 |
| Diodes | 30,000 | 0.01 |
| Transistors | 10,000 | 0.04 |
| Connections | 70,000 | 0.001 |

Assuming independence and no replacements, compute the mean time to failure for the system and the probability that no system failures will occur in an eight-hour period if the components are in "series" (chain reliability).

2. Show that if a pulse is passed through an amplifier whose gain-frequency characteristic is $A(\omega)$, the areas of the input and output pulses

$$\sigma_i = \int_{-\infty}^{\infty} v_i \, dt, \qquad \sigma_o = \int_{-\infty}^{\infty} v_o \, dt$$

are related by the expression

$$\sigma_o = |A(0)|\sigma_i$$

This result has been applied in component testing to the amplification of areas under waveforms.

# 8

# CIRCUIT DESIGN

# AND OPTIMIZATION

It will be assumed that the kind of logic to be performed has been decided upon (Chaps. 2–4) and the circuit configuration has been chosen (Chap. 5) and has been analyzed to the point that the dependence of the performance on the component characteristics is known (Chap. 6). It will also be assumed that the component characteristics have been determined throughout the expected range of the operating conditions (Chap. 7). Circuit design will be started with the equations of the circuit as obtained by analysis; these may be empirical in nature, and they may not provide all the information needed for a unique design. Thus additional relations must be obtained from system requirements. It may be that the circuit performance must be optimized in some way: for example, it may be desirable to minimize the product of cost and delay in a logic circuit. If a speed specification is furnished, the circuit will then be designed for minimum cost. Such a circuit design procedure yields a unique result.

One of the requirements furnished by a complete specification is the reliability level that should be achieved. *Worst-case design* is intended to produce a circuit design in which the probability of wear-out failures at the end of the design life is zero. *Statistical design* is intended to produce a circuit design in which the probability of wear-out failures at the end of the design life is a small but acceptable quantity.

Both kinds of design technique will be illustrated by showing their application to a circuit in which the design equations are very simple. A realistic example of worst-case design and optimization will then be considered.

## 8.1  WORST-CASE DESIGN; DIODE CIRCUIT

Consider the diode logic circuit in Fig. 8.1. $C_1$, $C_2$, and $C_3$ have values as indicated and are assumed to be fixed. However, they can be considered to

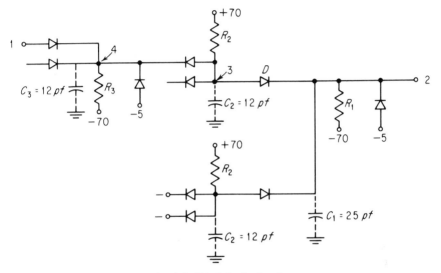

**Fig. 8.1.** Diode logic circuit.

be statistically distributed. The problem will be idealized to simplify calculations and to better illustrate principles.

*Assumptions:*

1. Diodes are ideal (no leakage, no drop, no storage effects).
2. All inductances are negligible.
3. Supply voltages having the same values come from one point; i.e., +70 feeds two places, thus these two appearances of +70 are assumed to be identical.
4. All resistors have a tolerance of ±5 per cent.
5. All voltages are within ±5 per cent of the nominal value.
6. In Fig. 8.1, point 2 swings between −5 ± 5 per cent and 0. Rise and fall times should not exceed 100 nsec at point 2 for a step input at point 1 (Fig. 8.1).

*Fall time (max)* (point 3 in Fig. 8.1 falls at the same rate as point 2). The fall time is given by

$$T_f = \frac{C_1 \Delta V_2}{I}$$

where

$$I = \frac{E_1 - \Delta V_2/2}{R_1}$$

The determination of the values of the parameters which yield the maximum value of $T_f$ is a problem in the determination of extremes and usually cannot be solved by the calculus or similar techniques. In this case, the problem can be solved as follows.

By inspection,

$$T_f^+ = \frac{C_1 \Delta V_2^+}{I^-} \tag{8.1a}$$

$$I^- = \frac{E_1^- - \Delta V_2^-/2}{R_1^+} \tag{8.1b}$$

However, $\Delta V_2$ cannot be at both extremes of its range ($\Delta V_2^+$, $\Delta V_2^-$) simultaneously; the same value of $\Delta V_2$ must be used in Eqs. (8.1a) and (8.1b). Examination of Eqs. (8.1a) and (8.1b) shows that $T_f$ is a monotonically increasing function of $\Delta V_2$. Hence, the maximum value of $T_f$ occurs when $\Delta V_2$ has its maximum value.

Therefore

$$T_f^+ = \frac{C_1 \Delta V_2^+}{I^-} \tag{8.1a$'$}$$

where

$$I^- = \frac{E_1^- - \Delta V_2^+/2}{R_1^+} \tag{8.1b$'$}$$

It is not always possible to solve such a problem by inspection. When such cases occur, one must usually make trial designs for the multiplicity of possibilities and choose among them using engineering judgment. In this example, this would correspond to finding $R_1^+$ for several values of $\Delta V_2$ within its permissible range of variation and choosing the *smallest* value of $R_1^+$ so obtained (the calculus can be of occasional assistance here).

Proceeding and using Eq. (8.1a$'$) one will have

$$T_f^+ = \frac{C_1 \Delta V_2^+}{I^-} = \frac{25 \times 10^{-12} \times 5(1.05)}{I^-} = 10^{-7}$$

Solution of the equation above yields

$$I^- = 1.312 \text{ ma}$$

From Eq. (8.1b$'$)

$$I^- = \frac{0.95 \times 70 - 1.05 \times 5 \times 0.5}{R_1 \times 1.05} = \frac{63.9}{1.05R_1}$$

Hence

$$R_1 = \frac{63.9}{1.05 \times 1.312 \times 10^{-3}} = \underline{46.3 \text{ K}} \qquad \text{(nominal value)}$$

*Rise time (max), equivalent circuit* (Fig. 8.2). For 0.1 $\mu$sec rise time,

$$I^- = \frac{C \,\Delta V_4^+}{T_R^+} = \frac{37 \times 10^{-12} \times 5.25}{10^{-7}} = 1.943 \text{ ma}$$

(from $T_R^+ = C \,\Delta V_4^+ / I^-$). Hence

$$1.943 + 1.61 = (I_2)_{min} = 3.55 \text{ ma}$$

$$R_2^+ = \frac{66.5 - [0 + (-5.25)]/2}{3.55 \times 10^{-3}} = \frac{69.1}{3.55 \times 10^{-3}} = 19.4 \text{ K}$$

$$R_2 = \frac{19.4}{1.05} = \underline{18.5 \text{ K}}$$

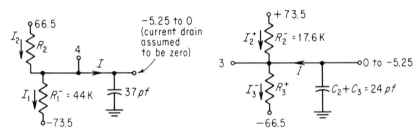

Fig. 8.2.

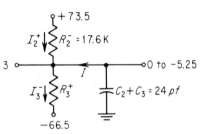

Fig. 8.3.

*Fall time (max), equivalent circuit* (Fig. 8.3). Diode $D$ is assumed to have zero voltage across it during the fall time (also zero current through it).

$$I^- = \frac{C \,\Delta V_3^+}{T_F^+} = \frac{24 \times 10^{-12} \times 5.25}{10^{-7}} = 1.26 \text{ ma} \qquad \left(\text{from } T_f^+ = \frac{C \,\Delta V_3^+}{I^-}\right)$$

$$I_2^+ = \frac{73.5 - [0 + (-5.25)]/2}{17.6} = \frac{76.1}{17.6} = 4.32 \text{ ma}$$

$$I_3^- = 4.32 + 1.26 = 5.58 \text{ ma}$$

$$R_3^+ = \frac{66.5 + [0 + (-5.25)]/2}{5.58 \times 10^{-3}} = \frac{63.9}{5.58 \times 10^{-3}} = 11.43 \text{ K}$$

$$R_3 = \frac{11.43}{1.05} = \underline{10.9 \text{ K}}$$

(Current required from the driving circuit can be determined by the rise-time condition at point 4 in Fig. 8.1.)

*Summary:*

$$R_1 = 46.3\text{K}, \qquad V_1 = +70\text{v}$$
$$R_2 = 18.5\text{K}, \qquad -V_2 = -70\text{v}$$
$$R_3 = 10.9\text{K}, \qquad -V_3 = -5\text{v}$$

## 8.2  PROBABILITY ANALYSIS*

Since the above design was a worst-case design, the probability that the rise and fall times at point 2 in Fig. 8.1 exceed 100 nsec is zero. Such a design may be overly costly in that performance may have been sacrificed for excessive reliability with regard to wear-out failures. The point of interest here is to find out how to design a circuit so that the probability of wear-out failure at the end of the design life is a small nonzero quantity. The advantage of this type of design is that a minimum of overdesign exists such that increased speed or efficiency can sometimes be obtained from a circuit at no additional cost or a circuit with a given speed can be produced at less cost since the components can be allowed to have greater parameter tolerances. Factors which work to increase the design cost include the fact that statistical design requires more effort and more knowledge about the component parameter distributions: in purchasing the components, one may have to specify the shapes of their distributions, so that in some cases the cost of the item is increased. Furthermore, in worst-case design there may be sufficient margins to cover up a design error which, if it occurred in a statistical design, would have disastrous consequences. When the number of circuit parameters that affect its performance is of the order of two or three, there is little to be gained from statistical design. However, the improvements in operation and cost increase as the number of circuit parameters increases.

The first approach will be that of making a probability analysis of the diode circuit just designed.

The probability will now be determined that the rise and fall times will exceed some value less than 100 nsec.

An equation is needed of the form:

$$\delta T = \hat{a}_1 \, \delta V_1 + \hat{a}_2 \, \delta V_2 + \cdots + \hat{b}_1 \, \delta R_1 + \hat{b}_2 \, \delta R_2 + \cdots$$

in which $\delta T$ is expressed as a sum of random variables. $\delta T$, $\delta V_1$, etc. are the deviations of the respective quantities from some reference values (such as their means). The distribution of $\delta T$ will then be obtained (Appendix II). The $\hat{a}$'s and $\hat{b}$'s can be obtained from equations for the rise and fall times.

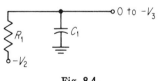

Fig. 8.4.

## 8.3  DERIVATION OF EQUATIONS FOR RISE AND FALL TIMES

*Point 2 fall time* (Fig. 8.4).

$$T_{f2} = \frac{C_1 \, \Delta E}{I} = \frac{C_1 V_3 R_1}{V_2 - (V_3/2)}, \qquad V_2 V_3 > 0$$

* This development was taken in part from Ref. 4.

*Point 2 rise time* (Fig. 8.5).

$$T_{r2} = (C_1 + C_2)\frac{\Delta E}{I} = \frac{(C_1 + C_2)V_3}{-\dfrac{V_2 - (V_3/2)}{R_1} + \dfrac{V_1 + (V_3/2)}{R_2}}$$

$$= \frac{(C_1 + C_2)V_3 R_1 R_2}{R_1[V_1 + (V_3/2)] - R_2[V_2 - (V_3/2)]}, \qquad V_1, V_2, V_3 > 0$$

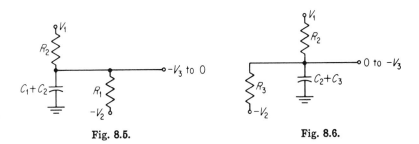

Fig. 8.5.          Fig. 8.6.

*Point 3 fall time* (Fig. 8.6).

$$T_{f3} = (C_2 + C_3)\frac{\Delta E}{I} = \frac{(C_2 + C_3)V_3 R_2 R_3}{[V_2 - (V_3/2)]R_2 - R_3[V_1 + (V_3/2)]}$$

$T_{r2}$ will be considered as being a representative quantity for illustrative purposes.

$$T_{r2_{nom}} = \frac{37 \times 10^{-12} \times 5 \times 46.3 \times 18.5 \times 10^6}{46.3 \times 10^3(70 + 2.5) - 18.5 \times 10^3(70 - 2.5)}$$

$$= 75 \text{ nsec}$$

Changes due to changes of variables can be obtained by evaluating partial derivatives or by experiment. The latter is often easier whereas the former is sometimes difficult; judgment is required in choosing the method to be used.

That is,

$$\delta T_{r2} = \frac{\partial T_{r2}}{\partial R_2}\delta R_2 + \frac{\partial T_{r2}}{\partial R_3}\delta R_3 + \frac{\partial T_{r2}}{\partial V_1}\delta V_1 + \frac{\partial T_{r2}}{\partial V_2}\delta V_2 + \frac{\partial T_{r2}}{\partial V_3}\delta V_3$$

which are the leading terms of a Taylor series expansion of $\delta T_{r2}$ in terms of $\delta R_2$, $\partial R_3$, $\delta V_1$, $\delta V_2$, and $\delta V_3$. This expression is an approximation to the dependence of $\delta T_{r2}$ on the circuit parameters and is obtained because it is quite difficult to work with the actual function. (See Ref. 5 at the end of this chapter.)

The partial derivatives are:

$$\frac{\partial T_{r2}}{\partial V_1} = -\frac{(C_1 + C_2)V_3R_1^2R_2}{D^2} = -1.64 \times 10^{-9} \text{ sec/volt}$$

$$\frac{\partial T_{r2}}{\partial V_2} = \frac{(C_1 + C_2)V_3R_1R_2^2}{D^2} = 0.657 \times 10^{-9} \text{ sec/volt}$$

$$\frac{\partial T_{r2}}{\partial V_3} = (C_1 + C_2)R_1R_2 \frac{R_1V_1 - R_2V_2}{D^2} = 13.8 \times 10^{-9} \text{ sec/volt}$$

$$\frac{\partial T_{r2}}{\partial R_1} = -(C_1 + C_2)V_3R_2^2 \frac{V_2 - (V_3/2)}{D^2} = -0.959 \times 10^{-12} \text{ sec/ohm}$$

$$\frac{\partial T_{r2}}{\partial R_2} = (C_1 + C_2)V_3R_1^2 \frac{V_1 + (V_3/2)}{D^2} = 6.44 \times 10^{-12} \text{ sec/ohm}$$

$$D = R_1\left(V_1 + \frac{V_3}{2}\right) - R_2\left(V_2 - \frac{V_3}{2}\right) = 2.11 \times 10^6 \text{ volt ohms}$$

Thus (5 per cent change):

|  |  | $\delta T_{r2}$ |
|---|---|---|
| $\delta V_1 = 3.5$ | Due to $\delta V_1$: | 5.74 nsec |
| $\delta V_2 = 3.5$ | Due to $\delta V_2$: | 2.30 nsec |
| $\delta V_3 = 0.25$ | Due to $\delta V_3$: | 3.45 nsec |
| $\delta R_1 = 2.32$ K | Due to $\delta R_1$: | 2.22 nsec |
| $\delta R_2 = 0.925$ K | Due to $\delta R_2$: | 5.96 nsec |
|  |  | 19.67 nsec |

The total change in $T_{r2}$ should be the worst-case value of 25 nsec but works out to be about 20 nsec. The difference is due to the neglect of the higher-order terms in the Taylor series expansion of $T_{r2}$. This can be understood by referring to a plot of a function which depends on a variable in a nonlinear manner (Fig. 8.7).

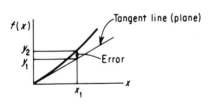

Fig. 8.7.

The actual value of $f(x)$ at $x_1$ is $y_2$. The Taylor series approximation gives $y_1$. If the function is approximated by the chordal line

$$f_c(x) = x\left(\frac{y_2}{x_1}\right)$$

then $f(x) \cong f_c(x)$, $0 \le x \le x_1$ for most functions of interest. It can easily be shown that the chordal line approximation* is very nearly

$$\delta y = \tfrac{1}{2}[f'(0) + f'(x_1)] \, \delta x$$

Applying this to the problem requires the evaluation of the partial derivatives at $T_{r2} = 100$ nsec. These are

$$\frac{\partial T_{r2}}{\partial V_1} = -2.64 \times 10^{-9} \text{ sec/volt} \qquad \frac{\partial T_{r2}}{\partial R_1} = -1.872 \times 10^{-12} \text{ sec/ohm}$$

$$\frac{\partial T_{r2}}{\partial V_2} = 1.162 \times 10^{-9} \text{ sec/volt} \qquad \frac{\partial T_{r2}}{\partial R_2} = 9.58 \times 10^{-12} \text{ sec/ohm}$$

$$\frac{\partial T_{r2}}{\partial V_3} = 18 \times 10^{-9} \text{ sec/volt}$$

The mean values of the partial derivatives are

$$\left(\overline{\frac{\partial T_{r2}}{\partial V_1}}\right) = -2.14 \times 10^{-9} \text{ sec/volt} \qquad \left(\overline{\frac{\partial T_{r2}}{\partial V_3}}\right) = 15.9 \times 10^{-9} \text{ sec/volt}$$

* The derivation of this chordal line approximation is as follows:

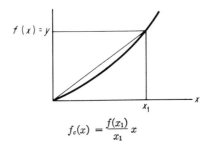

$f(x) = y$

$x_1$

Straight line: 
$$f_c(x) = \frac{f(x_1)}{x_1} x$$

Let $f(x) = f(0) + \dfrac{f'(0)}{1!} x + \dfrac{f''(0)}{2!} x^2 + \cdots$. Then

$$f(0) = 0; \qquad \therefore \quad f(x) \cong f'(0)x + \frac{f''(0)}{2} x^2$$

$$f'(x) = f'(0) + f''(0)x$$

$$f'(x_1) = f'(0) + f''(0)x_1$$

$$f(x_1) = f'(0)x_1 + \frac{f''(0)}{2} x_1^2$$

$$\therefore \quad f_c(x) = \left[ f'(0) + \frac{f''(0)}{2} x_1 \right] x$$

$$= \left[ f'(0) + \frac{f'(x_1) - f'(0)}{2} \right] x$$

$$f_c(x) = \frac{1}{2} [f'(0) + f'(x_1)] x$$

$$\left(\overline{\frac{\partial T_{r2}}{\partial V_2}}\right) = 0.910 \times 10^{-9} \text{ sec/volt} \qquad \left(\overline{\frac{\partial T_{r2}}{\partial R_1}}\right) = -1.416 \times 10^{-12} \text{ sec/ohm}$$

$$\left(\overline{\frac{\partial T_{r2}}{\partial R_2}}\right) = 8.01 \times 10^{-12} \text{ sec/ohm}$$

Thus (5 per cent changes in $V$'s and $R$'s)

$$\delta T_{r2}$$

|                     |            |
| ------------------- | ---------- |
| Due to $\delta V_1$:  | 7.49 nsec  |
| Due to $\delta V_2$:  | 3.19 nsec  |
| Due to $\delta V_3$:  | 3.98 nsec  |
| Due to $\delta R_1$:  | 3.28 nsec  |
| Due to $\delta R_2$:  | 7.42 nsec  |

25.36 nsec (should be 25 nsec)

The numbers obtained will be corrected in the following way. For the chordal approximation the coefficients will be multiplied by $25/25.36$ and for the Taylor approximation by $25/19.67$ to get

$$\delta T_{r2} = -2.085 \, \delta V_1 + 0.835 \, \delta V_2 + 17.55 \, \delta V_3 - 1.218 \, \delta R_1 + 8.19 \, \delta R_2 \text{ nsec} \tag{8.2}$$

for the adjusted Taylor approximation and

$$\delta T_{r2} = -2.11 \, \delta V_1 + 0.897 \, \delta V_2 + 15.7 \, \delta V_3 - 1.398 \, \delta R_1 + 7.9 \, \delta R_2 \text{ nsec} \tag{8.3}$$

for the adjusted chordal approximation. In these two equations, $\delta V$ is in volts and $\delta R$ is in kilohms.

One point which should be mentioned here has to do with the advisability of treating the supply-voltage deviations as independent random variables. They can be so treated if they arise from the deterioration of circuit components such as those in the power-supply voltage regulators. However, in the absence of such regulators, or if the chief source of voltage variation arises from voltage drops and other load-dependent disturbances in the power-supply system, the voltage deviations could not be considered as independent random variables and possibly not even as random variables. In this case, the partial derivatives with respect to the other component values would have to be evaluated with the supply voltages at the worst-case limits in order to include their effects.

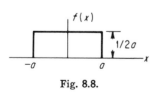

Fig. 8.8.

However, in order to illustrate a procedure it will be assumed that the

$\delta V$ and $\delta R$ are uniformly distributed as in Fig. 8.8 and are independent random variables. Equations (8.2) or (8.3) can be written

$$X = X_1 + X_2 + X_3 + X_4 + X_5 \qquad (8.4)$$

where the $X_i$ are given in Table 8.1. The $a$'s are the limiting values of the $X_i$ and are in nsec (Table 8.2). $a_1$ is calculated as follows for the adjusted Taylor approximation:

**TABLE 8.1**

|        | Adjusted Taylor | Adjusted chordal |
|--------|-----------------|------------------|
| $X_1$  | $-2.085\,\delta V_1$ | $-2.11\,\delta V_1$ |
| $X_2$  | $0.835\,\delta V_2$  | $0.897\,\delta V_2$ |
| $X_3$  | $17.55\,\delta V_3$  | $15.7\,\delta V_3$ |
| $X_4$  | $-1.218\,\delta R_1$ | $-1.398\,\delta R_1$ |
| $X_5$  | $8.19\,\delta R_2$   | $7.9\,\delta R_2$ |

**TABLE 8.2**

|        | Adjusted Taylor | Adjusted chordal |
|--------|-----------------|------------------|
| $a_1$  | 7.3    | 7.38 |
| $a_2$  | 2.92   | 3.14 |
| $a_3$  | 4.39   | 3.93 |
| $a_4$  | 2.82   | 3.24 |
| $a_5$  | 7.58   | 7.31 |
| Total  | 25 nsec | 25 nsec |

$$a_1 = 2.085\,\delta V_1 = 2.085 \times 0.05 \times 70 = 7.3 \text{ nsec}$$

From Appendix II, the piecewise polynomial (approximating from the right) is

$$g(x, x_0, k) = \frac{(x_0 - x)^k}{k!}, \qquad x < x_0$$

$$g(x, x_0, k) = 0, \qquad\qquad x > x_0$$

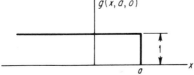

$g(x, a, 0)$ is shown in the accompanying figure. Hence for the uniform distribution,

$$f(x) = \frac{1}{2a} [g(x, a, 0) - g(x, -a, 0)]$$

The characteristic function of this distribution is from the pair (Appendix II)

$$g(x, x_0, k) \longleftrightarrow \frac{e^{jtx_0}}{(jt)^{k+1}}$$

$$f(x) \longleftrightarrow \phi(t) \tag{8.5}$$

$$\phi(t) = \frac{1}{2a} \left[ \frac{e^{jta}}{jt} - \frac{e^{-jta}}{jt} \right]$$

The characteristic function given by Eq. (8.5) suffices for any of the variables $X_i$ if the proper $a_i$ is taken from Table 8.2. Now if the $X_i$ are treated as independent random variables, the characteristic function of the distribution of $X$ and, hence, $\delta T_{r2}$ is the *product* of the characteristic functions of the individual distributions given by Eq. (8.5). This is

$$\phi(t) = \frac{1}{2^5 a_1 a_2 a_3 a_4 a_5} [e^{jta_1} - e^{-jta_1}][e^{jta_2} - e^{-jta_2}]$$

$$\cdots [e^{jta_5} - e^{-jta_5}] \frac{1}{(jt)^5} \tag{8.6}$$

The critical points of the distribution of $T_{r2}$ are at

$$\pm a_1 \pm a_2 \pm a_3 \pm a_4 \pm a_5 \tag{8.7}$$

Of interest are those near the maximum value of $\delta T_{r2}$ of 100 nsec. The first few from the right are given in Table 8.3 calculated from Eq. (8.7). Mul-

**TABLE 8.3**

| Critical point | Adjusted Taylor | Adjusted chordal | Calculated form (adjusted Taylor only) |
|---|---|---|---|
| $x_1$ | 25 nsec | 25 nsec | $a_1 + a_2 + a_3 + a_4 + a_5$ |
| $x_2$ | 19.36 nsec | 18.72 nsec | $a_1 + a_2 + a_3 - a_4 + a_5$ |
| $x_3$ | 19.16 nsec | 18.52 nsec | $a_1 - a_2 + a_3 + a_4 + a_5$ |
| $x_4$ | 16.22 nsec | 17.14 nsec | $a_1 + a_2 - a_3 + a_4 + a_5$ |

tiplying out Eq. (8.6) and substituting the values from Table 8.3 yields Taylor:

$$\phi_X(t) = \frac{1.563 \times 10^{-5}}{(jt)^5} [e^{j25t} - e^{j19.36t} - e^{j19.16t} - e^{j16.22t} + \cdots]$$

Chordal:

$$\phi_X(t) = \frac{1.446 \times 10^{-5}}{(jt)^5} \left[ e^{j25t} - e^{j18.72t} - e^{j18.52t} - e^{j17.14t} + \cdots \right]$$

These are the characteristic functions of the distribution of $\delta T_{r2}$ obtained according to two approximations. Carrying out the substitution of the $g$ functions yields:

Taylor:

$$f_X(x) = 0; \quad x > 25 \text{ nsec (as in worst-case design)}$$

$$f_X(x) = \frac{1.563 \times 10^{-5}}{4!} (25 - x)^4; \quad 19.36 < x < 25 \text{ nsec}$$

$$f_X(x) = \frac{1.563 \times 10^{-5}}{4!} [(25 - x)^4 - (19.36 - x)^4];$$

$$19.16 < x < 19.36 \text{ nsec}$$

. . .

Chordal:

$$f_X(x) = 0; \quad x > 25 \text{ nsec (as in worst-case design)}$$

$$f_X(x) = \frac{1.446 \times 10^{-5}}{4!} (25 - x)^4; \quad 18.72 < x < 25 \text{ nsec}$$

$$f_X(x) = \frac{1.446 \times 10^{-5}}{4!} [(25 - x)^4 - (18.72 - x)^4]; \quad 18.52 < x < 18.72 \text{ nsec}$$

. . .

To calculate the probability that $T_{r2} \geq 95$ nsec, calculate the probability that $\delta T_{r2} > 20$ nsec. This is

$$P(x > 20) = \int_{20}^{\infty} f_X(x) \, dx$$

For the adjusted chordal case

$$P(x > 20) = 3.8 \times 10^{-4}$$

For the adjusted Taylor case

$$P(x > 20) = 4.1 \times 10^{-4}$$

That is, on the average only one circuit out of 2500 so designed will have a rise time greater than 95 nsec. If the values of the probability obtained using the two approximations differed markedly, it would be quite correct to doubt the validity of the results. However, the fact that in this example the results obtained using the two different approximations are in close agreement does not necessarily mean that the true value of the probability lies, for example, between the two values obtained. The true function,

$\delta T_{r2}$, of the five variables describes a surface in a six-dimensional space. The two approximations represent two different plane surfaces passing through the points $\delta T_{r2} = 0, 25$ nsec. When the tail of the $\delta T_{r2}$ distribution is affected chiefly by the component values at the extremes of their respective distributions, one would expect as suggested by K. G. Ashar (Ref. 1) that best results could be obtained by choosing the plane surface that is tangent to the true surface at $\delta T_{r2} = 25$ nsec, the worst-case limit. From the derivatives evaluated at $T_{r2} = 100$ nsec, one has for the equation of this tangent plane

$$\delta \hat{T}_{r2} = 2.64 \, \delta \hat{V}_1 + 1.162 \, \delta \hat{V}_2 + 18 \, \delta \hat{V}_3 + 1.872 \, \delta \hat{R}_1 + 9.58 \, \delta \hat{R}_2 \text{ nsec}$$

(8.8)

where

$$\delta \hat{T}_{r2} = T_{r2}^+ - T_{r2}, \qquad T_{r2}^+ \geq T_{r2}$$
$$\delta \hat{V}_1 = V_1 - V_1^-, \qquad V_1 \geq V_1^-$$
$$\delta \hat{V}_2 = V_2^+ - V_2, \qquad V_2^+ \geq V_2$$
$$\delta \hat{V}_3 = V_3^+ - V_3, \qquad V_3^+ \geq V_3$$
$$\delta \hat{R}_1 = R_1 - R_1^-, \qquad R_1 \geq R_1^-$$
$$\delta \hat{R}_2 = R_2^+ - R_2, \qquad R_2^+ \geq R_2$$

All these quantities are the deviations from the values at the worst-case limit so arranged that they are all positive quantities. K. G. Ashar has also suggested a modification to the procedure which simplifies the arithmetic in this case. The frequency functions are piecewise approximated from left to right with the worst-case limit at the origin of coordinates such that $x_1 = 0$ (see Fig. II.4, Appendix II). The conjugate of the characteristic function of a distribution is

$$\phi^*(t) = \int_{-\infty}^{\infty} f(x)e^{-it} \, dt$$

where $X$ and the $X_i$ are independent random variables and if $X = X_1 + X_2 + \cdots + X_n$, then from Eq. (II.5), Appendix II,

$$\phi_X^*(t) = \phi_{X_1}^*(t)\phi_{X_2}^*(t) \cdots \phi_{X_n}^*(t)$$

(8.9)

where $\phi_X^*(t)$, $\phi_{X_1}^*(t)$, etc. are the conjugates of the characteristic functions of the respective distributions. Hence, Eq. (II.15) becomes

$$f(x, x_0, k) \longleftrightarrow \frac{e^{-jtx_0}}{(jt)^{k+1}}$$

(8.10)

with

$$f(x, x_0, k) = 0, \qquad x \leq x_0$$

(8.11)

$$f(x, x_0, k) = \frac{(x - x_0)^k}{k!}, \qquad x > x_0$$

If the component and voltage deviations in Eq. (8.8) are uniformly distributed as in Fig. 8.9, then

$$f_{X_i}(x) = \frac{1}{A_i}\left[f(x, 0, 0) - f(x, 0, A_i)\right]$$

and

$$\phi_{X_i}^*(t) = \frac{1}{A_i}\left[1 - e^{-jtA_i}\right]\frac{1}{jt}$$

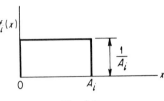

Fig. 8.9.

If the component and voltage deviations in Eq. (8.8) are independent, the conjugate of the characteristic function of the distribution of $\delta T_{r2}$ is, from Eq. (8.9),

$$\phi_X^*(t) = \frac{1}{A_1 \cdot A_2 \cdot A_3 \cdot A_4 \cdot A_5}\left[1 - e^{-jtA_1}\right]\left[1 - e^{-jtA_2}\right] \cdots \left[1 - e^{-jtA_5}\right]\frac{1}{(jt)^5}$$

(8.12)

where $A_1 = 0.1 \times 70 \times 2.64 = 18.4$ nsec

$A_2 = 0.1 \times 70 \times 1.162 = 8.15$ nsec

$A_3 = 0.1 \times 5 \times 18 = 9.00$ nsec

$A_4 = 0.1 \times 46.3 \times 1.872 = 8.66$ nsec

$A_5 = 0.1 \times 18.5 \times 9.58 = 17.70$ nsec

The computation of the $A_i$ differs from the computation of the $a_i$ in that $A_i = 2a_i$. Starting at the origin, the first few critical points of the distribution of $\delta T_{r2}$ are at

$$x_1 = 0, \quad x_2 = 8.15 \text{ nsec}, \quad x_3 = 8.66 \text{ nsec}, \quad \cdots$$

Hence, Eq. (8.12) becomes

$$\phi_X^*(t) = 4.85 \times 10^{-6}\left[1 - e^{-j8.15t} - e^{-j8.66t} - \cdots\right]\frac{1}{(jt)^5}$$

arranged with the exponential terms in order of increasing magnitude of their arguments; and using Eq. (8.10), the frequency function of the distribution of $\delta \hat{T}_{r2}$ is obtained as

$$f_X(x) = 4.85 \times 10^{-6}\left[f(x, 0, 4) - f(x, 8.15, 4) - f(x, 8.66, 4) - \cdots\right]$$

Hence

$$f_X(x) = 0, \qquad\qquad\qquad\qquad x \leq 0$$

$$f_X(x) = \frac{4.85 \times 10^{-6}}{4!}x^4, \qquad\qquad 0 \leq x \leq 8.15 \text{ nsec}$$

$$f_X(x) = \frac{4.85 \times 10^{-6}}{4!}\left[x^4 - (x - 8.15)^4\right], \qquad 8.15 \leq x \leq 8.66$$

· · ·

Now

$$P(T_{r2} > 95 \text{ nsec}) = P(\delta \hat{T}_{r2} < 5 \text{ nsec})$$

Hence

$$P(T_{r2} > 95 \text{ nsec}) = \frac{4.85 \times 10^{-6}}{4!} \int_0^5 x^4 \, dx = 1.27 \times 10^{-4} \quad (8.13)$$

The results obtained are summarized in Table 8.4 vs. the approximation used.

**TABLE 8.4**

| Approximation used | $P(T_{r2} > 95 \text{ nsec})$ |
|---|---|
| Adjusted Taylor | 4.1  $\times 10^{-4}$ |
| Adjusted chordal | 3.8  $\times 10^{-4}$ |
| Tangent plane at worst-case limit | 1.27 $\times 10^{-4}$ |

Insight can be gained into the source of the differences in the figures obtained by comparing what values of $T_{r2}$ the various approximations predict with the actual value for several conditions. This is done in Table 8.5. In the last line of the table $V_2$ was kept at the nominal value. This was

**TABLE 8.5.** VALUES OF $T_{r2}$

| Case | Actual | Adjusted Taylor | Adjusted chordal | Tangent plane |
|---|---|---|---|---|
| Nominal | 75 nsec | 75 nsec | 75 nsec | 66 nsec |
| Worst-case | 100 nsec | 100 nsec | 100 nsec | 100 nsec |
| Worst-case except $V_2 = +70$ | 96 nsec | 97 nsec | 97 nsec | 96 nsec |

done to determine approximately where $V_2$ would have to be to produce a rise time of 95 nsec used in the probability calculations. $V_2$ was chosen because of all the quantities it has to change the maximum amount to affect $T_{r2}$ by 5 nsec. In this example, it can be seen that the tangent plane is the best approximation to the $T_{r2}$ dependence on the circuit parameters in the range of interest. Hence, it would be expected that the probability calculated, using the tangent-plane approximation at the worst-case limit, is closest to the correct value.

It can be noted in Table 8.5 that the tangent-plane approximation yields a value which in the last line differs by about one nsec from what the other two approximations predict. This implies that the error due to the approximations shows up as distortions of the axis of the random variable, which in this case should be about a one-nsec displacement. This is borne out by a calculation of the upper limit required in Eq. (8.13) needed to give the results predicted by the adjusted Taylor and adjusted chordal approximations. The result is

$$P(T_{r2} > 93.7 \text{ nsec}) = 4 \times 10^{-4}$$

showing the presence of a 1.3-nsec displacement along the $T_{r2}$ axis.

The above discussion emphasizes the importance of the choice of the best approximation. The method of calculating the probabilities depends highly on the accuracy in the range of interest of the approximation used. In this example, the adjusted chordal and adjusted Taylor approximations gave more conservative results than the approximation based on the tangent plane at the worst-case limit, but this does not mean that they will always do so.

It is of interest to see what the central limit theorem predicts. It states that the distribution of a sum of independent random variables approaches a normal distribution (whose mean is the sum of the means of the individual distributions and whose standard deviation is the square root

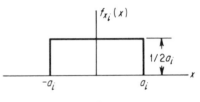

Fig. 8.10.

of the sum of the squares of the individual standard deviations) as the number of random variables gets large.

The $X_i$ are distributed as in Fig. 8.10. The mean is

$$m_{X_i} = \int_{-\infty}^{\infty} x f_{X_i}(x)\, dx = 0$$

The standard deviation squared is

$$\sigma_{X_i}^2 = \int_{-\infty}^{\infty} f_{X_i}(x)(x_i - m_i)^2\, dx = \int_{-a_i}^{a_i} \frac{x^2}{2a_i}\, dx = \frac{a_i^2}{3}$$

Hence

$$\sigma_X^2 = \frac{1}{3}(a_1^2 + a_2^2 + a_3^2 + a_4^2 + a_5^2)$$

for the sum distribution ($X = \delta T_{r2}$).

$\sigma_X^2 = 48.8$ (adjusted Taylor),      $\sigma_X^2 = 40.0$ (adjusted chordal)

For the normal distribution,

$$P(X > b) = \frac{1}{\sigma\sqrt{2\pi}} \int_b^\infty e^{-(x^2/2\sigma^2)} \, dx$$

$$= \frac{1}{2}\left[1 - I\left(\frac{b}{\sigma\sqrt{2}}\right)\right], \qquad I = \frac{2}{\sqrt{\pi}} \int_0^x e^{-x^2} \, dx$$

$$= 2 \times 10^{-3} \qquad\qquad (b = 95 - 75 = 20 \text{ nsec})$$

This figure is about sixteen times larger than the best estimate that we have computed previously using the tangent plane at the worst-case limit.

However, as the number of component parameters increases, the probabilities computed using the central limit theorem will approach more closely those computed by the method based on characteristic functions above. This is of practical importance, since the labor involved in the computation using characteristic functions increases rapidly as the number of component parameters increases.

### 8.4 STATISTICAL DESIGN

In most practical cases, one may find the probability expressions too complicated to permit the writing of design equations. Industry practice in this situation has been to use a variation of the method of successive approximations. As applied to this circuit the procedure would be the following.

(a) Arrive at suitable values of the probabilities that $T_{r2}$, $T_{f2}$ exceed specified values from reliability considerations and specifications.
(b) By worst-case design, obtain an initial estimate of $R_1$.
(c) Determine $T_{f2}$ value, using the method above, that satisfies the specified probability.
(d) Using the value obtained in (c), correct the value of $R_1$ obtained in (b).
(e) Repeat until there is no change.
(f) Go on to $R_2$.

As an illustration, consider $T_{f2}$ with the requirement of

$$P(T_{f2} > 100 \text{ ns}) = 10^{-4}$$

$$T_{f2} = \frac{C_1 V_3 R_1}{V_2 - (V_3/2)}$$

The partial derivatives are

$$\frac{\partial T_{f2}}{\partial V_2} = -\frac{C_1 V_3 R_1}{D^2}, \qquad \frac{\partial T_{f2}}{\partial V_3} = \frac{V_2 C_1 R_1}{D^2}$$

$$\frac{\partial T_{f2}}{\partial R_1} = \frac{C_1 V_3}{V_2 - (V_3/2)}, \qquad D = V_2 - \frac{V_3}{2}$$

The mean value of $T_{f2}$ and the values of the partial derivatives for $R_1 = 46.3\text{K}$ (nominal value of $R_1$ obtained by worst-case design) are

$$T_{f2} = 85.6 \times 10^{-9} \text{ nsec}$$

$$\frac{\partial T_{f2}}{\partial V_2} = -1.27 \text{ nsec}$$

$$\frac{\partial T_{f2}}{\partial V_3} = 17.8 \text{ nsec}$$

$$\frac{\partial T_{f2}}{\partial R_1} = 1.85 \text{ nsec}$$

Hence, using the adjusted Taylor approximation,

$$
\begin{aligned}
\delta V_2 &= 3.5, & a_1 &= 3.5 \times 1.27 = & 4.44 \\
\delta V_3 &= 0.25, & a_2 &= 0.25 \times 17.8 = & 4.45 \\
\delta R_1 &= 2.32\text{K}, & a_3 &= 2.32 \times 1.85 = & 4.29 \\
\end{aligned}
$$

$$\text{max } \delta T_{f2} = 13.18 \text{ nsec}$$

Max $\delta T_{f2}$ should be $100 - 85.6 = 14.4$ nsec.

Corrected values of $a_1$, $a_2$, $a_3$ are obtained by multiplying the above values by $14.4/13.18$ to obtain

$$
\begin{aligned}
a_1 &= 4.85 \\
a_2 &= 4.86 \\
a_3 &= 4.68 \\
\hline
&14.39
\end{aligned}
$$

The characteristic function for the distribution assuming that $\delta V_2$, etc., are uniformly distributed is

$$\phi_X(t) = \frac{1}{2^3 a_1 a_2 a_3} \left[ e^{jt4.85} - e^{-jt4.85} \right] \left[ e^{jt4.86} - e^{jt4.86} \right]$$

$$\cdot \left[ e^{jt4.68} - e^{-jt4.68} \right] \frac{1}{(jt)^3}$$

$$= 0.0013 \left[ e^{jt14.4} - e^{jt5.03} - \cdots \right] \frac{1}{(jt)^3}$$

Hence for the probability density function for the distribution of $\delta T_{f2}$, one obtains

$$f_X(x) = 0, \qquad\qquad\qquad\qquad x > 14.4 \text{ nsec}$$

$$f_X(x) = 5.65 \times 10^{-4}(14.4 - x)^2, \qquad 5.03 < x < 14.4$$

If it is required to have $P(X > b) = 10^{-4}$, then from

$$P(X > b) = \int_b^\infty f_X(x) \, dx$$

it is found that $b = 13.6$. Hence

$$P(T_{f2} > 99.2 \text{ nsec}) = 10^{-4}$$

since $99.2 = 85.6 + 13.6$.

A corrected value of $R_1$ is approximately [for $P(T_{f2} > 100 \text{ nsec}) = 10^{-4}$]

$$\frac{100}{99.2} \times 46.3 \text{ K} = 46.7 \text{ K}$$

Since

$$\delta T_{f2} = \frac{\partial T_{f2}}{\partial V_2} \delta V_2 + \frac{\partial T_{f2}}{\partial V_3} \delta V_3 + \frac{\partial T_{f2}}{\partial R_1} \delta R_1$$

it is possible to find the new value of $R_1$ from this relation.

$$\delta T_{f2} = 100 - 99.2 = 0.8$$

Hence

$$0.8 = \frac{\partial T_{f2}}{\partial V_2} \cdot 0 + \frac{\partial T_{f2}}{\partial V_3} \cdot 0 + 1.85 \ \delta R_1 \ (\delta R_1 \text{ in kilohms})$$

$$\delta R_1 = 0.43 \text{ K}$$

$$R_1 = 46.3 + 0.43 = \underline{46.73 \text{ K}}$$

Because there is no easily applied rigorous method available to determine the error of the calculated probabilities arising from the approximation used, one may wish to use a method that does not depend on such an approximation as a check of a final design. One such method is the "Monte Carlo" method. In it, as applied to this circuit, the rise and fall times would be calculated without approximation, using many sets of parameter values taken from tables of numbers having the expected parameter distributions. After a sufficient number of calculations, the resulting numbers would be distributed in such a way as to approximate the distribution of rise and fall times. Since the error in this approximation varies roughly inversely as the square root of the number of parameter sets taken, the large number of computations required makes mandatory the use of a high-speed computer. However, in the instances where such computations have been undertaken and completed by both methods, good agreement has been found to exist between the results.

Furthermore, it does not happen often that mathematical expressions are available that accurately describe the dependence of circuit performance on parameter values. Frequently one has to be content with empirical equations obtained from experimental results. In such cases it may not be worthwhile or even possible to resort to expensive Monte Carlo calculations where the approximation technique described may suffice.

**8.5** STATISTICS AS APPLIED TO TIMING CALCULATIONS

The timing calculations illustrated in Chap. 4 were made on a worst-case basis. It is possible to apply statistical techniques to timing calculations, such as the determination of delays through chains of logic stages, thereby achieving either cost savings or increased speeds of operation.

Let the delay of the $i$th logic stage in a chain of such stages be $D_i$. The delay through $n$ such stages (assuming that the delays are additive) is

$$T = \sum_{i=1}^{n} D_i$$

Since the logic stages are usually supplied with power from common power-supply busses, the delays $D_i$ will not be independent when considered as random variables. This fact must be taken into account in computing the probabilities.

A simplified approach will be adopted and it will be assumed that the stages are all alike, although the method is applicable to the case where this simplification cannot be made. Let the components in each stage have values $R_1, R_2, \ldots, R_p$ and the applied voltages be $V_1, V_2, V_3, \ldots, V_q$. Assume that the delay of the $i$th stage can be expressed as a linear approximation of the type previously discussed. Then

$$D_i = \hat{b}_1 R_1 + \hat{b}_2 R_2 + \cdots + \hat{b}_p R_p$$
$$+ \hat{a}_1 V_1 + \hat{a}_2 V_2 + \cdots + \hat{a}_q V_q$$

Hence

$$D = \hat{b}_1 R_1 + \hat{b}_2 R_2 + \cdots + \hat{b}_p R_p \quad \text{(stage 1)}$$
$$+ \hat{b}_1 R_1 + \hat{b}_2 R_2 + \cdots + \hat{b}_p R_p \quad \text{(stage 2)}$$
$$\vdots$$
$$+ \hat{b}_1 R_1 + \hat{b}_2 R_2 + \cdots + \hat{b}_p R_p \quad \text{(stage } n\text{)}$$
$$+ n\hat{a}_1 V_1 + n\hat{a}_2 V_2 + \cdots + n\hat{a}_q V_q \tag{8.14a}$$

Hence if $\hat{b}_1 R_1, \hat{b}_2 R_2, \ldots, \hat{a}_1 V_1, \hat{a}_2 V_2, \ldots$ are random variables and the mean values of the distributions of $\hat{b}_1 R_1, \hat{b}_2 R_2, \ldots$ are $m_1, m_2, \ldots$ respectively and the mean values of the distributions of $\hat{a}_1 V_1, \hat{a}_2 V_2, \ldots$ are $\hat{m}_1, \hat{m}_2, \ldots$, then

$$D_{\text{mean}} = n m_1 + n m_2 + \cdots + n m_p$$
$$+ n\hat{m}_1 + n\hat{m}_2 + \cdots + n\hat{m}_q \tag{8.14b}$$

and if the above random variables are independent,

$$\sigma^2 = n\sigma_1^2 + n\sigma_2^2 + \cdots + n\sigma_p^2$$
$$+ n^2\hat{\sigma}_1^2 + n^2\hat{\sigma}_2^2 + \cdots + n^2\hat{\sigma}_q^2 \tag{8.14c}$$

where $\sigma_1, \sigma_2, \ldots$ are the standard deviations of the distributions of $\hat{b}_1 R_1, \hat{b}_2 R_2, \ldots$ respectively, and $\hat{\sigma}_1, \hat{\sigma}_2, \ldots$ are the standard deviations of $\hat{a}_1 V_1, \hat{a}_2 V_2, \ldots$ respectively. Note that the voltage and component values are treated differently. This is because for the component values, there are as many random variables as appearances of given component designations $(n \times p)$ while for the voltage there are only as many random variables as voltages $(q)$ independent of the number of appearances of a given voltage in the logic chain under consideration. Usually Eq. (8.14a) contains such a large number of terms that the central limit theorem can be used with little error. This means that the distribution of $D$ is approximately normal with a mean $D_{\text{mean}}$ and a standard deviation $\sigma$.

Probability calculated using this distribution must be interpreted as being the fraction of logic chains having such delay ranges. The timing calculations in Chap. 4 can be statistically reformulated in the above way.

## 8.6 STATISTICS AS APPLIED TO COMPONENT SPECIFICATION

The design of a circuit using the statistical methods described previously in this chapter is a time-consuming and arduous procedure. In some instances it is possible to reap some of the benefits of statistical design by applying statistics to component specification. The development of a worst-case specification for diode recovery time was discussed in Chap. 7. If such a specification were used as the basis of a worst-case design, then the design when completed would make it possible to state a maximum limit on the required recovery time, $T_R$. Such a conclusion is true for any worst-case design. However, it would be advantageous to choose a parameter to which the cost of the device is very sensitive. This might be the common-emitter current gain $\alpha_{FE}$, of a transistor in a logic circuit. The value of $\alpha_{FE}$ required to give satisfactory operation in a circuit would be

$$\alpha_{FE} = f(R_1, R_2, \ldots, R_p, V_1, V_2, \ldots, V_q)$$

from which the minimum required $\alpha_{FE}$ can be determined. However, let it be assumed that $R_1, R_2, \ldots, V_1, V_2, \ldots$ have known distributions. Then the minimum required $\alpha_{FE}$ for a given circuit has a distribution which can be determined by the Monte Carlo technique or by one of the approximation techniques. Denote the frequency function of this distribution by $f_{\text{req}}(x)$. Assume that the frequency function of the distribution of the $\alpha_{FE}$ values of available transistors is $f_{\text{av}}(x)$. Summarizing, the distribution of required $\alpha_{FE}$ is described by $f_{\text{req}}(x)$ and that of the available $\alpha_{FE}$ by $f_{\text{av}}(x)$. These random variables are clearly independent so that their joint distribution is

$$X = \text{required } \alpha_{FE}, \qquad Y = \text{available } \alpha_{FE}$$

$$P(x < X \leq x + dx, y < Y \leq y + dy) = f_{\text{req}}(x) f_{\text{av}}(y) \, dx \, dy$$

The probability that a circuit will not work (the fraction of nonworking circuits assembled from the available components) is

$$P(-\infty < X \le \infty, 0 < Y - X \le \infty) = \int_{-\infty}^{\infty} \int_{x}^{\infty} f_{\text{req}}(x) f_{\text{av}}(y) \, dy \, dx$$

since the required $\alpha_{FE}$ must be greater than the available $\alpha_{FE}$ for any given circuit to work. Letting $z = x - y$ yields

$$P = \int_{-\infty}^{\infty} \int_{0}^{\infty} f_{\text{req}}(x) f_{\text{av}}(x - z) \, dz \, dx$$

This integral has been discussed in Chap. 7, where a simple method of evaluating it has been given when $f_{\text{req}}(x)$ and $f_{\text{av}}(x)$ are approximately normal.

The result of such a technique is the possibility of using some transistors whose $\alpha_{FE}$ is lower than the worst-case limit. To do this requires that the distribution of available $\alpha_{FE}$ be adjusted to make $P$ an acceptably small nonzero quantity.

### 8.7 OPTIMIZATION*

Heretofore it has been implied to some extent that analysis, design, and optimization proceed after *one* circuit has been chosen. This implication was made to limit the size of the conceptual meal the student must digest so he could limit his efforts to developing a grasp of the more basic principles. The time has now come to broaden our view of the design process to encompass those considerations that have been ignored. It will be assumed that the aim is to design a solid-state large-scale electronic digital computer meeting a performance specification including high speed, and at minimum cost. It is also assumed that logical design has specified the general nature of the requirements for addition, subtraction, etc. The next step is the evaluation of the available circuits.

The general types of circuits that can be classified (Chap. 5) are these: *Pulse envelope* (nonreturn to zero). Four basic types can be selected.

1. One, as opposed to two, levels of logic in the basic logical block. (The existence of more than two levels becomes impractical owing to gain and speed required.)
2. Inversion to be or not to be included in basic logical block (that is, grounded emitter as opposed to two grounded emitters or an emitter follower).
3. Diode logic as opposed to transistor logic (that is, whether or not diodes are to be used).
4. Are transistors to be allowed to go into saturation or not? (That is, delays to include storage time or not.)

* Adapted in part from Ref. 6.

The above four categories imply sixteen types of circuits. In addition, each type can be represented by a number of possible circuits.

In the case of RZ circuits square-loop magnetic devices can be rejected because of comparatively low efficiency. Hence, only transformer-transistor circuits need be considered. Two major types of these circuits exist: (a) feedback circuits (blocking oscillators, and so forth) fit for timing, storage, and pulse forming with diode logic, (b) transformer logic.

In order to evaluate all types of circuits to be used, it would be necessary to build test systems which could simulate the actual system. For conclusions to be critical, each test system should be designed with as much care as the final system. This would involve a prohibitive amount of work. However, it is practical to build about six test systems which simulate, for example, the work of complete adders. The design of these adders may not be the optimum one, although the validity of conclusions depends on each design being truly representative of the capability of the type of circuit.

The results of each design consist of:

(a) Addition time. This may differ considerably from the desired period, since the design may optimize speed irrespective of the specification requirement.
(b) Cost of components.
(c) Numbers of components having relatively low reliability such as transistors, diodes and other special devices.

The number of components can be combined into a kind of merit factor in order to uniquely represent the advantage of one circuit as opposed to another. Of course, such a merit factor may assign erroneous weights to the various performance numbers, and therefore over-reliance on a merit factor should be avoided.

For example:

| Factor | Symbol |
|---|---|
| Cost of parts | $C$ in $ |
| Addition time | $T$ in $\mu$sec |
| Number of transistors | $N_t$ |
| Number of diodes | $N_d$ |
| Merit factor | $M$ |

If a diode is considered three times more reliable than a transistor,

$$M = \left(\frac{1}{TC}\right)\left(\frac{1}{N_t + N_d/3}\right)$$

In addition there are a number of other factors which we will call intangibles. Some of these intangibles are:

1. Possible forms of packaging.
2. Labor in packaging.
3. Power and clock tolerances and cost.
4. Frame construction.
5. Noise pick-up.
6. Debugging and service.
7. Marginal checking.

Another important factor to be considered is the type of circuit with which the project personnel are most familiar. By comparing the performance of a standard circuit with that of the circuit being developed, the circuit offering the greatest advantage can be chosen. In sum, and without going further into a description of the test system process, the pulse-envelope type of circuitry will be selected employing single-level diode logic and saturated transmission operation with inversion.

We are now ready to proceed to the worst-case design and optimization of the circuit. Once the problem of the evaluation of the types of circuits has been reduced to the consideration of only one circuit, the process can become more rigorous and thorough.

The worst-case for d-c will be discussed first. Figure 8.11 shows the circuit for two buffer-inverters.

The transistor in the first circuit is in the on state and produces a large collector current. The transistor in the second circuit is off. The on and off conditions of the transistors can be defined as follows:

*ON condition*
Emitter-collector voltage $(V_{ec}) = V_{ec(on)}$
Output current $= n \times I_i$ ($n =$ fan-out of 3)
Input voltage $(V_{i(off)}) = E_3 - I_{tL}R_3$ ($I_{tL} \leq 250$ $\mu a$)
Emitter-base voltage $(V_{eb}) = V_{b(on)} \leq 0.6$ volts.
*OFF condition*
Emitter-base voltage $(V_{eb}) = 150$ mv,
$I_b = 0$ and $I_c = I_{tL}$ ($\leq 250$ $\mu a$).

Since $V_b$ versus $I_b$ is nonlinear (Fig. 8.12) and varies greatly from transistor to transistor, it is difficult to make a general statement on the precise values of $V_b$ and $I_b$ to be used in design. It has been found that best overall circuit performance was obtained (using a Surface-Barrier transistor) when the design was based around the off point ($I_b = 0$). This off point was optimum because this transistor has a relatively low value of $\alpha_{FE}$ for a very small base current. The $I_b = 0$ point corresponds at (25°C) to a collector current of less than 250 $\mu a$.

The worst-case equations for nodes $A$, $B$ and $C$ are shown in Table 8.6.

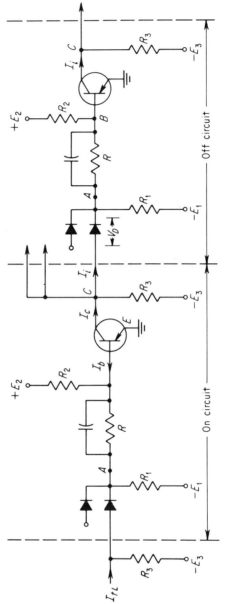

**Fig. 8.11.** Two stages of the basic logic circuit.

**TABLE 8.6.** Table of Equations

| Node | | Equations |
|---|---|---|
| OFF | ON | |
| $C$ | $A$ | $E_3^- - I_{tL}^+ R_3^+ - V_{n(\text{off})} = \dfrac{E_1^+ - V_{b(\text{on})}^+}{R_1^- + R^+} R^+ + V_{b(\text{on})}^+$ |
| | $B$ | $I_{b(\text{on})}^- = \dfrac{E_1^- - V_{b(\text{on})}^+}{R_1^+ + R^+} - \dfrac{E_2^- + V_{b(\text{on})}^+}{R_2^-}$ |
| | Transistor | $I_{b(\text{on})}^- \alpha_{FE}^- = I_c^+$ |
| | $C$ | $I_c = \dfrac{E_3^+ - (V_{ce(\text{on})}^+ + V_d^+)}{R_1^-} + nI_i^+ + mI_{dL}^+$ <br> $n = $ fan-out; $m = $ number of diodes in driven gates |
| $A$ | | $I_i^+ = \dfrac{E_1^+ - (V_{c(\text{on})}^+ + V_d^-)}{R_1^-} - \dfrac{(V_{b(\text{off})} + V_{n(\text{on})} + V_{ce(\text{on})} + V_d^+)}{R^+}$ |
| $B$ | | $V_{b(\text{off})} = \dfrac{1}{R_2^+ + R^-}$ <br> $[E_2^- R^- - I_{b(\text{off})} R^- R_2^+ - R_2(V_{n(\text{on})} + V_{ce(\text{on})} + V_d^+)]$ |

At node $A$ of the on circuit, the diode should be reverse biased to assure a zero input-current. That is, the voltage at node $C$ of the off circuit plus the noise voltage induced in the input line ($V_{n(\text{off})}$) should not be positive with respect to the voltage at node $A$ of the on circuit.

At node $B$ of the on circuit, $I_{b(\text{on})}^-$ and $I_c^+$ should be maintained.

At node $C$ of the on circuit, $I_c^+$ should exceed the load current ($nI_i$), the diode leakage current ($mI_{dL}$), and the current into $R3$.

The voltage at node $B$ of the off circuit should assure that the transistor is turned off ($I_{b(\text{off})} \leq 0$). In Table 8.6, there are six equations with twenty unknowns. These unknowns (dropping maximum and minimum superscripts) are:

$I_{tL}, I_{dL}, I_{b(\text{on})}, I_{b(\text{off})}, I_c, I_i,$ and $\alpha_{FE}$
$E_1, E_2, E_3, R_1, R_2, R_3,$ and $R$
$V_{n(\text{on})}$ and $V_{n(\text{off})}$
$V_{b(\text{on})}, V_{b(\text{off})}, V_{c(\text{on})},$ and $V_d$

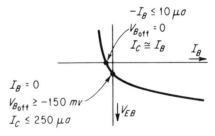

$-I_B \leq 10\,\mu a$
$V_{B\text{off}} = 0$
$I_C \cong I_B$
$I_B$

$I_B = 0$
$V_{B\text{off}} \geq -150\ mv$
$I_C \leq 250\,\mu a$
$V_{EB}$

Fig. 8.12. $V_{EB}$ versus $I_B$ for typical transistor.

To define a unique circuit, it is necessary to determine fourteen independent unknowns in the process of optimization.

$V_{b(on)}$, $V_{b(off)}$, $V_d$, $I_{tL}$, $I_{dL}$ and $I_{b(off)}$ are determined so that a high percentage of the produced diodes and transistors can be used. $V_{n(on)}$ and $V_{n(off)}$ are determined through noise measurements (which will be discussed further).

As a zero approximation for the solution, $I_{b(on)}$ is assumed to be such as to allow operation in the range where $\alpha_{FE}$ is maximum (upper end of this range). This assumption should be re-examined at the end of the optimization because iterative corrections of the value of $I_{b(on)}$ may be necessary. $V_{c(on)}$ can be determined by assuming values for four independent variables and calculating (from equations in Table 8.6) the relationship of $\alpha_{FE}$ vs. $V_{c(on)}$. On the other hand, transistor measurements give the available $\alpha_{FE}$ vs. $V_{c(on)}$ for the end of transistor life (aged transistor). Comparison of the rates of change of $\alpha_{FE}$ with $V_{c(on)}$ (expressed as $d\alpha_{FE}/dV_{c(on)}$) of the two curves shown in Fig. 8.13 allowed for the determination of an optimum value of 0.3 volts for $V_{c(on)}$.

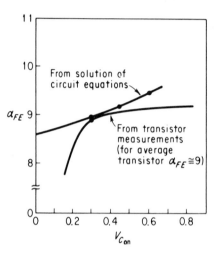

Fig. 8.13. $\alpha_{FE}$ versus $V_{c(on)}$.

We found that $E_2$, so long as it exceeded 10 volts, had very little effect on the operation of the circuit. To minimize power-supply requirements, the value of $E_2$ was selected to be 12 volts. Consequently, six equations with nine unknowns still need to be solved. The remaining independent unknowns are determined through optimization of speed.

The maximum-delay situation will now be considered.

The delay of a step function through a transistor depends on whether it is turning off or on, since the worst loading conditions are different for the two switching directions. Therefore, delay is conveniently measured across two levels—one switching in one direction and the other switching in the opposite direction (each being loaded for its own worst-case of delay). When the transistor is turning on, its $\alpha_{FE}$ and gain bandwidth should be the minimum allowable, its load should be maximum, and the worst diode leakage should be present.

When the transistor is turning off, the worst condition occurs when the load is minimum and the $\alpha_{FE}$ and storage time are maximum. This condition oversaturates the transistor as much as possible, thereby producing the maximum hole-storage delay. If hole storage did not constitute an appreciable portion of the total delay for the SB100 transistor, the worst loading condition for the transistor turning off would have to be re-examined.

## 8.8 MEASURING TECHNIQUE

The breadboard set-up for delay measurements is shown in Fig. 8.14.

The first gate gives input rise and fall times comparable to what would be expected in a chain of logic. To simulate wiring capacity, 50 pf of lumped capacity were added from all collectors to ground. Diode and transistor leakage were also added where appropriate.

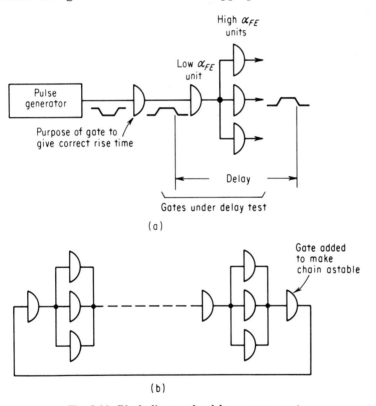

**Fig. 8.14.** Block diagram for delay measurements.

The delay was measured from collector to collector, usually 1 volt below ground, since this is approximately where the following stage is fully turned on during the transient period. If the trailing edges of the wave-shape at the first and third collectors are identical, it does not matter from which point on the trailing edge the delay is measured. However, if the trailing edges are not identical, the delay measured between a fixed point on the two edges will be either pessimistic or optimistic, depending on whether the output fall time to the point of measurement is greater or less than the corresponding fall time on the driving edge.

Standard delays were measured by observing the recirculation frequency of a chain of amplifiers shown in Fig. 8.14(b). The odd level of gating must be added in order to make the chain astable. Here the minimum load is

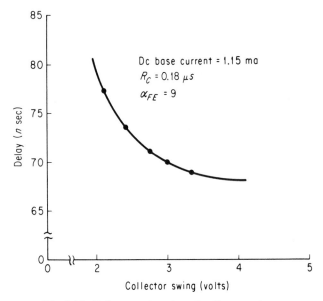

**Fig. 8.15.** Delay as a function of collector swing.

one-third. For a given delay per stage, any desired pulse width may be obtained by varying the number of stages. This method of measuring has the advantage that the input and output waveforms of any given stage are assured of being those which would be expected in a long chain of logic. In this type of experiment, wiring capacitance must be simulated.

As shown in Fig. 8.15, $E_3$ can be determined by designing circuits for a number of $E_3$ values and then measuring the delays. The upper value of $E_3$ is limited by the breakdown voltage of the transistors. For longer transistor life, $E_3$ was selected to be 3 volts. The graph shows that 4 volts for $E_3$ would improve the speed only slightly.

The next parameter to be optimized was the value of $R_3$. This is shown in Fig. 8.16, where the delay is plotted as a function of the current in $R_3$. We see that optimum speed is obtained when

$$\frac{E_3/R_3}{I_i} = 3.3$$

Now there is left one independent variable, namely $\alpha_{FE}$. Although speed can be increased with the increase in $\alpha_{FE}$, $\alpha_{FE} = 9$ has been selected as the end of the transistor's life. As directed by the specifications, this is the minimum allowable $\alpha_{FE}$ for assuring a maximum delay of 40 nsec per level of logic with three loads. The value of the capacitor should now be varied

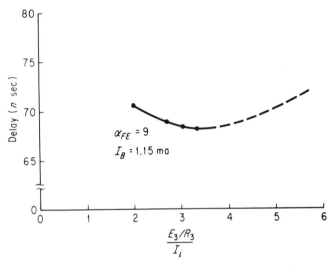

**Fig. 8.16.** Delay as a function of the current through $R_3$.

to obtain maximum speed for all pulse widths propagated through the levels of gating.

The process of optimization requires the design of a large number of circuits (less than 100). Each design implies solution of six simultaneous nonlinear equations. The amount of computation involved clearly indicated the advantage of processing the computations on a computer.

Transient analysis of circuit performance was conducted experimentally (as shown by the delay measurements). The transient performance was calculated using the methods of Chap. 6. The results of such analyses were qualitative and helpful in understanding the factors involved, but were not sufficiently accurate for the design of the circuits.

## REFERENCES

**1.** Ashar, K. G., "An Improvement in the Use of Piecewise Approximations to Reliability and Statistical Design," *Proc. I.R.E.*, **48**:10 (Oct. 1960), 1788.

2. Cramér, H., *Elements of Probability Theory* (New York: John Wiley & Sons, 1955), pp. 57–75—elementary notions, pp. 71–86—means, moments, pp. 108–116—normal distribution.

3. Cramér, H., *Mathematical Methods of Statistics* (Princeton, N.J.: Princeton University Press, 1946), p. 185—characteristic functions.

4. Gray, Harry J., "An Application of Piecewise Approximations to Reliability and Statistical Design," *Proc. I.R.E.*, **47**:7 (July 1959), 1226–1231.

5. Parzen, Emmanuel, *Modern Probability Theory and Its Applications* (New York: John Wiley & Sons, 1960), pp. 316–333.

6. Prywes, N. S., H. Lukoff, and J. Schwarz, "Univac-Larc High Speed Circuitry: Case History in Circuit Optimization," *I.R.E. Transactions on Electronic Computers*, **EC-10**:3 (September 1961), 426–446.

## PROBLEMS

**1.** A group of 10-K resistors have the following distribution:

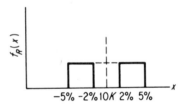

**Fig. P8.1.**

During use each resistor drifts from its initial value by an amount $\delta$. The distribution of $\delta$ is normal. The mean of the distribution of $\delta$ is in this case zero but its standard deviation is 2 per cent (200 $\Omega$). Determine and plot the distribution of resistor values at end of life. [*Hint:* End-of-life value = $x + \delta$; assume $x$ and $\delta$ are independent random variables and use the convolution integrals.]

**2.** For $P(T_{f2} > 100 \text{ nsec}) = 10^{-4}$, determine $R_1$ (Fig. 8.1) using the tangent plane at worst-case limit approximation. Use the voltages and capacitances appearing in Fig. 8.1.

**3.** For $P(T_{r2} > 100 \text{ nsec}) = 10^{-4}$, determine $R_2$ using for $R_1$ the value obtained in Prob. 2. Use the tangent plane at worst-case limit approximations.

**4.** In a given diode circuit as designed in Probs. 2 and 3 what is the probability that $T_{f2} > 100$ nsec and $T_{r2} > 100$ nsec simultaneously? See Chap. 10 for a transistor specification problem.

# 9

# PULSE AND D-C POWER

# TRANSMISSION SYSTEMS

There are the two problems of signal delay and noise on pulse transmission systems. In connection with signal delay, the reader should refer to the adequate treatments appearing in the references given at the end of Appendix III. That appendix includes a brief discussion of the transient analysis of lossless transmission lines.

There are two kinds of noise that appear on pulse transmission lines. One kind is produced by reflections from improper line terminations and from discontinuities in the transmission line. On lines having delays that are much less than the signal transition times (short lines), the effect of these reflections is usually referred to as "ringing," and the character of this noise is predictable on the basis of either a lumped circuit or transmission line analysis. The ringing usually has a very high frequency and is easily minimized by simple damping elements. It is usually not excessive and can often be tolerated when the line terminating impedances differ from the characteristic impedance of the line by not more than a factor of two or three. When the delay of the transmission line approaches or exceeds the signal transition times, it is almost always necessary to properly terminate the transmission lines with the characteristic impedance at either the sending or receiving ends and to avoid the occurrence of discontinuities. The size of the reflections introduced by the presence of unavoidable discontinuities or the unavoidable tolerances in the characteristic impedance and the terminating impedances can be predicted by conventional transmission line theory (Appendix III and its references). When the load is nonlinear, satisfactory results can sometimes be obtained by adjusting the circuit constants so that the characteristic impedance of the transmission line is equal to the ratio of the changes in load voltage and current. Sometimes this condition can also yield a satisfactory termination for delay lines.

The other kind of noise occurs because of the presence of stray electromagnetic fields interacting with a given pulse line. These fields arise from sources external to the system and from the operation of circuits in the system itself. The effect of fields from the former sources can be controlled by shielding, as is common engineering knowledge. The analysis and control of the noise due to the latter source of fields (crosstalk) is the main subject of this chapter.

### 9.1 CROSSTALK IN TRANSMISSION SYSTEMS

The early digital computers such as ENIAC operated at relatively low speeds with wide margins to allow for the deterioration of components and for noise. In those days, one often used such things as heavy braided ground straps to assure good "grounding," but very few people, if any, understood in detail what was going on. This mode of thinking has persisted to some extent, with adverse effects on the reliability of equipment. Crosstalk control is an old problem in telephone systems, and satisfactory solutions have been found for many of the problems encountered there. However, in the telephone lines with which most people are familiar, signal frequencies in excess of two or three thousand cycles are rarely encountered. As will be seen, crosstalk is proportional to the signal frequency. If, in a high-speed computer, frequency components of 200 mcps are encountered, we may expect about one hundred thousand times the amount of crosstalk signals in computer wiring as in physically similar telephone system wiring.

There are two separate subjects under the heading of crosstalk: (1) the theory involved and the principles of crosstalk control, (2) the application of this knowledge to the design of circuits, packages, frame, and wiring such that a system will work within the noise it generates. Most of this chapter will be concerned with the first subject.

The first question that arises is: in what places will crosstalk cause difficulty?

Consider a chain of logic circuits between two pulse formers as in Fig. 9.1. It will be assumed that in normal operation, a clock pulse will set pulse former 1 and a step will propagate through the chain of logic and will arrive at the clock gate of pulse former 2. The signal at the input of this clock gate must settle down to one of the binary states by the time the clock samples the state of the signal on line $C$. The signal at $C$ must stay in a given state while it is being sampled in order that pulse former 2 will be put in an unambiguous state. Any spurious signals, including those

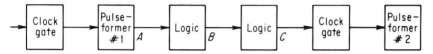

**Fig. 9.1.** Clocked synchronous system.

arising from crosstalk, must not appear on line $C$ during the time the clock pulse is sampling the state of $C$. However, noise occurring on line $C$ at any other time will cause no harm. It would be possible for noise introduced at $A$ or $B$ at other than clock-pulse time to be delayed by the logic and to arrive at $C$ at clock-pulse time. In systems where the delay through the logic is more than about half the time interval available for the logic delay, care must be taken to minimize crosstalk to the logic circuits. In systems where the delay through the logic is less than about half the time interval available for the logic delay, not as much care needs to be taken, but in both kinds of systems the gain through the logic circuits for a noise pulse must be less than unity, or the noise may appear at clock time on a second or higher pass through the logic circuits and therefore would propagate throughout the entire system, producing malfunction. In all systems, care must be taken to avoid the possibility that noise will upset flip-flops.

In asynchronous logic systems, there is rarely, if ever, any use of clocks. Therefore, care must be taken to minimize noise pick-up in all circuits at all times.

In order to compute crosstalk signals accurately it is required that the solution of a large set of partial differential equations for the package and backboard wiring systems be obtained, which at present is not practicable. However, approximate calculations can be made for idealized systems which help one understand what is occurring, and in some cases highly accurate results can be obtained. In practice, when the sources of any inaccuracies have been found, they have been seen to be errors in estimating rates of change of voltages and of currents, inaccurate data on the geometry, or misapplication of the theory. Eventually the numerical values obtained should be verified, however, on carefully considered and constructed models of the package, backboard, and wiring system.

## 9.2  ELEMENTARY CROSSTALK CALCULATIONS

Consider first the system in Fig. 9.2. The generator may be a *logic circuit* or it may be a *switch* or *relay contact*.

Schelkunoff (Ref. 7) has formulas for computing values for the crosstalk voltages ($V_1$, $V_2$) and currents if the lines in Fig. 9.2 are not too tightly coupled. If they are tightly coupled, the crosstalk will usually be excessive. With regard to the length of lines, in high-speed computers it usually turns out that when their length becomes comparable to the wavelengths of the higher-frequency signal components, the crosstalk signal becomes so large that it is often necessary to use coaxial lines. Thus it is usually (but not always) possible to make the division of cases shown in Table 9.1.

**TABLE 9.1**

| Type of wiring | Distance | Analysis approach |
|---|---|---|
| Open wire, etc. | intraunit | lumped circuit |
| Coaxial line | interunit | distributed |

Intraunit wiring may be random, but fortunately a lumped-circuit analysis approach is often possible. In some instances, as in the parallel transmission of a word from register to register and especially in the internal wiring of memories such as core memories, a large number of wires may

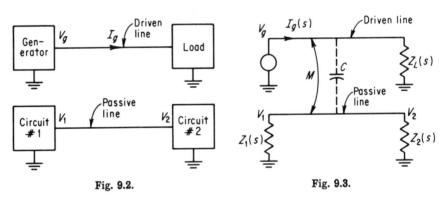

Fig. 9.2.        Fig. 9.3.

run close together over appreciable distances. In such cases, a distributed analysis must often be made; this will be considered later. When the signal transition times are of the order of 10 nsec or more, crosstalk problems with coaxial lines are often negligible for logic signal transmission over the distances for which attentuation is not a serious problem—distances of the order of one hundred feet or so. For longer distances the transmission system becomes a digital communication system, often requiring special modulation techniques, repeaters, etc., and will not be discussed here. Also, when signal transition times become very short, such as less than a nanosecond, extreme care must be taken in choosing the coaxial cable to be used.

First, intraunit wiring (that is, wiring inside the computer cabinets) will be considered in more detail. Recall that currents flow in circuits rather than on single wires. $M$ shall be defined as the mutual inductance between the two loops or circuits in Fig. 9.2 and $C$ as the mutual capacitance between the driven line and the passive line (see Fig. 9.3).

Using Laplace transforms, solution of the equations for Fig. 9.3 yields (initial conditions are assumed to be zero) approximately

$$V_1(s) = sCV_g(s) \frac{Z_1 Z_2}{Z_1 + Z_2} + sMI_g(s) \frac{Z_1}{Z_1 + Z_2}$$

$$V_2(s) = sCV_g(s) \frac{Z_1 Z_2}{Z_1 + Z_2} - sMI_g(s) \frac{Z_2}{Z_1 + Z_2}$$

$$(9.1)$$

where $V_g(s) \cong Z_L(s)I_g(s)$ if the driven line is short. In the case of lines driven by switches which may produce steps having rise times of the order of 1 nsec or less, $I_g \cong V_g/Z_0$ for times of the order of the line delay where $Z_0$ is the characteristic impedance of the driven line.

If the impedances in Fig. 9.3 are resistive, then Eqs. (9.1) become

$$V_1 = C \frac{R_1 R_2}{R_1 + R_2} \frac{dV_g}{dt} + M \frac{R_1}{R_1 + R_2} \frac{dI_g}{dt}$$

$$V_2 = C \frac{R_1 R_2}{R_1 + R_2} \frac{dV_g}{dt} - M \frac{R_2}{R_1 + R_2} \frac{dI_g}{dt}$$

$$(9.2)$$

Each of Eqs. (9.2) has two terms, one proportional to $C$ called the capacitive crosstalk component and one proportional to $M$ called the inductive crosstalk component.

Note that these crosstalk components are respectively proportional to the rate of change of the voltage and current in the driven line.

The capacitive component was predominant in computer circuits using vacuum tubes where large voltages and small currents were involved. It was reduced just by having the wires far apart or else shielded from each other. This was easy to do because of the size of these machines.

When the voltages are small and the currents are large, the inductive component of crosstalk may be large compared to the capacitive component. This is often but not always the case with solid-state circuits. Whichever is the case can be determined by examining $V_1$ and $V_2$. If $V_g$ is a

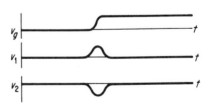

Fig. 9.4. Characteristic waveforms for capacitive and inductive crosstalk when $M > 0$ and inductive crosstalk predominates.

positive ramp, we can construct the following Table 9.2 by inspection from Eqs. (9.2) for $R_1 = R_2 = Z_L$. The case corresponding to the second line in Table 9.2 is illustrated in Fig. 9.4.

TABLE **9.2**

| $V_1$ | $V_2$ | $M$ | Type of crosstalk predominating |
|-------|-------|-----|---------------------------------|
| pos. | pos. | $+$ if $V_1 > V_2$<br>$-$ if $V_2 > V_1$ | capacitive |
| pos. | neg. | $+$ | inductive |
| neg. | pos. | $-$ | inductive |

**9.3**  GROUND NOISE

Mention is often made of "ground noise" and of the need for a good ground to minimize this noise. Let us examine this kind of noise by considering the system in Fig. 9.5. In this figure a long wire is shown grounded at one end and running above a ground plane to point 3 where, for example, the base of a transistor may be connected having its emitter connected to point 4.

Fig. **9.5.** Wire over ground.

It is desired to determine the noise appearing across terminals 3 and 4 arising from current flowing in the ground plane.

If the dotted line from 4 to 3 indicates a circuit element connected across these two points, the voltage rise from 3 to 4 is, by definition, in terms of the electric field at every point in space

$$V = - \int_3^4 \mathbf{E} \cdot \mathbf{ds}$$

Using one of Maxwell's equations

$$\oint \mathbf{E} \cdot \mathbf{ds} = -\frac{d\Phi}{dt}$$

where $\Phi$ is the magnetic flux through the loop 12341, then

$$\int_1^2 \mathbf{E} \cdot \mathbf{ds} + \int_2^3 \mathbf{E} \cdot \mathbf{ds} + \int_3^4 \mathbf{E} \cdot \mathbf{ds} + \int_4^1 \mathbf{E} \cdot \mathbf{ds} = -\frac{d\Phi}{dt}$$

Since there is no current flowing through the wire, $\mathbf{E} = 0$ tangential to its surface. Hence

$$\int_3^4 \mathbf{E} \cdot \mathbf{ds} + \int_4^1 \mathbf{E} \cdot \mathbf{ds} = -\frac{d\Phi}{dt}$$

Assume a current $I$ flows through the ground plane, which is assumed to have an effective resistance from 4 to 1 of $R$. Then

$$- \int_3^4 \mathbf{E} \cdot \mathbf{ds} = V = RI + \frac{d\Phi}{dt}$$

Thus, the "ground noise" consists of an ohmic component arising from currents flowing in the ground plane and of a component that is the inductive crosstalk component. The sources of noise may be summarized as (a) capacitive crosstalk, (b) inductive crosstalk, and (c) coupling through common resistances.

## 9.4  MUTUAL CAPACITANCES

The capacitance crosstalk is by Eq. (9.2) directly proportional to the mutual capacitance and the voltage swing on the driven line and inversely proportional to the rise time. In order to determine how the mutual capacitance depends on geometry, consider a few simple cases (Fig. 9.6).

If the wires can be considered to be essentially infinite in length, the capacitance between the wires (defined as the charge on a conductor divided by the potential difference) for a length $l$ is

$$C = \frac{\pi \epsilon l}{\cosh^{-1} \frac{D}{2a}} = \frac{\pi \epsilon l}{\log_e \left[ \frac{D}{2a} + \sqrt{\left(\frac{D}{2a}\right)^2 - 1} \right]} \quad \text{farads (MKS)}$$

$$C \cong \frac{\pi \epsilon l}{\log_e \frac{D}{a}} \quad \text{if } \frac{a}{D} \text{ is small}$$

This, however, is not the mutual capacitance we are looking for.

In multiconductor systems,

$$\delta V_1 = p_{11} \, \delta Q_1 + p_{12} \, \delta Q_2 + \cdots + p_{1n} \, \delta Q_n$$

$$\delta V_2 = p_{21} \, \delta Q_1 + p_{22} \, \delta Q_2 + \cdots + p_{2n} \, \delta Q_n$$

$$\cdots \qquad\qquad (9.3)$$

$$\delta V_n = p_{n1} \, \delta Q_1 + p_{n2} \, \delta Q_2 + \cdots + p_{nn} \, \delta Q_n$$

$$p_{21} = p_{12}, \text{ etc.}$$

where $\delta V_i$ is the change in potential of conductor $i$, and $\delta Q_j$ is the change in charge on conductor $j$.

These equations may be solved for the $\delta Q_j$ in terms of the $\delta V_i$. For the case of a number of parallel thin wires above ground, these relations may be used to find all of the capacitances including the mutual capacitances.

Consider the arrangement in Fig. 9.7. From potential theory the effect

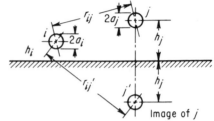

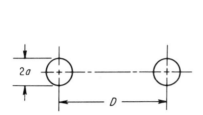

Fig. 9.6. Two parallel round wires in free space.

Fig. 9.7.

of a change of the charge per unit length on conductor $j$ and its image on the potential of conductor $i$ is, for small-diameter wires,

$$p_{ij}\,\delta Q_j = \frac{\delta q_i}{2\pi\epsilon}\log_e \frac{r'_{ij}}{r_{ij}}, \qquad i \neq j$$

and also

$$p_{jj}\,\delta Q_j = \frac{\delta q_j}{2\pi\epsilon}\log \frac{2h_j}{a_j}$$

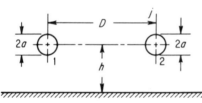

Fig. 9.8. Two parallel round wires above a ground plane.

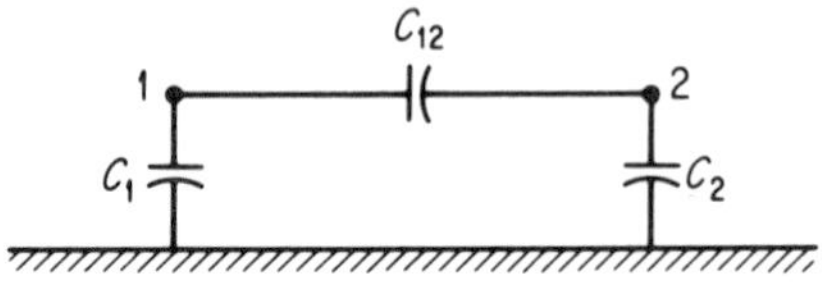

Fig. 9.9. Equivalent circuit.

The equivalent circuit for the configuration of Fig. 9.8 is given in Fig. 9.9.

$$\begin{aligned} \delta Q_1 &= (C_1 + C_{12})\,\delta V_1 - C_{12}\,\delta V_2 \\ \delta Q_2 &= -C_{21}\,\delta V_1 + (C_2 + C_{12})\,\delta V_2 \end{aligned} \tag{9.4}$$

Equations (9.3) become:

$$\delta V_1 = p_{11}\,\delta Q_1 + p_{12}\,\delta Q_2$$

$$\delta V_2 = p_{21}\,\delta Q_1 + p_{22}\,\delta Q_2$$

These may be solved to express $C_1$, $C_2$, and $C_{12}$ in terms of the $p_{ij}$.

$$C_1 = \frac{p_{22} - p_{12}}{\Delta}, \qquad C_2 = \frac{p_{11} - p_{12}}{\Delta}, \qquad C_{12} = \frac{p_{12}}{\Delta}$$

$$\Delta = p_{11}p_{22} - p_{12}p_{21}$$

For the configuration of Fig. 9.8,

$$p_{11} = \frac{1}{2\pi \epsilon l} \log_e \frac{2h}{a}$$

$$p_{12} = p_{21} = \frac{1}{2\pi \epsilon l} \log_e \frac{\sqrt{D^2 + 4h^2}}{D}$$

$$p_{22} = \frac{1}{2\pi \epsilon l} \log_e \frac{2h}{a}$$

Hence, explicitly, for $h \gg a$, $D \gg a$,

$$C_{12} = \frac{2\pi \epsilon l \log_e \left[ \dfrac{\sqrt{D^2 + 4h^2}}{D} \right]}{\log_e \left[ \dfrac{2h\sqrt{D^2 + 4h^2}}{a} \dfrac{}{D} \right] \log_e \left[ \dfrac{2hD}{a\sqrt{D^2 + 4h^2}} \right]} \quad \text{farads} \quad (9.5)$$

where $\epsilon = 8.85 \times 10^{-12}k$ farads/meter, $l$ is in meters, $k$ is the dielectric constant of the medium. An alternate form is

$$C_{12} = \frac{2\pi \epsilon \log_e \dfrac{\sqrt{D^2 + 4h^2}}{D}}{\left[ \log \dfrac{2h}{a} \right]^2 - \left[ \log_e \dfrac{\sqrt{D^2 + 4h^2}}{D} \right]^2} \quad \text{farads/meter} \quad (9.5a)$$

For a pair of 40-mil diameter wires 100 mils apart and 1 in. off ground, $C_{12}$ by Eq. (9.5) is 13.7 pf/meter in air. This is the mutual capacitance (induction). $D$, $h$, and $a$ can be in any consistent set of units. Note that the mutual capacitance is directly proportional to the length of the wire.*

Capacitances for other configurations can be calculated by the methods given above. However, an upper bound on the capacitive crosstalk can be easily estimated if the case of a single wire (passive) surrounded by a group of driven wires each carrying the same signal is considered. The effect would be roughly equivalent to the single wire coaxial to a cylinder carrying the signal (Fig. 9.10). The capacitance between the cylinders is given by

$$C = \frac{2\pi \epsilon}{\log_e (b/a)} \quad \text{farads/meter}$$

For wires located as in Fig. 9.11, $C < 40$ pf/meter. This value of capacitance is less than three times the value obtained from Eq. (9.5) for two wires. Thus the capacitive crosstalk is not greatly increased by the presence of additional wires above that existing for one active wire.

(In practice, it is preferable to measure the capacitances and also the

---

* The published literature in English on crosstalk is very sparse. There are, however, many references in German. Three important references are Refs. 1, 2, and 4 at the end of this chapter.

crosstalk, especially if it has a capacitive component. The formulas enable one to get only an approximate value for any configuration as, among other things, it is difficult to take into account the effect of the wire insulation.)

Summarizing, the capacitive crosstalk is:

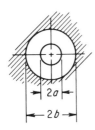

Fig. 9.10. Coaxial cylinders.

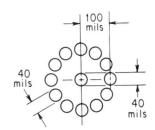

Fig. 9.11.

1. directly proportional to the signal voltage on the driven wires;
2. directly proportional to the distance over which the wires are near each other;
3. directly proportional to the dielectric constant of the medium;
4. inversely proportional to the signal rise times;
5. directly proportional to functions of the logarithms of the distances involved.

Even though the spacings appear as arguments of the logarithms and the logarithms are slowly varying functions of the arguments, an appreciable reduction in crosstalk can be obtained by dealing with the spacings.

## 9.5 INDUCTIVE CROSSTALK

The type of crosstalk that appears in most (but not all) solid-state computer circuits arises chiefly from inductive coupling between driven and passive lines. The mutual inductance between two such lines, if uniformly constructed, is proportional to their lengths such that Eq. (9.2) may be written (inductive component):

$$\begin{bmatrix} \text{crosstalk} \\ \text{voltage} \end{bmatrix} = \begin{bmatrix} \text{function of} \\ \text{circuit constants} \end{bmatrix} \times \begin{bmatrix} \dfrac{\text{current level} \times \text{line length}}{\text{rise-time}} \end{bmatrix}$$
$$\times \begin{bmatrix} \text{function} \\ \text{of spacings} \end{bmatrix} \quad (9.6)$$

A circuit designed for high computing speeds must have small margins for noise because time is uselessly consumed in swinging a voltage or current through a range in which nothing is done. Crosstalk is not controlled efficiently by designing large margins for noise into the circuits. In this connection, it will be shown later that an optimum margin exists for a given wiring configuration. For this and other reasons it is not practicable to reduce crosstalk appreciably by reducing the first term of Eq. (9.6). In fact the worst case is in Fig. 9.5, which makes the first term unity. With given circuits, the current level appearing in Eq. (9.6) is fixed. It is preferable to pick an entirely different circuit type, if possible, if the current level of the type used is excessively high, rather than designing the circuit for a lower current level, because a given circuit has an optimum current level and too much deviation from this optimum will result in poor performance. The line lengths are determined by packaging and logical considerations and given a specific machine logic; the only thing that can be done is to increase the packaging efficiency. The rise time is also fixed by the circuit type so that the second term of Eq. (9.6) can be reduced only by improving the package and backboard design to minimize wire lengths. This is also desirable for other reasons such as the reduction of wiring delays and machine size. Therefore, it is possible to reduce crosstalk in any given situation most effectively by reducing the third term of Eq. (9.6). Ways of doing this will now be discussed in connection with several wiring systems that have been used in the past.

There are essentially two kinds of wiring in computers. These are (intraunit): (a) package wiring, (b) backboard wiring. It must be remembered that any signal must pass over the package wiring *twice* and over the backboard wiring *once*. *Both* types of wiring must be considered for effective crosstalk control. Since package and backboard wiring problems are both mechanical and electrical, their solution requires the close cooperation of both mechanical and electrical engineers and the abandonment of notions that do not have any good solid reasons for their existence.

Four ways of doing package wiring (not all possible ways) in approximate order of decreasing crosstalk are:

1. Printed-circuit wiring laid out on the basis of purely mechanical considerations.
2. Printed-circuit wiring laid out on the basis of both mechanical and electrical considerations.
3. Printed-circuit wiring using microstrip or similar techniques.
4. Twisted pair for some or all signal lines.

These are not necessarily in the order of increasing mechanical complexity or cost.

Six ways of doing backboard wiring so as to control crosstalk in approximate order of decreasing crosstalk and increasing mechanical complexity are (an optimum then exists for any system):

1. Cabled or "neat" wiring with ground busses.
2. Point-to-point wiring over a ground plane, which may be the chassis.

A lattice of interconnected wires may, in some cases, be as effective as using the chassis as circuit ground.

3. The use of special cables.
4. Point-to-point wiring using twisted pair.
5. The use of coaxial line.
6. The use of multishielded coaxial line.

One method of engineering a wiring system requires: (a) The determination by experiment of the circuit margins. These are usually greater than one would obtain by calculation. (b) The use of the wiring techniques stated above, trying to minimize cost while allowing no more crosstalk than permitted by the circuit margins.

Several methods of backboard wiring will now be discussed. Some of the discussion also applies to package wiring.

Consider the wiring system which is outlined in Fig. 9.12. The generator is on card $A$ and drives a circuit on card $B$. The line $C$-$D$ is the passive line.

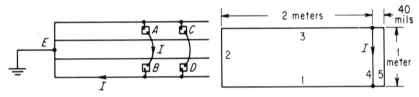

**Fig. 9.12.** "Neat" wiring with ground busses.

**Fig. 9.13.**

The "go" current, $I$, is on the line from $A$ to $B$. The return current has to traverse the loop $ABEA$. The mutual inductance between this loop and loop $CDEC$ would be expected to be considerable, so that appreciable inductive crosstalk voltage would be produced on line $CD$. Another way of looking at the situation is that the self-inductance of loop $ABEA$ would be much larger than the self-inductance of loop $ABDCA$, so that the return current would try to return to $A$ by line $DC$ rather than the long way round $(BEA)$, thus producing noise in line $CD$. The mutual inductance of the two loops can be calculated using published formulas. (See Ref. 3.) For a comparison of systems, numbers will be obtained for similar geometries.

A calculation for the system of Fig. 9.12 is made in the footnote* below,

* The calculation of the mutual inductance of the configuration of Fig. 9.12: The equivalent configuration is as in Fig. 9.13. Dimensions assumed are shown. Wires 1, 2, and 3 will be assumed to be 250 mils in dia. Wires 4 and 5 will be assumed to be 20 mils in dia. From Grover (Ref. 3), the mutual inductance between the circuits is

$$M = M_{11} + M_{12} + M_{13} + M_{14}$$
$$+ M_{21} + M_{22} + M_{23} + M_{24}$$
$$+ M_{31} + M_{32} + M_{33} + M_{34}$$
$$+ M_{51} + M_{52} + M_{53} + M_{54}$$

where 6.82 $\mu$h is obtained for the mutual inductance between the loops under consideration.

Before proceeding further it would be wise to review the theory. *Mutual* inductance refers to the inductance between *circuits* or *loops* and *self* inductance refers to the inductance of a *circuit* or *loop*. It is not proper to speak of the inductance of a wire, since the definition of inductance involves the flux through an *area* which must be bounded by conductors. (Formulas that give the inductance of wires not in closed circuits or the mutual inductance, for example, of lengths of straight wires as in the example above are the results of the evaluation of Neumann's formula [Eq. (9.9)] for these circuit parts.

For the sake of brevity, however, it is usual to neglect mentioning this fact and to say that these formulas give the mutual inductance between the circuit parts or the self inductance of the circuit part. An example of the use of these formulas to get the mutual inductance between circuits is given in the preceding footnote.

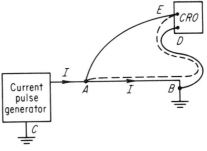

Fig. 9.14. Current pulse applied to wire.

For example, consider the application of a current pulse to a piece of wire as in Fig. 9.14. The cathode-ray oscilloscope (CRO) is connected as shown. If the CRO vertical input

---

The values of the various mutuals are:

| | | | | | |
|---|---|---|---|---|---|
| $M_{11}$ = | 2.56 $\mu$h | $M_{23}$ = | 0 | $M_{51}$ = | 0 |
| $M_{12}$ = | 0 | $M_{24}$ = | −0.049 | $M_{52}$ = | −0.049 |
| $M_{13}$ = | −0.33 | $M_{31}$ = | −0.33 | $M_{53}$ = | 0 |
| $M_{14}$ = | 0 | $M_{32}$ = | 0 | $M_{54}$ = | 1.316 |
| $M_{21}$ = | 0 | $M_{33}$ = | 2.56 | Total = | 6.82 $\mu$h |
| $M_{22}$ = | 1.14 | $M_{34}$ = | 0 | | |

The mutual inductance of two filaments at right angles is zero. The mutual inductance of two parallel filaments is

$$M = 0.2l \left[ \log_e \left( \frac{l}{d} + \sqrt{1 + \frac{l^2}{d^2}} \right) - \sqrt{1 + \frac{d^2}{l^2}} + \frac{d}{l} \right] \; \mu\text{h}$$

where $l$ is their length in meters and $d$ is their separation. If the conductors are not filaments, $d$ is replaced by the "geometric mean distance." The geometric mean distance of a circle of radius $a$ from itself is $0.779a$.

For $M_{11}$, for example, $d = 0.779 \times 0.125 \times 2.54 \times 10^{-2} = 2.5 \times 10^{-3}$ meters, $d/l = 1.25 \times 10^{-3}$, hence

$$M_{11} = 0.2 \times 2 \times \left[ \log_e \frac{4}{2.5} \times 10^3 - 1 \right] = 2.56 \; \mu\text{h} = M_{33}$$

See Ref. 3.

is connected to point $A$ as shown by the solid line, a deflection may be observed proportional to the derivative of the current pulse. The proportionality constant is *not* the "inductance" of the wire $AB$ but is the mutual inductance of loops $ABCA$ and $AEDBA$. This is dramatically illustrated by deforming the lead $AE$ to follow the dotted line, which results in the lowering of the mutual inductance and the observed differentiated pulse amplitude by reducing the area of loop $AEDBA$. The rate of rise of current in the loop $ABC$ is affected by the *self* inductance of that loop.

These ideas may be quantitatively expressed if we consider $n$ loops in space carrying currents $I_1, I_2, \ldots, I_n$. The flux through the $i$th loop is

$$\Phi_i = \int \mathbf{B} \cdot \mathbf{dS}_i$$

Since $\mathbf{B} = \nabla \times \mathbf{A}$, and using Stokes' theorem,

$$\Phi_i = \int (\nabla \times \mathbf{A}) \cdot \mathbf{dS}_i = \oint \mathbf{A} \cdot \mathbf{dl}_i$$

But for a distribution of current density $\mathbf{J}$, in space, the well-known relation for the vector potential $\mathbf{A}$ is

$$\mathbf{A} = \frac{\mu}{4\pi} \int \frac{\mathbf{J}}{r} \, dv$$

which, for $n$ loops, becomes for the $i$th loop

$$\mathbf{A} = \frac{\mu}{4\pi} \sum_{j=1}^{n} \oint \frac{I_j \mathbf{dl}_j}{r_{ij}}$$

where $r_{ij}$ is the distance between the points of interest on loop $i$ and loop $j$.
Hence

$$\Phi_i = \frac{\mu}{4\pi} \sum_{j=1}^{n} \oint \oint I_j \frac{\mathbf{dl}_i \cdot \mathbf{dl}_j}{r_{ij}} \qquad (9.7)$$

If the current in each loop is independent of position, Eq. (9.7) may be written

$$\Phi_i = \sum_{j=1}^{n} L_{ij} I_j, \qquad i = 1, 2, \ldots, n \qquad (9.8)$$

$$L_{ij} = \frac{\mu}{4\pi} \oint \oint \frac{\mathbf{dl}_i \cdot \mathbf{dl}_j}{r_{ij}} \qquad (9.9)$$

Equation (9.9) is known as Neumann's formula.

For three loops, Eq. (9.8) when written out is

$$\Phi_1 = L_{11} I_1 + L_{12} I_2 + L_{13} I_3$$
$$\Phi_2 = L_{21} I_1 + L_{22} I_2 + L_{23} I_3 \qquad (9.10)$$
$$\Phi_3 = L_{31} I_1 + L_{32} I_2 + L_{33} I_3$$

$L_{11}$, $L_{22}$, and $L_{33}$ are the self inductance of loops 1, 2, and 3, respectively, while $L_{13}$ is the mutual inductance between loops 1 and 3 [$L_{13} = L_{31}$ from Eq. (9.9)], $L_{23}$ is the mutual inductance between loops 2 and 3, etc.

From Eq. (9.9), the inductances are functions of the current distributions on the wires. At high frequencies the current is distributed close to the surface of the wire, and since crosstalk is a high-frequency phenomenon it is reasonable to assume that the current lies on the wire surface (this is equivalent to neglecting the internal self inductance of the wire). A uniform distribution of current on the surface is reasonable to assume, except when the wires are very close together (proximity effects occurring at high frequencies). The effect of these assumptions is that both the self and mutual inductances can be computed from Eq. (9.9) considering the wires as filaments on the wire axes even when the wires are almost in contact (see references at the end of this chapter). Proximity effects could at most change the value of the mutual inductance by 20 per cent (see Ref. 3).

Returning to the configuration of Fig. 9.12, insight into why such a high figure was obtained for the mutual inductance between the two loops can be obtained by considering the configuration of Fig. 9.15. The mutual

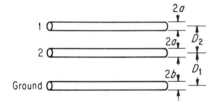

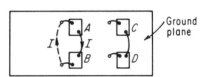

**Fig. 9.15.** Two circuits with common ground bus.     **Fig. 9.16.** Point-to-point wiring over a ground plane.

inductance between circuit 1 and circuit 2 is given by (in air for long wires):

$$M = 0.2 \log_e \frac{D_1(D_1 + D_2)}{bD_2} \quad \mu\text{h per meter} \tag{9.11}$$

If $D_1 = 1$ in., $D_2 = 1$ in., and $a = b = 10$ mils (No. 24 wire), $M = 1.06 \, \mu\text{h}$ per meter. Note that the radius of the ground wire appears in the denominator of the argument of the logarithm. It is therefore inadvisable to use a wire as a common ground.

Figure 9.16 shows how the situation might be improved by wiring point-to-point over a ground plane. As before, the generator is at $A$ and line $CE$ is the passive line. The return current, $I$, is now free to return to $A$ by means of the dotted path (the image of the "go" wire). The mutual inductance between the two loops will be less than in Fig. 9.12. The system is equivalent to that shown in Fig. 9.17.

For long wires

$$M = 0.2 \log_e \frac{\sqrt{D^2 + 4h^2}}{D} \quad \mu\text{h per meter} \tag{9.12}$$

For $D = 40$ mils (10 mils of insulation on No. 20 wires in *contact*), $h = \frac{1}{2}$ in., and $a = 10$ mils, $M = 0.64$ $\mu$h per meter.

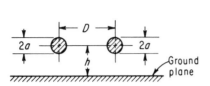

Fig. 9.17. Two wires over a ground plane.

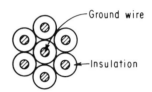

Fig. 9.18. Multi-wire cable.

## 9.6 SPECIAL CABLES

At various times attempts have been made to reduce the number of ground wires required below the number needed when twisted pairs are used. One such configuration is shown in Fig. 9.18.

In order for such a cable to be effective, the ground wire must be connected at both ends to circuit ground. Consider the geometry of Fig. 9.19 where there are two of the signal wires of Fig. 9.18 and the ground wires. For this

$$M = -0.2 \log_e \frac{ad}{r^2} \quad \mu\text{h per meter} \tag{9.13}$$

For $a = 10$ mils, $d = r = 40$ mils (10 mils of insulation), $M = +0.28$ $\mu$h

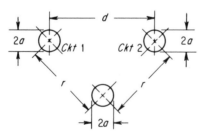

Fig. 9.19.

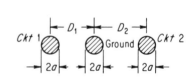

Fig. 9.20. Belt arrangement.

per meter. If $r = d = 1$ in. and $a = 10$ mils, $M = +0.92$ $\mu$h per meter. For the belt arrangement of Fig. 9.20,

$$M = -0.2 \log_e \frac{a(D_1 + D_2)}{D_2 D_1} \quad \mu\text{h per meter} \tag{9.14}$$

For $a = 10$ mils, $D_1 = D_2 = 40$ mils, $M = +0.14$ $\mu$h per meter. A belt containing more wires than shown in Fig. 9.20 can be analyzed as a circuit element by using Eq. (9.8) after all the $L_{ij}$ are obtained. The presence of the wire radius in the arguments of the logarithms in Eqs. (9.13) and (9.14) makes the corresponding configurations undesirable.

## 9.7 TWISTED PAIR

The calculation of the mutual inductance between two twisted pairs which are close to each other is complicated by the difficult geometry. However, it is possible to obtain an approximation to the mutual inductance. The geometry of two parallel pairs is shown in Fig. 9.21. The mutual inductance between the two circuits is given by

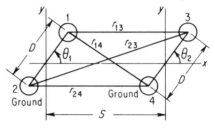

Fig. 9.21. Parallel pairs.

$$M = \frac{\mu}{2\pi} \log_e \frac{r_{23}r_{14}}{r_{13}r_{24}} \quad \text{henrys per meter}$$

where

$$r_{14}^2 = S^2 + \frac{D^2}{2} - SD \cos \theta_1 - SD \cos \theta_2 + \frac{D^2}{2} \cos (\theta_2 - \theta_1)$$

$$r_{24}^2 = S^2 + \frac{D^2}{2} + SD \cos \theta_1 - SD \cos \theta_2 - \frac{D^2}{2} \cos (\theta_2 - \theta_1)$$

$$r_{23}^2 = S^2 + \frac{D^2}{2} + SD \cos \theta_1 + SD \cos \theta_2 + \frac{D^2}{2} \cos (\theta_2 - \theta_1)$$

$$r_{13}^2 = S^2 + \frac{D^2}{2} - SD \cos \theta_1 + SD \cos \theta_2 - \frac{D^2}{2} \cos (\theta_2 - \theta_1)$$

Hence for the parallel pairs

$$M = \frac{\mu}{4\pi} \log_e \frac{\left[S^2 + \frac{D^2}{2} + \frac{D^2}{2} \cos (\theta_2 - \theta_1)\right]^2 - [SD \cos \theta_1 + SD \cos \theta_2]^2}{\left[S^2 + \frac{D^2}{2} - \frac{D^2}{2} \cos (\theta_2 - \theta_1)\right]^2 - [SD \cos \theta_1 - SD \cos \theta_2]^2}$$

For two twisted pairs, with pitches $p_1$ and $p_2$,

$$\theta_1 = \frac{z}{p_1}, \qquad \theta_2 = \frac{z}{p_2}$$

and, approximately,

$$M = \int_0^l M(z) \, dz \tag{9.15}$$

Equation (9.15) is an approximation because the fields for a parallel pair are transverse, while for a twisted pair they are not. Equation (9.15) is integrable in closed form if $p_1 = p_2 = p$. Hence for $p_1 = p_2 = p$,

$$M = \frac{\mu}{4\pi} \int_0^{2\pi} \log_e \frac{(S^2 + D^2)^2 - 4S^2 D^2 \cos^2 \theta}{S^4} \, d\theta \quad \text{henrys/meter}$$

This may be put into the form

$$M = \frac{\mu}{8\pi} \int_0^\pi \log_e \left( \frac{S^4 + D^4}{S^2} - \frac{2D^2}{S^2} \cos \alpha \right) d\alpha$$

From the definite integral (Peirce No. 540)

$$\int_0^\pi \log_e (a \pm b \cos x) \, dx = \pi \log \left( \frac{a + \sqrt{a^2 - b^2}}{2} \right), \qquad a \geq b$$

thus

$$M = \frac{\mu}{8} \log 1 = 0 \tag{9.16}$$

As Eq. (9.16) is an approximation, this does not definitely prove that the coupling between two twisted pairs is zero. However, it is quite small and arises chiefly because of end effects, other nonuniformities, and wave propagation phenomena; for specific values, it is best to resort to measurement.

### 9.8  COAXIAL LINE

The calculation of mutual inductance for the configuration of Fig. 9.22 using the above methods also yields zero. However, the mutual impedance between the two coaxial lines is not zero. This is because the resistance of the outer conductor gives rise to a longitudinal electric field, which can be considered to be the electric-field component of an electromagnetic wave propagating radially from the driven line. This wave will have some effect on the passive line. The effect might become a problem in interunit cabling, especially if the outer conductor is braided and not solid. The equivalent mutual inductance from this effect could be as large as 0.006 $\mu$h per meter for lines nearly in contact.

Fig. 9.22.

### 9.9  MULTIPLE SHIELDED LINES

Crosstalk between coaxial lines can be reduced by putting a conducting or magnetic coating over the outer conductor and insulated from the outer conductor. The external electromagnetic wave is appreciably absorbed by this coating.

## 9.10 SUMMARY OF INDUCTIVE CROSSTALK

Values of inductive crosstalk voltage are given in Table 9.3 for 10 ma switched in 20 nsec and for 3 volts switched by a mechanical switch. (The characteristic impedance of the driven line is assumed to be 150 Ω; for the switched line, the rise time is assumed to be 1 nsec.) The values given in Table 9.3 are evaluated on the basis of one meter of line-length for one driven line; however, these values should be considered only as illustrative examples, especially in the case of twisted pairs of lines, where values of a lesser order of magnitude have been observed. *If there is more than one driven line and all are driven at the same time, the crosstalk voltages produced by each in the passive line are additive.* The figures in the table should, therefore, be modified to take this into account.

TABLE **9.3.** COMPARISON OF SYSTEMS

| Wiring system | Mutual ind. ($\mu$h/m) | Crosstalk (volts per meter) | |
|---|---|---|---|
| | | 10 ma in 20 nsec* | 3 v in 150 Ω† |
| "NEAT" | 1–7 | 0.5–3.5 | 3 |
| Point-to-point over a ground plane | 0.64 | 0.32 | 2 |
| Special cables | 0.3 | 0.15 | 0.9 |
| Twisted pairs | 0.06 | 0.03 | 0.2 |
| Coaxial pairs | 0.006 | 0.003 | 0.02 |
| Multiple-shielded coaxial | As small as necessary | | |

\* From M di/dt
† From Eqs. 9.29

## 9.11 SWITCHED LINES

The large figures for the crosstalk due to switched voltages lead to the conclusion that this crosstalk must be reduced by increasing the rise time to a value equal to or larger than that occurring in the logic circuits. There are several ways of doing this using resistors when operating logic circuits. An example appears in Fig. 9.23. Note that the line is charged and discharged through resistors. A capacitor, $C$, may be placed on the line to degrade the rise and fall times further.

It is preferable not to use inductive elements to increase the rise times in mechanically switched lines unless certain precautions are taken, which will become evident in the following discussion. Consider a T filter used

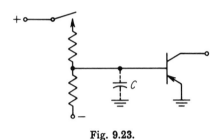

as in Fig. 9.24. No difficulties are experienced when the switch is closed. However, when it is opened, the current in $L$ is interrupted rapidly, producing a high voltage at point $A$ and the possibility of both capacitive and inductive crosstalk. The situation can be improved by placing an RC network across the switch as shown. When a $\pi$ filter is

**Fig. 9.23.**

used (Fig. 9.25), the switch must charge the input capacitor in nanoseconds through a resistance which is a fraction of an ohm. For example, assume

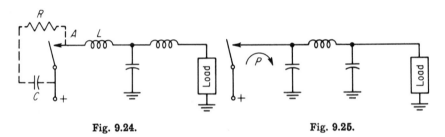

**Fig. 9.24.**                                        **Fig. 9.25.**

150 volts is switched. Assume 0.1-ohm loop resistance, 0.002 $\mu$h mutual inductance between the loop $p$ and a passive line in the computer, and 0.004 $\mu$h loop inductance. The crosstalk voltage is

$$\frac{150}{4 \times 10^{-9}} \times 2 \times 10^{-9} = 75 \text{ volts peak}$$

and it decays exponentially with a time constant of about 20 nsec. The crosstalk voltage pulse *area* may be reduced by increasing the resistance of the loop as in Fig. 9.26. If the switches are in a remote console, there is the

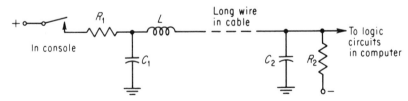

**Fig. 9.26.** Filter.

possibility of crosstalk in the cable connecting the computer or of noise pick-up due to external fields. The capacitor $C_2$ can be used to reduce this noise. The resistor $R_2$ serves to establish the voltage level of the switched line when the switch is open.

## 9.12  WIDENING OF AN IMPULSE

Crosstalk signals occur only while a current or voltage is changing. If the signal change takes 20 nsec, the crosstalk will last 20 nsec. However, circuits and wiring can widen this crosstalk pulse, and how this occurs will be indicated. Assume a current impulse carrying a charge $q$ is representative of a crosstalk signal. This impulse is applied to the base of a transistor as in Fig. 9.27.

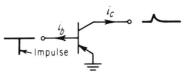

**Fig. 9.27.**

If

$$I_c(s) = \frac{\alpha_{FE}I_B(s)}{1 + s\dfrac{\alpha_{FE}}{\omega_T}}$$

then

$$I_c(s) = \frac{\alpha_{FE}q}{1 + s\dfrac{\alpha_{FE}}{\omega_T}} \quad \text{and} \quad i_c(t) = \omega_T q e^{-(\omega_T t)/\alpha_{FE}}$$

The peak value of the collector current is $\omega_T q$ and the area under the collector current waveform is $\alpha_{FE}q$. Therefore, the transistor *will amplify* even an impulse.

## 9.13  OPTIMUM MARGINS

With a given wiring system and layout, it is possible to estimate what the optimum circuit margins should be. In Fig. 9.28, the needed voltage

**Fig. 9.28.**

and current excursion for a circuit are $v$ and $i$ but current and voltage margins of $v_m$ and $i_m$ are needed. Therefore the actual swings are $v + 2v_m$ and $i + 2i_m$. The voltage and current crosstalk signals are

$$v_c = \frac{M}{T} (i + 2i_m)$$

$$i_c = \frac{C}{T} (v + 2v_m)$$

and should be less than $v_m$ and $i_m$ respectively. In the extreme case

$$v_m = \frac{M}{T} (i + 2i_m)$$

$$i_m = \frac{C}{T} (v + 2v_m)$$

Solving for $v_m$ and $i_m$ yields

$$v_m = \frac{\dfrac{M}{T} i + \dfrac{2MC}{T^2} v}{1 - \dfrac{4MC}{T^2}}$$

$$i_m = \frac{\dfrac{C}{T} v + \dfrac{4MC}{T^2} i}{1 - \dfrac{4MC}{T^2}}$$

(9.17)

For example, with open wiring and with one foot of wiring assume $M = 0.3$ $\mu$h and $C = 13$ pf. When the denominator of Eq. (9.17) vanishes, no computer can be built. This is for a switching time of $T = 2\sqrt{MC}$. Using the assumed numbers, $T = 4$ nsec.

The margins for $v = 3$ volts and $i = 10$ ma for 20-nsec switching times are

$$v_m = 0.22 \text{ v} \quad \text{and} \quad i_m = 2.3 \text{ ma.}$$

### 9.14  CROSSTALK ON MULTIPLE TRANSMISSION LINES

This section will discuss the problem of calculating the crosstalk that exists between multiple transmission lines that are too long to be considered as lumped-constant circuits. Such lines may exist in regions where a word is transferred over a set of parallel busses and in some kinds of core storage units. The results, however, also confirm the validity of the approximate inductive crosstalk calculation techniques previously discussed in that these are found to be exact when the lines are properly terminated and the signal rise times are large compared to the line delays.

Consider $n$ wires running parallel over a ground plane as in Fig. 9.29. The equations for such an assembly of lines are

$$\frac{dV_i}{dx} = - \sum_{k=1}^{n} Z_{ik}I_k, \quad i = 1, 2, \ldots, n$$

$$\frac{dI_i}{dx} = - \sum_{k=1}^{n} Y_{ik}V_k, \quad i = 1, 2, \ldots, n$$

(9.18)

The $Z_{ik}$ are the self and mutual impedances and the $Y_{ik}$ are the self and mutual admittances. For example, $Z_{11}$ is $R_{11} + sL_{11}$ where $R_{11}$ and $L_{11}$ are respectively the resistance and inductance per unit loop length of line 1. $Z_{12}$ is $sL_{12}$ where $L_{12}$ is the mutual inductance per unit length between lines 1 and 2 [see Sec. 9.4 and Eqs. (9.10)].

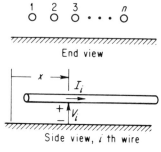

End view

Side view, $i$ th wire

Fig. 9.29.

If $n - 1$ lines in Fig. 9.29 talk into a single line, this line in turn talks into all the other lines, affecting the waveforms on them. This second interaction is taken into account in Eqs. (9.18) as are all higher-order interactions. However, in most cases it is a valid approximation to neglect the second- and higher-order interactions, calculating the crosstalk voltage and current in a single line and neglecting the effect that the single line has on the others. The size of the error introduced in this way can be estimated by calculating the crosstalk due to the crosstalk. Also, it is required only to calculate the crosstalk from a single active line into the passive line, as in this approximate method the effect of several active lines can be obtained by superposition. (See Fig. 9.31 for results in a form useful for calculation.)

Consider two transmission lines as in Fig. 9.30. It will be assumed that both lines have the same characteristic impedance, $Z_0$, and propagation

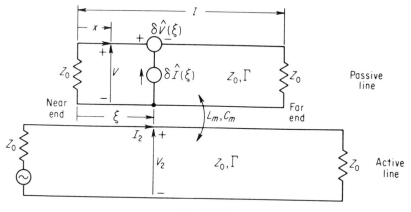

Fig. 9.30.

constant, $\Gamma$, and are terminated at both ends in $Z_0$. Coupling is loose and is via the mutual inductance per unit length, $L_m$, and the mutual capacitance per unit length, $C_m$. A wave is assumed to be propagating from left to right in the active line and at the point $\xi$ has the values

$$I_a = I_0 e^{-\Gamma\xi}$$
$$V_a = Z_0 I_a \tag{9.19}$$

These produce at the point $\xi$ in the passive line the differential crosstalk signals

$$\delta\hat{I}(\xi) = sC_m V_a$$
$$\delta\hat{V}(\xi) = sL_m I_a \tag{9.20}$$

Differential crosstalk signals inserted at the point $\xi$ propagate in both directions without reflection. For example, for $x < \xi$ we have for the differential crosstalk voltage $\delta V(x, \xi)$ and differential crosstalk current $\delta I(x, \xi)$ due to the differential crosstalk signals,

$$\delta V(x, \xi) = \frac{\delta\hat{V}(\xi)}{2} e^{-\Gamma(\xi-x)} + Z_0 \frac{\delta\hat{I}(\xi)}{2} e^{-\Gamma(\xi-x)}, \qquad x < \xi$$
$$\delta I(x, \xi) = -\frac{\delta\hat{V}(\xi)}{2Z_0} e^{-\Gamma(\xi-x)} - \frac{\delta\hat{I}(\xi)}{2} e^{-\Gamma(\xi-x)}, \qquad x < \xi \tag{9.21}$$

For $x > \xi$, $\delta V(x, \xi)$ and $\delta I(x, \xi)$ are

$$\delta V(x, \xi) = -\frac{\delta\hat{V}(\xi)}{2} e^{-\Gamma(x-\xi)} + Z_0 \frac{\delta\hat{I}(\xi)}{2} e^{-\Gamma(x-\xi)}, \qquad x > \xi$$
$$\delta I(x, \xi) = -\frac{\delta\hat{V}(\xi)}{2Z_0} e^{-\Gamma(x-\xi)} + \frac{\delta\hat{I}(\xi)}{2} e^{-\Gamma(x-\xi)}, \qquad x > \xi \tag{9.22}$$

Equations (9.21) and (9.22) are partly derived in Ref. 7. However, they can also be written down using superposition, the properties of incident waves (Appendix III), and the fact that the input impedance of the passive line at $\xi$ is $Z_0/2$. The total crosstalk voltage and current on the passive line is obtained by integrating the differential voltages and currents, given in Eqs. (9.21) and (9.22), over the region of interaction, which in this case is the length of the passive line

$$V(x) = \int_0^l \delta\hat{V}(x, \xi) \, d\xi$$
$$I(x) = \int_0^l \delta\hat{I}(x, \xi) \, d\xi \tag{9.23}$$

Equations (9.19) through (9.23) become

$$V(x) = \int_0^x \left[ -\frac{sL_m I_0 e^{-\Gamma\xi}}{2} e^{-\Gamma(x-\xi)} + Z_0 \frac{sC_m Z_0 I_0 e^{-\Gamma\xi}}{2} e^{-\Gamma(x-\xi)} \right] d\xi$$

$$+ \int_x^l \left[ \frac{sL_m I_0 e^{-\Gamma\xi}}{2} e^{-\Gamma(\xi-x)} + Z_0 \frac{sC_m Z_0 I_0 e^{-\Gamma\xi}}{2} e^{-\Gamma(\xi-x)} \right] d\xi$$

$$(9.24)$$

$$I(x) = \int_0^x \left[ -\frac{sL_m I_0 e^{-\Gamma\xi}}{2Z_0} e^{-\Gamma(x-\xi)} + \frac{sC_m Z_0 I_0 e^{-\Gamma\xi}}{2} e^{-\Gamma(x-\xi)} \right] d\xi$$

$$+ \int_x^l \left[ -\frac{sL_m I_0 e^{-\Gamma\xi}}{2Z_0} e^{-\Gamma(\xi-x)} - \frac{sC_m Z_0 I_0 e^{-\Gamma\xi}}{2} e^{-\Gamma(\xi-x)} \right] d\xi$$

Evaluation of Eq. (9.24) yields

$$V(x) =$$

$$-\frac{sL_m I_0}{2} \left[ \left( 1 - Z_0^2 \frac{C_m}{L_m} \right) x e^{-\Gamma x} + \frac{1}{2\Gamma} \left( 1 + Z_0^2 \frac{C_m}{L_m} \right) (e^{-\Gamma(2l-x)} - e^{-\Gamma x}) \right]$$

$$(9.25)$$

$$I(x) =$$

$$-\frac{sL_m I_0}{2Z_0} \left[ \left( 1 - Z_0^2 \frac{C_m}{L_m} \right) x e^{-\Gamma x} - \frac{1}{2\Gamma} \left( 1 + Z_0^2 \frac{C_m}{L_m} \right) (e^{-\Gamma(2l-x)} - e^{-\Gamma x}) \right]$$

Equations (9.25) may be used to compute the crosstalk voltages and currents after inverse Laplace transforming. However, in many cases

$$Z_0 = \sqrt{\frac{L}{C}} = \sqrt{\frac{L_m}{C_m}} \qquad (9.26)$$

whereupon, Eqs. (9.25) become

$$V(x) = \frac{sL_m I_0}{2\Gamma} (e^{-\Gamma x} - e^{-\Gamma(2l-x)})$$

$$(9.27)$$

$$I(x) = -\frac{sL_m I_0}{2Z_0 \Gamma} (e^{-\Gamma x} - e^{-\Gamma(2l-x)})$$

Equations (9.27) predict that the far-end crosstalk ($x = l$) is zero. This agrees with that obtained from Eqs. (9.1) if Eq. (9.26) is assumed valid. The near-end crosstalk is obtained by setting $x = 0$ in Eqs. (9.27) to obtain

$$V_1(s) = \frac{sL_m I_0(s)}{2\Gamma} (1 - e^{-2\Gamma l})$$

$$(9.28)$$

$$I_1(s) = -\frac{sL_m I_0(s)}{2Z_0 \Gamma} (1 - e^{-2\Gamma l})$$

Since in a lossless line, $\Gamma = s\sqrt{LC} = sT/l$ where $T$ is the delay, Eqs. (9.28) become

$$V_1(s) = \frac{L_m I_0(s)}{2\sqrt{LC}}\,(1 - e^{-2sT})$$

$$I_1(s) = -\frac{V_1(s)}{Z_0} \tag{9.29}$$

What the first of Eqs. (9.29) predicts is plotted in Fig. 9.31; it has been confirmed by experiment for a typical pulse on the active line for the case

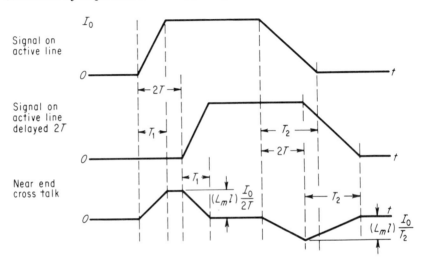

**Fig. 9.31.** Near end crosstalk voltage when $T_1 < 2T < T_2$.

when the round-trip delay on the passive line is greater than the rise and less than the fall time of the signal on the active line. *Note the peak amplitudes and their dependence on the total mutual inductance, the current, and the rise and fall times.* These results show that the crosstalk is simply $M(di/dt)$ when the signal transition time is greater than twice the line delay. Since the near-end crosstalk is the sum of differential contributions propagating toward that end, the near-end crosstalk for cases when the near end is not terminated in $Z_0$ is given by the product of Eqs. (9.29) and the appropriate transmission coefficient. The far-end crosstalk then becomes equal to the product of Eqs. (9.29), the appropriate near-end reflection coefficient, and exp $(-\Gamma l)$.

## 9.15 FORMULAS FOR CROSSTALK CALCULATION

In order to calculate the crosstalk in the case of multiple transmission lines, the sum of the mutual inductances between the passive circuit and all of the active circuits must be frequently calculated. When a large number of lines exists, this calculation is tedious and time-consuming. However, in some cases closed-form expressions are available giving upper bounds. Such expressions are given below for some geometries together with their parent formulas. The frequency is assumed to be high enough so that skin depth is negligible. The formulas were derived assuming that the wires are in air and are infinitesimal filaments. Many of the formulas have been checked experimentally and have been found to give accurate results. All logarithms are to the base $e$.

1. Wires over a ground plane—current returns through ground plane. (Fig. 9.32).

Fig. 9.32.

$$M = 0.2 \log \sqrt{\frac{(h_2 + h_1)^2 + D^2}{(h_2 - h_1)^2 + D^2}} \quad \text{microhenrys/meter}$$

If $h_1 = h_2 = h$,

$$M = 0.2 \log \frac{\sqrt{4h^2 + D^2}}{D} \quad \mu\text{h/m}$$

2. Summation formula for wires over a ground plane—current returns through ground plane (Fig. 9.33).

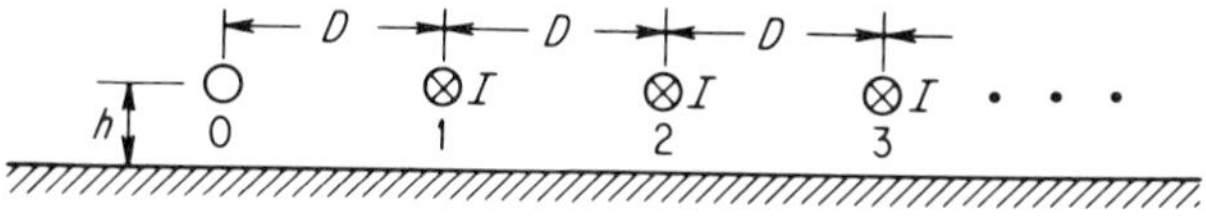

Fig. 9.33.

$$\sum_{n=1}^{\infty} M_{0i} = 0.1 \log \frac{\sinh\left(\frac{2\pi h}{D}\right)}{\left(\frac{2\pi h}{D}\right)} \quad \mu\text{h/m}$$

3. Wires between conducting planes—current returns through either plane or divides between them (Fig. 9.34).

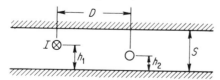

Fig. 9.34.

$$M = 0.2 \log \sqrt{\frac{\cosh^2 \dfrac{\pi D}{2S} - \cos^2 \dfrac{\pi(h_1 + h_2)}{2S}}{\cosh^2 \dfrac{\pi D}{2S} - \cos^2 \dfrac{\pi(h_1 - h_2)}{2S}}} \quad \mu h/m$$

(Derived via conformal transformation $w = \cosh \alpha_z$.) If $h_1 = h_2$ and $S = 2h$,

$$M = 0.2 \log \coth \frac{\pi D}{4h} \quad \mu h/m$$

4. Summation results for wires between conducting planes (Fig. 9.35). The formula for $\sum\limits_{n=1}^{\infty} M_{on}$ can be expressed in terms of theta functions.

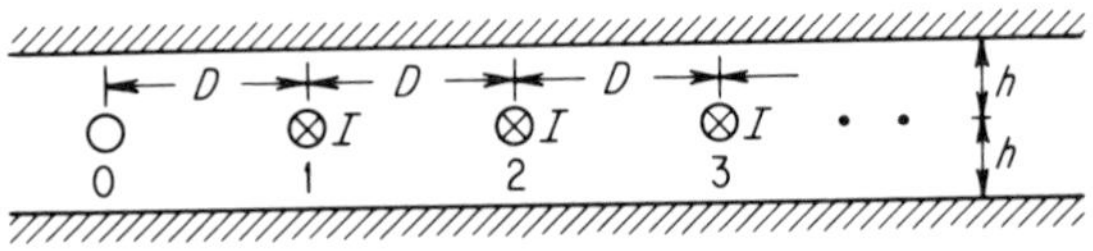

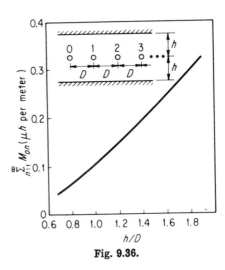

Fig. 9.35.

However, direct calculation is quicker and the results are plotted in Fig. 9.36.

Fig. 9.36.

5. Parallel pairs in free space (Fig. 9.37).

$$M = 0.2 \log \left[ 1 - \left(\frac{W}{D}\right)^2 \right] \quad \mu h/m$$

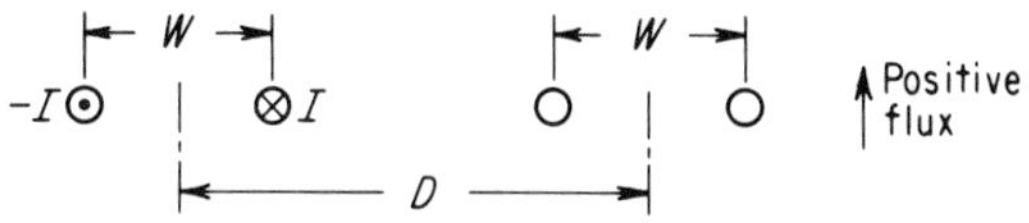

Fig. 9.37.

6. Summation formula—parallel pairs in free space (Fig. 9.38).

$$\sum_{n=1}^{\infty} M_{on} = 0.2 \log \frac{\sinh \dfrac{\pi W}{D}}{\dfrac{\pi W}{D}} \quad \mu h/m$$

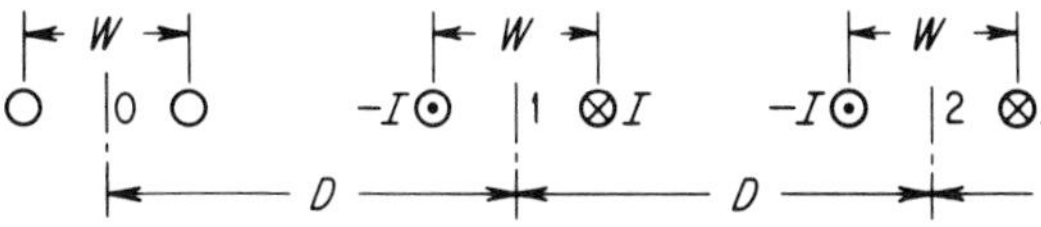

Fig. 9.38.

7. Parallel pairs near a ground plane (Fig. 9.39).

$$M = 0.2 \log \left[ \frac{(D^2 - W^2)(D^2 + 4h^2)}{D^2 \sqrt{(D+W)^2 + 4h^2} \sqrt{(D-W)^2 + 4h^2}} \right] \quad \mu h/m$$

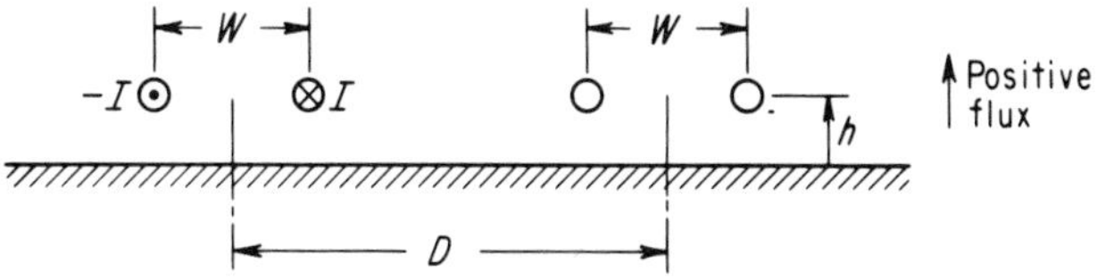

Fig. 9.39.

8. Parallel pairs near a ground plane—summation formula (Fig. 9.40).

$$\sum_{n=1}^{\infty} M_{on} = 0.2 \log \frac{\tanh \left( \dfrac{\pi h}{W} \right)}{\left( \dfrac{\pi h}{W} \right)} + 0.1 \log \left[ 1 + \left( \dfrac{2h}{W} \right)^2 \right] \quad \mu h/m$$

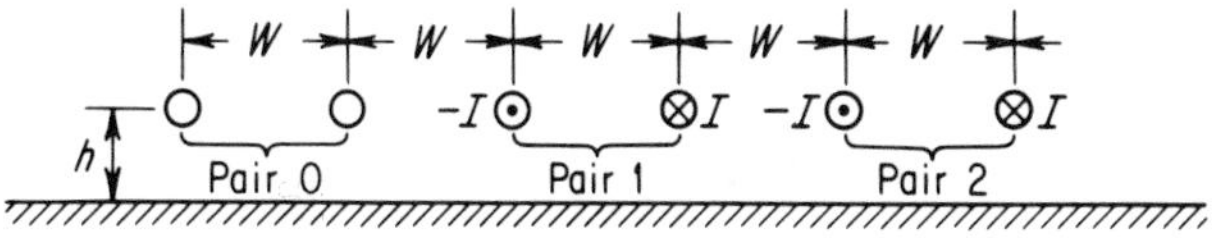

Fig. 9.40.

9. Parallel pairs between two plane conducting surfaces (Fig. 9.41).

$$M = 0.2 \log \frac{\left[\coth \dfrac{\pi D}{4h}\right]^2}{\left[\coth \dfrac{\pi(D-W)}{4h}\right]\left[\coth \dfrac{\pi(D+W)}{4h}\right]} \quad \mu h/m$$

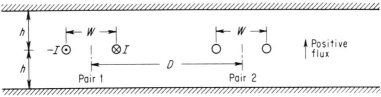

Fig. **9.41.**

10. Summation result for parallel pairs between two plane conducting surfaces (Fig. 9.42).

$$\sum_{n=1}^{\infty} M_{on} = 0.0564 \quad \mu h/m$$

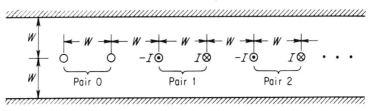

Fig. **9.42.**

### 9.16 D-C POWER TRANSMISSION SYSTEMS

In computer circuit design, it is assumed that the voltages supplied to a circuit fall between certain specified tolerance limits. Several things serve to cause the voltages to deviate from their nominal values. We may determine what these are by examining the typical d-c power distribution system for a computer shown in Fig. 9.43.

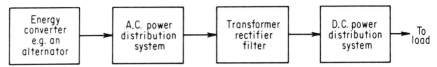

Fig. **9.43.** Source of computer power.

All the elements in Fig. 9.43 have the equivalent of internal resistance and reactance so that changes of load will produce changes in supply voltages. It will be assumed that the reader can adequately analyze the response of the first three boxes to transient load changes and can design them to have the appropriate performance using the methods of electrical engineering. The reader will be reminded that if the output voltage is not to change appreciably under transient load changes, sufficient energy storage must be provided in the system shown in Fig. 9.43.

An equivalent circuit of a d-c power distribution system is shown in Fig. 9.44. The sources of voltage changes at point $A$, the point at which a circuit receives its power, are three. These are:

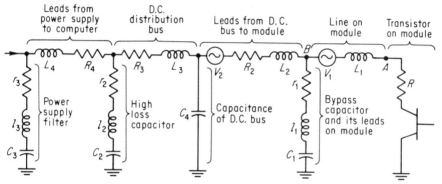

**Fig. 9.44.** Typical d-c power distribution system.

(a) Static drops in the distribution system and power-supply drift and regulation.
(b) Transient changes because of the finite impedance of the distribution system.
(c) Inductive crosstalk from signal leads and other d-c leads into the d-c distribution system.

In Fig. 9.44, $V_1$ and $V_2$ are generators representing the inductive crosstalk voltages. In some cases these may provide a voltage change which is several times that resulting from the finite impedance of the distribution system. As drawn in Fig. 9.44, the d-c distribution system is a lumped-constant transmission line. For this reason, transmission-line theory can be used to obtain an approximate design. For minimum ringing, each $L$ section in Fig. 9.44 should be designed to approximately match the adjacent sections. As we proceed from right to left, each section should have sufficient high-frequency losses so that the signal incident on the power supply has little energy at frequencies above the cutoff frequency of the power-supply voltage regulator.

To illustrate the order of magnitude of the quantities involved, assume that 1000 transistors, each capable of simultaneously drawing 10 ma with a rise time of 10 nsec, are to be furnished with power at 5 volts with only

0.3 per cent of noise allowable due to the finite impedance of the d-c distribution system. Assume ten circuits are on a module so that each lead from the d-c bus carries 100 ma. If the line on the module has an inductance of 0.01 $\mu$h, the transient voltage across it is

$$e = L\frac{di}{dt} = 10^{-8}\frac{10^{-2}}{10^{-8}} = 0.01 \text{ volts}$$

This is a third of the allowable transient change of $0.006 \times 5 = 0.03$ volts.

Since 100 ma is drawn at point $B$, the impedance looking to the left at that point should be less than

$$Z = \frac{\Delta V_B}{\Delta I} = \frac{0.03 - 0.01}{0.1} = 0.2 \text{ ohms}$$

If the leads from the d-c bus to the module have an inductance of 0.1 $\mu$h, then assuming that the impedance of that point is $\sqrt{L/C}$

$$C = \frac{L}{R^2} = \frac{10^{-7}}{4 \times 10^{-2}} = 2.5 \text{ } \mu\text{f}$$

This would be a lower bound on the size of the required bypass capacitor on the module. Because such capacitors have internal and lead inductance and resistance, it would be necessary to refer to data giving the impedance of commercial items as a function of frequency in order to make a specific choice. However, the capacitance of the d-c bus is negligible, so that the inductance of the d-c bus should have been included in the above capacitance calculation. Determination of the inductance of the d-c bus is partly a problem in optimization. However, let us assume that it produces the same inductive voltage drop as the leads from the module, so that its inductance should be of the order of 0.001 $\mu$h. This requires that at least 5 $\mu$f be used as a bypass on the module. Such low values

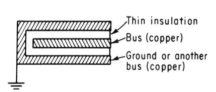

Thin insulation
Bus (copper)
Ground or another bus (copper)

Fig. 9.45. Strip-line.

of inductance can be achieved at reasonable cost using strip-line such as in Fig. 9.45. The inductance per unit length of two parallel strips in air having a width $W$ and spacing $d$ is approximately

$$L = \frac{\mu_0 d}{W} = 4\pi \times 10^{-7}\frac{d}{W} \quad \text{henrys/meter} \qquad (9.30)$$

If $d = 0.005$ in. and $W = 6.25$ in., the inductance of a meter length is, from Eq. (9.30), 0.001 $\mu$h/meter. When folded as in Fig. 9.45, the assembly is a little over 3 in. wide.

The high-loss capacitor should terminate the d-c bus in its characteristic impedance over as wide a frequency range as possible. The total impedance in this example is

$$R = \frac{\Delta V}{\Delta I} = \frac{0.02}{10} = 0.002 \text{ ohms}$$

This value can be economically achieved by paralleling moderately sized electrolytic capacitors until their net impedance as determined from data on their characteristics has this value. Care should be taken so that the leads to the capacitors have low inductance. This can be achieved, for example, by using short lengths of flexible strip-line as leads. The loss resistance results from dielectric hysteresis in the capacitors such that the proper choice of capacitor is essential for economy. Excessive capacitor requirements can sometimes be circumvented by using other lossy devices in shunt such as capacitor-coupled lossy chokes.

This chapter will be concluded with a brief outline of the application of the preceding theory to the design of the signal and d-c distribution system used in the UNIVAC-LARC computer.*

The logic circuit used for the most part was the diode-transistor buffer-inverter previously discussed in Chap. 5. With this circuit, most of the noise was produced by inductive crosstalk.

The response of the circuit to noise depends on both the amplitude and the frequency of the noise. The test set-up illustrated in Fig. 9.46 was de-

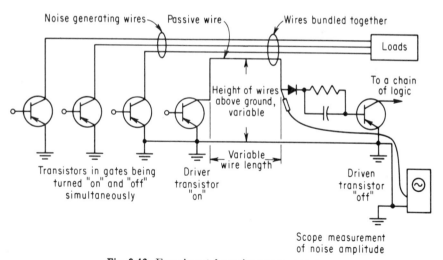

**Fig. 9.46.** Experiment for noise measurements.

signed to establish the amplitude and frequency for the worst-case of noise propagated through a circuit. First, it was established that the worst-case

* Adapted from Ref. 6.

corresponds to the condition when the driver circuit is on and heavily saturated. This condition represents almost a short circuit at the driving end of the passive line. The driven circuit represents the smallest load possible, and consists of a high-speed transistor which is lightly loaded at its output by a chain of gates. Voltages and components were also picked for the worst-case. The lead between the driver and the driven circuit is bundled together with leads originating from a number of other gates which are in the process of being turned on and off (these circuits have rise times of less than 20 nsec). The other ends of the wires, on which pulses are being propagated, are connected to various loads.

This experiment led to the following conclusions:

1. Noise generated in the passive wire is directly proportional to the length of the line and to the logarithm of the height of the wires above ground.
2. Noise will decrease with an increase in the distance between the passive wire and the generating wires.

In order to minimize noise, 30 gauge wire was used and the insulation was made thick to assure minimum spacing between wires. It was found that in the case of the seven tightly bundled wires from the basic gates, the noise generated in the passive wire (up to 15 in. long) had an amplitude below 400 mv. The total noise generated was divided between the backboard wiring and the wiring on the circuit packages. A 400-mv crosstalk noise on the backboard and 100 mv on the cards was allowed, giving a total of 500 mv of crosstalk noise (even though the static voltage margins, $V_m$, were 150 mv). This was satisfactory because it was found that noise was reduced appreciably when it was propagated through a chain of gates.

Upon studying the distribution of the intraunit wire length, it was found that a great majority of wires were less than 9 in. long. Therefore, it was feasible, without undue expense, to allow point-to-point signal-lead wiring over a ground plane for all wires up to 9 in. long (leaving a 6-in. margin for safety). For longer wires, twisted pairs were used in which one wire was the signal lead and the other was connected at its ends to the ground points at the driving and driven circuits. Interunit leads used coaxial cables. These studies showed that noise could be suppressed (at a sacrifice in cost) by using more expensive wires, such as twisted pairs and coaxial cables.

Since noise amplitude depends on the distance of the wires from ground, all metal parts in the circuit-card frames and the main frame constituted the ground system. In order to assure good ground conduction at all points (without the possibility of corrosion), gold plating was used in many places. By employing this method of grounding, the margins for noise were much smaller than the noise margins in previous computers.

Recall that ringing on signal leads is caused by unmatched terminations. It is difficult to terminate the sending end of the wire, since the transistor impedance changes greatly when it is turning on. The impedance of a single wire is approximately 300 ohms; the impedance of a twisted pair is approximately 200 ohms. The minimum terminating impedance at the receiving end of the leads was approximately 500 ohms and the maximum was approximately 1500 ohms. Smaller gate input impedances were desirable, but this was not possible because of the relatively low current level of the transistors being used (about 10 ma). The ringing noise resulting from the unmatched termination was still smaller than the crosstalk noise; therefore, it did not constitute a problem in this case. Generally, in the case where a choice was possible, lower gate input impedances resulted in reductions in ringing, noise amplitude, and circuit delay.

Another source of noise occurred when a number of circuits shared a common ground resistance. However, the latter proved to be negligible because of the precautions taken in designing the ground system.

The system of backboard wiring required an examination of its effect on the delays in propagation of information. It was found that for intraunit wiring, distances were always smaller than six feet. Since rise times were between 10 to 60 nsec, computation based on lumped circuitry, rather than distributed circuitry, provided reasonable accuracy. Therefore, in the delay measurements, the presence of wires was simulated by attaching a capacitance of 6 pf. per foot to the collectors of the transistors.

The d-c distribution used in LARC differed in only a few minor details from that shown in Fig. 9.44. The approximate values of the lumped com-

**TABLE 9.4**

| Component | Description | Order of magnitude |
|-----------|-------------|--------------------|
| $L_1$ | Printed line on module | 0.01 $\mu$h |
| $L_2$ | Lead to module | 0.1 $\mu$h |
| $L_3$ | DC bus (one of several) | 0.001 $\mu$h |
| $L_4$ | Power-supply leads | 10 $\mu$h |
| $l_1$ | Capacitor lead ($C_1$) | 0.01 $\mu$h |
| $l_2$ | Capacitor lead ($C_2$) | 1 $\mu$h |
| $C_1$ | Capacitor on circuit card | 10 $\mu$f |
| $C_2$ | High loss capacity | farads |
| $C_4$ | Capacitance of dc bus | 1000 pf |
| $R_2, R_3, R_4, r_1, r_2$ | Lead resistances | $10^{-4} - 1$ ohm |
| $R$ | Equivalent resistance of total load | 60 milliohm |

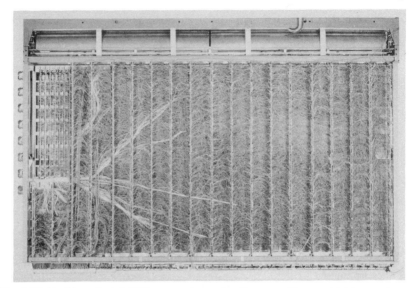

**Fig. 9.47.** Backboard of LARC computing unit. Courtesy Univac Division of Sperry Rand Corp.

ponents are given in Table 9.4 for the 3-volt, 100-amp supply excluding the power-supply filter capacitor whose characteristics are determined primarily by filtering requirements.

**Fig. 9.48.** LARC computing unit—top rear view. Courtesy Univac Division of Sperry Rand Corp.

Figures 9.47 and 9.48 illustrate the wiring and power distribution schemes. Figure 9.47 is a photograph depicting the backboard of the LARC computing unit. The heavier vertical lines are the d-c and clock distribution busses. The very dense point-to-point wiring (entirely covering the printed circuit connectors) can be seen between the busses. Figure 9.48 is an enlargement of the top of the backboard. On the left are shown the heavy power-supply cables; the two rows of cylinders are the large capacitor banks. These are connected to the vertical d-c busses projecting above the backboard. The leads from the busses to the circuit cards are shown at the lower right corner of Fig. 9.48.

## REFERENCES

1. Carson, J. R., and R. S. Hoyt, "Propagation of Periodic Currents over a System of Parallel Wires," *Bell System Technical Journal*, **6**, pp. 495–545 (1927).

2. Chapman, A. G., "Open Wire Crosstalk," *Bell System Technical Journal*, **13**, pp. 19–58, 195–238 (1934).

3. Grover, W. C., *Inductance Calculations* (Princeton, N.J.: D. Van Nostrand Co., 1946). Many formulas for the calculation of self and mutual inductance.

4. Klein, W., *Die Theorie des Nebensprenchens auf Leitungen* (Berlin: Springer-Verlag, 1955). Contains an extensive list of references.

5. Panofsky, W. K. H., and M. Phillips, *Classical Electricity and Magnetism* (Reading, Mass.: Addison-Wesley Publishing Co., 1955). A concise and mature text on electromagnetic field theory.

6. Prywes, N. S., H. Lukoff, and J. Schwarz, "UNIVAC-LARC High Speed Circuitry: Case History in Circuit Optimization," *I.R.E. Transactions on Electronic Computers*, **EC-10**:3, pp. 426–438 (Sept. 1961).

7. Schelkunoff, S. A., *Electromagnetic Waves* (Princeton, N.J.: D. Van Nostrand Co., 1943), p. 167, Capacitance in multiconductor systems; p. 204, Crosstalk.

8. Weber, E., *Electromagnetic Fields*, vol. I (New York: John Wiley & Sons, 1950). Typical text illustrating methods of calculating inductance and capacitance.

## PROBLEMS

1. A uniform lossless transmission line is shown below. Determine the voltage and current observed at each end as a function of time if (a) $e_g(t)$ is a 10-volt step, (b) $e_g(t)$ is as shown in the figure.

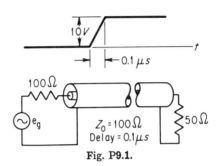

Fig. P9.1.

**2.** In the transmission line of Prob. 1, determine the inductance and capacitance per unit length.

**3.** The passive and active lines in a system run parallel 1 in. above a ground plane for a distance of 3 ft and are separated by a distance of 2 in. Calculate the mutual capacitance and inductance if No. 30 wire is used.

**4.** The lines in Prob. 3 are both terminated in resistances of 100 Ω at the far end. The active line is driven by a 3-volt pulse having 20-nsec rise and fall times. Calculate the crosstalk when the near end of the passive line is (a) open-circuited (b) grounded.

**5.** The wires in Prob. 3 are insulated with Teflon to an outside diameter of 0.1 in. Estimate an upper bound to the sum of the mutual capacitances to other wires of the same kind for a 15-in. long passive wire.

**6.** Five No. 22 wires are arranged as shown in the accompanying cross-sectional figure. Each wire is 2 ft long and wires 1, 2, 4, and 5 carry a current of 50 ma with a rise time of 0.1 μsec. Compute the inductive crosstalk component induced in the circuit involving wire No. 3 and the return wire.

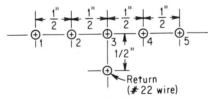

Fig. P9.2.

# 10

# APPLICATION OF COMPUTERS

# TO THE DESIGN OF COMPUTERS*

Because of the major advances in understanding in recent years, it is now possible to design very large and complex systems. It has even become possible to use computers in computer design. Furthermore, in the design of large systems such use is now almost imperative. The purpose of this chapter is to present and to illustrate a variety of techniques and areas in applying digital computers to the design of new computers. It would be very desirable if a process were found to take over the entire design of a computer; however, this is not in sight. The processes to be described are carried out partly by humans and partly by computers. Computers aid in the design by the take-over of routine work. They also allow the designer to take into account many more factors simultaneously. The savings involved are twofold: first, much of the engineering is performed by computers, thus eliminating manual work, and second, one can plan better and thus proceed more directly to the final design.

Appropriate techniques must be chosen for each individual area of application. Generally speaking, techniques and areas of applications can be divided into two classes: (1) mathematical techniques such as those using algebra, statistics, and numerical analysis which are applied primarily to circuit design, component design and specifications, etc., and (2) data-processing and symbol-manipulation techniques which are applied to the

* Adapted in part from Ref. 2.

309

layout of circuits, wiring information, and logical design. These two classes of techniques will be described separately since there is generally little overlap between them.

Several applications of computers to circuit design are described here and demonstrated by illustrations. The problem areas can be divided into the categories of evaluation of components, life-test, and design of circuits. Several mathematical techniques requiring use of computers can be applied to each of these categories as shown in Table 10.1.

TABLE 10.1. SUMMARY OF APPLICATIONS AND TECHNIQUES

| Application | | Technique used | | | |
|---|---|---|---|---|---|
| | | Symbol and data manipulation | Computational | Statistical | Experimental |
| Evaluation of components | Test data analysis | X | | | X |
| | Normalizing and analysis of distributions | | | X | |
| | Control of transistor production | | | X | X |
| | Prediction of life expectancy from elevated temperature accelerated life tests | | | X | X |
| Circuit design | Generation of DC circuit relations | X | | | |
| | Solution of worst case design equations | | X | | |
| | Optimization of speed | | X | | X |
| | Preparation of component specs | | | X | X |
| Reduction of noise | Calculation of lead delay | X | | | |
| | Calculation of lead worst case noise pickup | X | | | |

## 10.1  EVALUATION OF COMPONENTS

The purpose of a component evaluation program is to provide the designer with information about characteristics of components and distributions of such characteristics. If close cooperation with manufacturers is maintained, it is possible to correlate the distributions of the characteristics with the setting of controls in the manufacturing process, which will assure that, for the application at hand, the components made are the best that could be produced in the manufacturing process used. The mathematician facilitates this by designing experiments to aid in the determination of the effect of various changes in production. An example of such a process would be the selection of a transistor type for general computer use illustrated in Fig. 10.1. Transistors that are candidates for

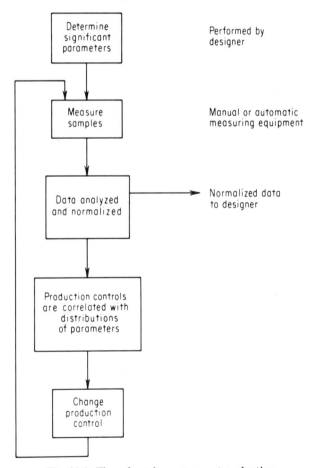

**Fig. 10.1.** Flow chart for component evaluation.

such use are studied to determine characteristics, such as rise time, storage time, current gain, current and power levels, and cost.

The evaluation program requires the testing of a large number of transistors to determine the distribution of parameters. The values are measured initially and at various times throughout life-tests. Statistical routines are applied using a computer to analyze and evaluate the available data. If the data are to be useful for evaluation by a designer, they must be greatly condensed and simplified. Statistical analysis of empirical data can be simplified if the variant under analysis is normally distributed. Since in practice this is rarely the case, the distributions must be transformed to ones that have Gaussian properties. Thus, the designer obtains simplified data in terms of means and standard deviations. The distributions are correlated with the various controls in production, such as controls of resistivity and etching time. A computer routine is then applied to perform the various analyses necessary for the identification of the statistically significant variables. The techniques involved include statistical analysis and programming. Further details about these programs are described in Ref. 1.

### 10.2 EVALUATION OF LIFE-TEST

Component life-expectancy is limited, owing to either mean time between catastrophic failures or degradation of parameters with time. It is the latter which is usually taken into account in circuit design, and which therefore is considered in the following. Because of the long life-expectancy of components it is often difficult to ascertain degradation rate of characteristics by life-tests in a reasonable time period. One of the most important components for which life-expectancy must be determined is the transistor. For this component it was found impossible to detect significant degradations in parameters over thousands of hours of life-tests in the operational environment. Accelerated life-tests are applied, which are run at elevated temperatures under severe humidity conditions or under vibration, with the purpose of producing significant deterioration in a reasonable time. This is followed by an effort to correlate such results with deterioration under normal usage. If such a relationship is found to exist, then extrapolation may yield a reasonably accurate prediction of life-expectancy.

In one case (Refs. 1, 2) experiments indicated that such correlation could be obtained from accelerated life-tests under elevated temperature. No correlation with the other accelerated life-tests was found. In this example transistors were placed on tests at 55, 65, 75, 85, and 100°C. The transistors involved were first tested for homogeneity by a study of the distribution of breakdown voltage. The voltage-breakdown parameter also appeared to be the major cause of transistor failure and therefore was the subject of the investigation. By studying the behavior of these homogeneous sets over a period of time it was hoped to obtain an estimate of transistor behavior at 25°C.

To illustrate the statistical methods used, the determination of transistor life using degradation of breakdown voltage as a criterion will be discussed. The circuit design indicated that the breakdown-voltage degradation to 3 volts implied a transistor failure.

The first step was to make a regression analysis of the breakdown voltage $V_p$ and the time $t$ by making a least-squares fit of the data to a straight line at several temperatures. The results of this analysis are given in Table 10.2.

**TABLE 10.2.** PUNCH-THROUGH VOLTAGE
ACCELERATED LIFE-TEST

| Temperature (°C) | Least-squares equation ($t$ in hours) |
|:---:|:---:|
| 55 | $10.6 - 0.0002t$ |
| 65 | $9.57 - 0.0004t$ |
| 75 | $11.9 - 0.0028t$ |
| 85 | $10.9 - 0.0058t$ |

Next the dependence of the slope of the lines on temperature was studied. Theoretical studies had suggested the dependence of the breakdown voltage on temperature and time as follows:

$$\sqrt{V_p} = A - Be^{-a/2T}\sqrt{t} \qquad (10.1)$$

where $V_p$ is the breakdown voltage, $T$ is the absolute temperature, and $t$ is the age of the transistor in hours. An exponential relationship was assumed. The least-squares straight line was obtained for the logarithm of the slope as a function of reciprocal temperature. The equation thus obtained was

$$m = -1.3 \times 10^{15}e^{-(14278/T)} \qquad (10.2)$$

where $m$ is a slope of the linear least-square equation and $T$ is the corresponding absolute temperature as shown in Fig. 10.2.

This equation was used to estimate the slope at 25°C, and the value was found to be approximately $2 \times 10^{-5}$ volts per hour. The results of a fit by eye made prior to the regression analysis on a computer indicated an average life of 211,000 hours as indicated in Fig. 10.3, wherein the constants in the plotted least-squares equations have all been adjusted to the same value for comparison purposes.

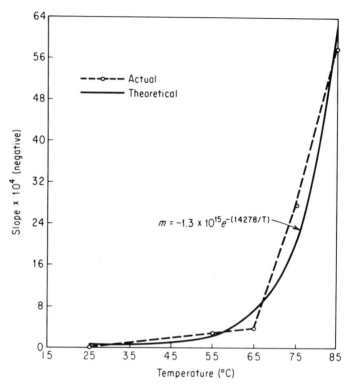

**Fig. 10.2.** Punch-through voltage slope prediction.

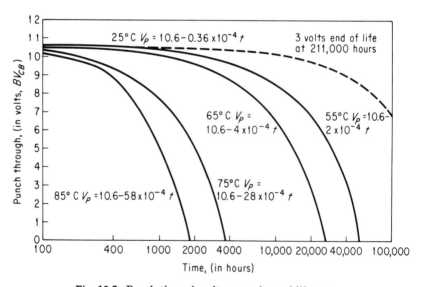

**Fig. 10.3.** Punch-through voltage accelerated life-test.

**10.3** STEADY-STATE CIRCUIT DESIGN AND OPTIMIZATION
USING WORSE-CASE TECHNIQUE

Mechanization of the various steps involved in circuit design has served
for some time as the basis for research, the ultimate objective of which is
to completely automate the design steps required in going from proposed
circuit schematic configurations to the development of an optimized circuit.
Such a process will consist primarily of computer programs using a detailed
mathematical model. There are two advantages to such a process:

1. Better circuit optimization in terms of cost and performance by
   utilizing the speed of computers.
2. The generation of component specifications which computer programs
   correlate with the capabilities of the designed circuit.

Circuit design and optimization processes would start with given circuit
schematic configurations and a performance requirement. In the case of
computer circuits, the latter can be stated, for instance, in terms of fan-in
(number of logical inputs), logical operation, fan-out (number of circuits
to which the output is connected), and the delay per circuit. The objectives
of the design are to single out one of several suggested circuit configurations
and determine component parameters so that cost is minimized.

The process can be roughly divided into three steps:

1. Generation of d-c circuit equations.
2. D-c circuit design.
3. Optimization of the circuit for reduced delay.

**10.3.1** Generation of D-C Circuit Equations

The advantage in obtaining a mathematical model by computer processing is in assuring the completeness of the model; i.e., all the independent
equations are obtained. A code must be first devised for transferring the
circuit information in a schematic diagram into the computer. The code
may be completely reversible; that is, the original circuit diagram can be
derived uniquely from the computer code. The following is an example of
such a code.

The nodes of the circuit are assigned a two-digit number $n_1 n_2$. Each
branch is uniquely determined by its endpoints (i.e., the branch with
nodes $m_1 m_2$ and $n_1 n_2$ as endpoints is called branch $m_1 m_2 n_1 n_2 p_1 p_2$). An
additional two-digit number $p_1 p_2$ is necessary to differentiate two or more
branches which have common endpoint nodes. After listing a number that
identifies a branch, the components of the particular branch are listed.
When this has been done for all branches, the circuit has been completely
described. Each component is associated with a letter of the alphabet

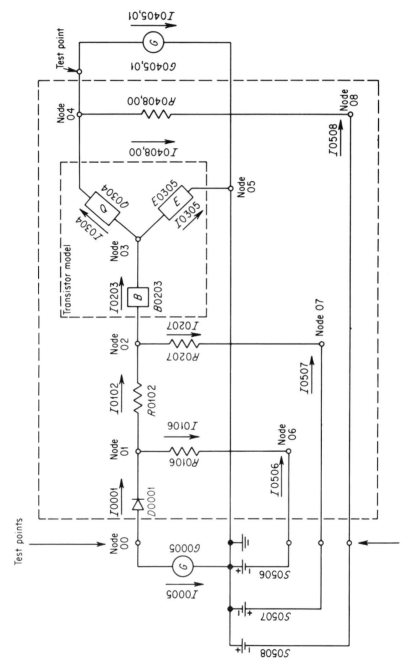

**Fig. 10.4.** Sample circuit for computer analysis.

316

(e.g., resistor $R$, emitter $E$, supply $S$, and diode $D$). As an example, the following is the format for the circuit shown in Fig. 10.4. Each component and its location is thus uniquely described.

| $m_1m_2$ | $n_1n_2$ | $p_1p_2$ | Components | |
|---|---|---|---|---|
| 00 | 01 | 00 | $D$ | |
| 00 | 05 | 00 | $G$ | |
| 01 | 02 | 00 | $R$ | |
| 01 | 06 | 00 | $R$ | |
| 02 | 03 | 00 | $B$ | |
| 02 | 07 | 00 | $R$ | |
| 03 | 04 | 00 | $Q$ | (10.3) |
| 03 | 05 | 00 | $E$ | |
| 04 | 05 | 01 | $G$ | |
| 04 | 08 | 00 | $R$ | |
| 05 | 06 | 00 | $S$ | |
| 05 | 07 | 00 | $S$ | |
| 05 | 08 | 00 | $S$ | |

There are two basic methods available for the generation of the circuit equations: the loop and the nodal-branch techniques. The nodal-branch derivation is preferred; it has an advantage which is extremely important from the standpoint of a computer solution in that the equations are derived very systematically. Thus, the process of mechanization, which will result in a set of nonredundant equations, is easily implemented.

The generation of nodal and branch equations can now proceed as follows. If there are $n$ nodes in the circuit, $n - 1$ independent nodal equations can be generated. (It can be shown that if the $n$th equation is generated, the result can be derived from the other $n - 1$ equations.) Referring to the circuit in Fig. 10.4, the $n - 1$ nodal equations generated are:

$$I_{0001} + I_{0005} = 0$$

$$-I_{0001} + I_{0102} + I_{0106} = 0$$

$$-I_{0102} + I_{0203} + I_{0207} = 0$$

$$-I_{0203} + I_{0304} + I_{0305} = 0 \qquad (10.4)$$

$$-I_{0304} + I_{0405} + I_{0408} = 0$$

$$-I_{0106} - I_{0506} = 0$$

$$-I_{0207} - I_{0507} = 0$$

$$-I_{0408} - I_{0508} = 0$$

The branch equations represent the total voltage drop across each branch. For the sample circuit in Fig. 10.4 the branch equations are as follows:

$$V_{00} - V_{01} = V_{D0001} = D0001 + R_D0001 \times I_{0001}$$

$$V_{00} - V_{05} = V_{G0005} = G0005$$

$$V_{01} - V_{02} = V_{R0102} = R0102 \times I_{0102}$$

$$V_{01} - V_{06} = V_{R0106} = R0106 \times I_{0106}$$

$$V_{02} - V_{03} = V_{B0203} = B0203 + R_B0203 \times I_{0203}$$

$$V_{02} - V_{07} = V_{R0207} = R0207 \times I_{0207}$$

$$V_{03} - V_{04} = V_{Q0304} = K_10304(I_{0304} - K_20304 \times I_{0203}) \qquad (10.5)$$

$$V_{03} - V_{05} = V_{E0305} = 0$$

$$V_{04} - V_{05} = V_{G0405} = G0405$$

$$V_{04} - V_{08} = V_{R0408} = R0408 \times I_{0408}$$

$$- V_{06} = V_{S0506} = S0506$$

$$- V_{07'} = V_{S0507} = S0507$$

$$- V_{08} = V_{S0508} = S0508$$

These eight nodal and thirteen branch equations, then, represent a complete set of irredundant equations which fully describe the system.

The voltage-current relationships are then introduced as shown above in the third column of the branch equations.

The current-voltage relation of diodes and transistors is nonlinear. In order to simplify computation, these nonlinear curves have been approximated and replaced by linear segments in the regions of operation that are of interest. Thus, whenever the voltage-current relationship of a diode is considered, the following condition is employed:

$$V_D = D + R_D I_D \qquad (10.6)$$

where $V_D$ and $I_D$ are the voltage and current respectively through the diode (see Fig. 10.5). The constants $D$ and $R_D$ are unknown quantities to be determined in the calculations. In effect, a variable $(V_D)$, which changes

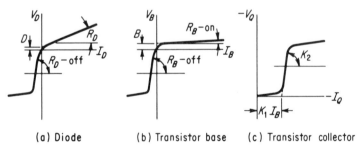

(a) Diode        (b) Transistor base        (c) Transistor collector

**Fig. 10.5.** Voltage-current characteristics of a diode, base, and collector of a transistor.

with input conditions, has been replaced by two quantities $(D, R_D)$ which remain constant through varied input conditions.

In a similar manner the following substitutions can be made for the transistor currents:

$$V_B = B + R_B I_B, \qquad V_Q = K_2(I_Q + K_1 I_B) \qquad (10.7)$$

where $B$, $R_B$, $K_1$, and $K_2$ are constants determining the two straight line approximations; $I_B$ and $I_Q$ are the currents through $B$ (base) and $Q$ (collector) respectively; and $V_B$ and $V_Q$ are the voltage drops across the base and collector. (See Fig. 10.5.)

As in the case of the diode, unknown quantities $(V_B, V_Q)$ which change with input conditions are replaced by quantities $(K_1, K_2, B, R_B)$ which remain constant through varied input conditions.

Both linear and nonlinear characteristics together with equivalent models for devices having more than two terminals are stored in the computer and automatically applied to the circuit schematic to derive the equations.

### 10.3.2   D-C Circuit Design

Consider as an example the case where the optimization of cost consists mainly of reducing the required $\alpha_{FE}$ of transistors used. The criteria for calculating the required $\alpha_{FE}$ consist of the worst-case design, discussed previously in Chap. 8.

The parameters, such as resistances, supply voltages, etc., are then multiplied by a factor which represents the maximum tolerances allowed so that the $\alpha_{FE}$ of the transistor involved becomes minimum.

### 10.3.3   Optimization of the Circuit

The optimization now follows the process described in Chap. 8. Examination of the above circuit equations shows that the number of unknown variables (including component parameters) exceeds the number of equations. Therefore there is no unique solution. Generally delay decreases with increase in $\alpha_{FE}$, although the delay would depend on many other parameters as well. The purpose of the optimization is then to determine a unique circuit having the lowest minimum $\alpha_{FE}$ requirement such that the maximum delay allowed in the circuit specifications is not exceeded.

The transient behavior of the circuit can be determined experimentally, analytically, or through statistical studies. These three techniques will now be discussed.

In the experimental study the unknowns in the circuit equations are divided into so-called dependent variables and independent variables. The number of the dependent variables is equal to the number of equations.

The determination of optimum values for the independent variables implies unique solution of the circuit equations, which represents the optimized circuit. The problem then is to vary the independent variables and determine experimentally the values corresponding to minimum delay. This can be an iterative process, where one of the independent variables is varied while the others are kept constant.

A large number of circuits have to be computed in this process, and the circuit equations involved are found to be nonlinear. Solution of the system of equations by computer is of significant advantage over manual computation, especially since the system of equations is nonlinear.

The analytical study of theoretical relationship between circuit delay and several circuit parameters has been found to be extremely unreliable for prediction purposes. The relations of Chap. 6 are very useful for qualitative analysis, and their use here is not advocated.

The third approach involves the statistical determination of the relationship between the circuit parameters and the circuit delay. Specifically, the determination of the regression of circuit delay on the transistor parameters has been established. This method is described in detail in Sec. 10.4.

## 10.4 TRANSIENT CIRCUIT DESIGN (INCLUDING DELAYS)

The engineer who has as his assignment the design of a transistor circuit to perform according to a predetermined functional specification has a choice of two courses in designing the circuit and in specifying the transistor. One approach in general use is to determine by measurements the worst parameters of a selected type of transistor, to employ these parameters as the limiting criteria in a worst-case design, and to choose the other components in the circuit to optimize speed or gain.

In the second approach to be discussed here, the engineer designs a circuit for a typical transistor which performs to the given functional specification. The other components are selected to optimize the operation with this transistor. The dependence of the functional operation of the circuit (for instance, its gain or delay) upon the parameters of the transistor is determined over a wide range of variations of these parameters through statistical studies. Transistor parameters are then determined for each of the ranges corresponding to the functional specifications.

Information on the dependence or correlation of parameters is valuable to both the transistor manufacturer and the circuit designer. One transistor parameter can be improved at the expense of another so that the transistor improves in production yield, cost, etc., without harmful effect on the operation of the circuit. A change in production controls can be helpful rather than harmful. Various types of transistors are candidates for use in the circuit without additional design or experimental work, and the same circuit can be used to satisfy a number of specifications, changing only the type of transistor. The circuit designer can use the same information for statistical circuit design as opposed to the worst-case design (discussed in Chap. 8), thus effecting additional savings.

The subject approach will be illustrated by a case history of a circuit design. To relate a given circuit specification to the transistor parameters involved, a considerable amount of computation is necessary, which requires the use of a computer.

*Description of the Circuit.* The functional specifications of this circuit were as follows:

Driving circuit: Flip-flop, of which the output voltage has
   exponential rise time to 70 per cent in 40 nsec.
Input voltage: Pulse from $-2.9$ v to $-0.3$ v.
Input current: Pulse from 0 ma to 4.5 ma.
Output voltage: Pulse from $-2.9$ v to 0 v.
Output current: Pulse from 0 ma to 52.0 ma.
Maximum output capacitance: 1000 pf.
Maximum load: 32 "standard" circuits.
Delay:

|                   | *Minimum* | *Maximum* |
|-------------------|-----------|-----------|
| High-speed range  | 22 nsec   | 165 nsec  |
| Medium-speed range| 33 nsec   | 205 nsec  |
| Low-speed range   | 44 nsec   | 245 nsec  |

The circuit configuration chosen is shown in Fig. 10.6. The delay of the circuit is measured from the beginning of the clock pulse driving the flip-

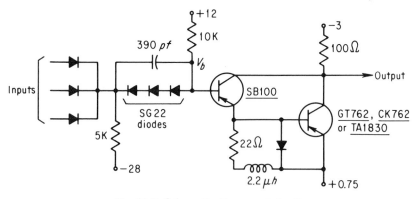

**Fig. 10.6.** Schematic diagram of circuit.

flop to the beginning of the output of the loading circuits. The delay measuring circuit is shown in Fig. 10.7.

Since the minimum delay was not critical in this configuration, the design conditions corresponded to the input and loading for maximum delay. Measurements were made when the transistor was turning off, since maximum delay occurs at that time. A typical transistor was selected to give a delay in the medium range. The values of the other components, in the circuit that would minimize delay, were then determined experimentally. The Surface-Barrier transistor (SBT) in the circuit (Fig. 10.6) had a relatively small effect on the delay of the entire circuit, and so the determination of worst parameters for the SBT was feasible. Therefore, we will deal only with the regression of the parameters of the second transistor on the performance of the circuit as a whole.

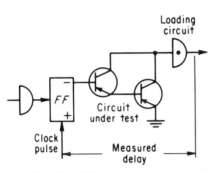

**Fig. 10.7.** Delay measurement.

*Parameters of the Transistors.* Four parameters including circuit delays were measured for each of 360 transistors. The six parameters normally specified by the manufacturer were breakdown voltage, leakage current, current gain ($\alpha_{FE}$), rise time ($T$), storage time ($S$), and peak base-to-emitter voltage ($V$). The first two, which affect mainly the d-c operation of the circuit, had no significant effect on circuit delay. The remaining four parameters, assumed a priori to affect circuit delay significantly, were measured in each transistor. Current gain ($\alpha_{FE}$) was measured at a constant collector voltage of $-0.6$. Because of d-c considerations, gain had to exceed 30 under these conditions. Total circuit delay ($\delta$) was assumed to be a function of $V$, $\alpha_{FE}$, $T$, and $S$. In addition, $\delta$ was measured for each transistor, with output loading that corresponded to maximum delay.

The transistors tested were in three groups: 236 transistors of type GT762 (taken from two production runs), 99 transistors of type CK762, and 25 transistors of type TA1830.

No theoretical relationship among the measured parameters was assumed. Each measurement was performed twice. Transistors whose values did not check within the accuracy limits of the measuring device were eliminated from further consideration, but the number of these was negligible.

*Statistical Studies.* Interdependence studies between the parameters and delay values were undertaken first. The tools of regression analysis (Ref. 3) were used to ascertain whether, in general, circuit delay can be predicted from known parameters of a transistor. The second step was the establishing of a functional relationship between circuit delay and the several known parameters. This function formed the basis for the successful determination of transistor parameters for the delay ranges.

*Studies in Regression Analysis.* To investigate whether there is any direct relationship between circuit delay ($\delta$) and any of the four transistor parameters listed, the measured value of circuit delay for 236 transistors, assuming these to be a representative sample of population of all GT762 transistors, was plotted against each of the parameters. It was assumed that the regression of $\delta$ on each of the parameters $V$, $\alpha_{FE}$, $T$, and $S$ was linear.

The scatter diagrams of $\delta$ versus each of the transistor parameters and fitting of linear regression equations are given in Figs. 10.8 through 10.11.

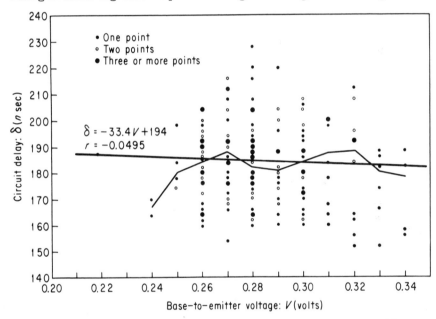

**Fig. 10.8.** Scatter diagram and regression line for circuit delay as a function of base-to-emitter voltage.

The mean $\delta$ values are connected in a line of best fit, shown as a light line; the line of regression, shown as a heavy line, is defined as the linear function of the form $y = mx + b$, which fits the means of arrays best, in the least-squares sense. The fitted linear regression equations are given below:

$$\delta = -33.4V + 194$$
$$\delta = -0.0812\alpha_{FE} + 197$$
$$\delta = 0.577T + 146.5$$
$$\delta = 12.4S + 171$$

(10.8)

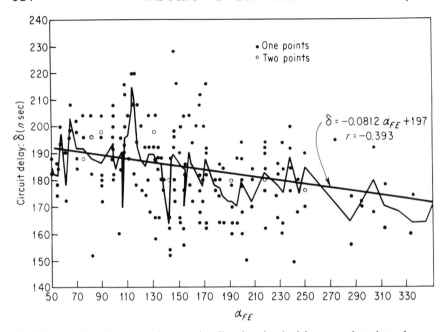

**Fig. 10.9.** Scatter diagram and regression line for circuit delay as a function of $\alpha_{FE}$.

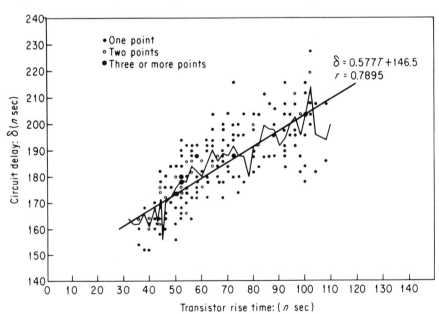

**Fig. 10.10.** Scatter diagram and regression line for circuit delay as a function of transistor rise time.

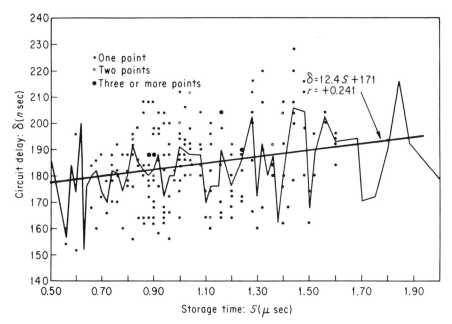

**Fig. 10.11.** Scatter diagram and regression line for circuit delay as a function of storage time.

By using $t$ tests (Ref. 4), it is found that the regression between $\delta$ and $V$ is not statistically significant but the regressions of $\delta$ on the other parameters are highly significant, i.e., at the 1 per cent level. There is a definite indirect relationship, then, among $\alpha_{FE}$, $T$, and $S$. The indirect relationships are obtained by using the last three of the above equations. Though the estimated coefficient regression between $\delta$ and $V$ is greater than the corresponding coefficient between $\delta$ and any other parameter, it is not statistically significant since the estimated variance of this coefficient is very high.

Further investigation, made to determine whether any direct relationship between the parameters $V$, $\alpha_{FE}$, $T$, and $S$ existed, indicated a strong direct relationship between both $V$ and $T$ and also between $T$ and $\alpha_{FE}$.

*Delay as a Function of Sixteen Expressions.* A program was used to find the linear fit and regression coefficients between $\delta$ and the following 16 parameter expressions:

$$V, \quad \alpha_{FE}, \ T, \quad S, \quad 1/\alpha_{FE}, \ T/\alpha_{FE}, \ T^2/\alpha_{FE}, \ T/\alpha_{FE}^2, \ V/\alpha_{FE}, \\ VT, \ TS, \ S/\alpha_{FE}, \ T^2, \ 1/\alpha_{FE}, \ 1/S, \quad VS, \tag{10.9}$$

It was assumed that the coefficients of regression between $\delta$ and other parameter expressions were not significant. The program revealed highest positive regression between $\delta$ and terms $T$, $T^2$, $T^2/\alpha_{FE}$, $VT$, $S/\alpha_{FE}$, and $TS$. These six parameter combinations were chosen for a function with linear constants as follows:

$$\delta = K_1T + K_2T^2 + K_3VT + \frac{K_4T^2}{\alpha_{FE}} + \frac{K_5S}{\alpha_{FE}} + K_6TS + K_7 \quad (10.10)$$

A second program was subsequently written to apply the least-squares fit criterion to the 234 sets of transistor data for the given equation. The normalized equations (seven equations, seven unknowns) of the fit were solved by the Crout method (Ref. 5). A third program was developed to test the curve fit; that is, to compare the calculated $\delta$ with the observed and to determine the individual term contributions. These programs revealed that the $K_5S/\alpha_{FE}$ and $K_6TS$ terms contributed little to the value and could be dropped, thus simplifying the function to the following:

$$\delta = K_1T + K_2T^2 + K_3VT + \frac{K_4T^2}{\alpha_{FE}} + K_7 \quad (10.11)$$

where $K_1 = 1.666$, $K_2 = 0.001$, $K_3 = 2.717$, $K_4 = -0.175$, and $K_7 = 129.135$.

A relatively simple evaluation of the normality of the distribution of errors based on this regression equation is indicated in Fig. 10.12. The

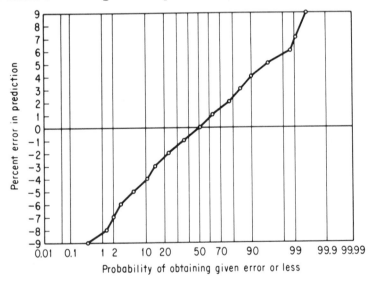

**Fig. 10.12.** Circuit delay prediction, 234 GT762 transistors test for normality of error distribution.

cumulative distribution of errors would appear perfectly linear in the representation of a normally distributed population.

*Discussion of Accuracy of Prediction Using the Function.* A lot of 99 type GT762 transistors, from a later shipment, was measured to determine the applicability of the derived functions, Eqs. (10.10) and (10.11). The distribution of errors between the equation prediction (10.11) and the observed values of delay appeared normal, with a mean of 8 per cent. A change in the constant term or inclusion of dependence on $S$ (Eq. 10.10) would correct the function as applied to this particular group and shift the mean to zero.

*Range Determination.* Since the circuit under design specifies use in one of three delay ranges, rather than a specific delay, a method for classifying transistors into the three ranges according to known parameters would serve the purpose. The method capitalizes on the relationship established in the search for a predictive function.

The 236 units first investigated were plotted on a $T$-ordinate, $\alpha_{FE}$-abscissa graph, and labeled with their observed $\delta$ values. Arbitrary $\delta$ ranges were found to separate themselves fairly well into various regions of the plot; rough borders were sketched between regions following the best range separations. These $T$ ($\alpha_{FE}$) curves descended exponentially at low $\alpha_{FE}$ values, and leveled off horizontally as $\alpha_{FE}$ increased, suggesting the functional relationship:

$$T = \hat{K}_1 + \hat{K}_2 e^{-\hat{K}_s \alpha_{FE}} \tag{10.12}$$

The $\delta$-labeled points were separated into the three designated groups: 0–155 nsec, 156–195 nsec, and 196–235 nsec, and the two borders were added. A program was devised to fit the border $\alpha_{FE}$-$T$ data to the suggested functional expression, yielding the constants $\hat{K}_1$, $\hat{K}_2$, $\hat{K}_3$ for each curve. The smooth exponential curves were drawn in to separate the data.

The results, for the first lot of 234 type GT762 transistors, are described as follows:

1. In the high range ($196 \leq \delta \leq 235$), 8 units out of 52 occurred that did not belong. Their values were 180, 180, 186, 192, 192, 192, 192, 194 nsec. Thus, there were only two outside the tolerance criterion, $\pm 10$ nsec. This tolerance was selected arbitrarily by adding the measurement tolerances of $T$ and $\delta$, each $\pm 5$ nsec.
2. In the medium range ($156 \leq \delta \leq 195$) 9 units out of 179 occurred that did not belong. One unit was below (152), and 8 units were above (196, 196, 196, 198, 198, 198, 200, 200). None of these was outside the $\pm 10$-nsec tolerance region.
3. The low range ($\delta \leq 155$) contained only two units, both of which were correctly placed.
4. The two border equations are as follows:

$$T = 30.97 + 60.58e^{-0.0157\alpha_{FE}} \qquad \text{at } \delta = 155 \qquad (10.13)$$

$$T = 62.18 + 112.41e^{-0.0166\alpha_{FE}} \qquad \text{at } \delta = 195 \qquad (10.14)$$

The results suggest a very accurate separation. The lowest region, where insufficient data were available, was checked on another set of transistors. The results are discussed below.

Figure 10.13 is a graph that can be used to sort transistors by $\alpha_{FE}$ and $T$ measurements. Once the measurements for each transistor are made, the $\alpha_{FE}$-$T$ point on the graph establishes the delay range of the unit.

*Discussion of Accuracy of Prediction Using Ranges Determined.* With the method just indicated, using the transistor delay-range chart with the originally derived borders (Fig. 10.13) the new lot of 99 type GT762

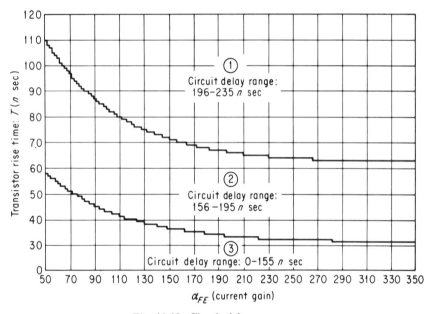

**Fig. 10.13.** Circuit delay ranges.

transistors was plotted. Twenty-eight transistors were correctly placed in the high range ($196 \leq \delta \leq 235$).

In the medium range ($156 \leq \delta \leq 195$), sixty-nine units occurred, of which eleven did not belong. Nevertheless, all were acceptable under the tolerance limits.

In the low delay range ($\delta \leq 155$), only two transistors occurred, both of which were correctly placed.

A linear shift in the borders of the $\delta$ ranges would take care of the errors of misplacement. These results are strongly indicative that the new lots of the transistor had some property changes that can affect the application, unless additional parameters such as storage time ($S$) are considered.

An excellent prediction for the TA1830 data was achieved by the transistor delay-range chart (Fig. 10.13). Of the 25 units tested, 22 fell within the predicted range and three were borderline. The borderline cases were so close that, within tolerance limits, they could be placed in the correct catagories.

In contrast to the broad range of delay values in the original 236 type GT762 transistors, these RCA TA1830 units were mostly confined to the lowest delay range.

## 10.5 MONTE CARLO ANALYSIS IN STATISTICAL CIRCUIT DESIGN

The assembling of circuits consists of picking components from bins and interconnecting them in a particular circuit configuration. The value of each component in a circuit is not known. The information available may be in form of the probability distribution of the parameter values, based on sample studies of the components in each bin. This would include some nominal or minimum specifications applied to all parts of the bin with tolerance limits.

The assembling of a circuit can then be regarded as an experiment which can be simulated on a computer. This is often also referred to as the Monte Carlo method. It consists of the following steps. First, the value of the parameter of a component in a circuit is determined as follows. A random-number generator is used which generates numbers having a rectangular frequency distribution between zero and one. Several easy-to-mechanize algorithms for random-number generators are available (Ref. 6). The number generated is applied to the probability distribution of a particular component, and a specific value of a component is thus obtained; i.e., the component value corresponds to the upper end of components having probability equal to the random number generated. This process is continued until all the components for individual circuit are selected.

In the second step of the process component values are used to calculate the circuit performance. For instance, the circuit in Fig. 10.4 has been previously discussed in Chap. 8, and an equation relating the output current of the circuit to the values of components and power supplies was given there. (See Table 8.6, table of equations.) This equation may be used to calculate the available output current of the circuit.

The last step in the process consists of repeating the above two steps several thousand times and obtaining a distribution of some critical characteristics of the circuit. One such important characteristic is that of the current available at the output of a circuit. In this way, without doing any laboratory work, the distribution of characteristics may be determined as a function of the distributions of components. Further studies may involve changing some of the tolerances and distribution of the performance characteristics.

The advantages of this method, as compared to the analytical methods of statistical design described in Chap. 8, are primarily in the general applicability to any circuit and freedom from making many simplifying assumptions which affect accuracy. Once the programs for carrying through the above steps have been prepared, the process is completely mechanical and rapidly provides useful and reliable information. One use for such information would be to indicate to logical designers the available output current from a circuit with a certain small probability of failure. In circuits

TABLE 10.3. TABLE OF PARAMETERS (CIRCUIT IN FIG. 8.11)

| | Variate | Definition | Distribution assumed | Toler-ance | Lower limit | Upper limit |
|---|---|---|---|---|---|---|
| 1 | $I_{tL}$ | Transistor leakage current | Rectangular | | 0.1 $\mu$a | 40 $\mu$a |
| 2 | $I_{dL}$ | Diode leakage current | Rectangular | | 0.1 $\mu$a | 30 $\mu$a |
| 3 | $I_{b(\text{off})}$ | Base cutoff leakage | Rectangular | | 0 | 40 $\mu$a |
| 4 | $E_1$ | | Lower limit* | 3% | | 10.7 |
| 5 | $E_2$ | Supply voltages | Upper limit* | 3% | | 12.4 |
| 6 | $E_3$ | | Upper limit* | 3% | | 3.1 |
| 7 | $R_1$ | | Rectangular | 2% | 4,900 | 5,100 |
| 8 | $R_2$ | Resistors | Rectangular | 2% | 26,460 | 27,540 |
| 9 | $R_3$ | | Rectangular | 2% | 735 | 765 |
| 10 | $R_4$ | | Rectangular | 2% | 1,470 | 1,530 |
| 11 | $V_{n(\text{on})}$ | Noise signals | Upper limit* | | | 0.1 v |
| 12 | $V_{n(\text{off})}$ | voltages | Upper limit* | | | 0.1 v |
| 13 | $V_{b(\text{on})}$ | Transistor base voltage | Rectangular | | 0.35 v | 0.6 v |
| 14 | $V_{ec(\text{on})}$ | Transistor emitter-to-collector voltage | Rectangular | | 0.05 v | 0.3 v |
| 15 | $V_d$ | Diode voltage drop | Rectangular | | | |
| 16 | $\alpha_{FE}$ | Transistor current gain | Obtained from data; mean = 12 | | 9 | 35 |

* Worst case assumed.

where a large number of components is involved this method doubles, and sometimes even triples, the available fan-out over that obtained in using worst-case design techniques. Therefore, the importance of this technique is evident.

This method can be further illustrated by applying it to the circuit used to explain the worst-case design and optimization method in Chap. 8. This circuit was shown in Fig. 8.11. An examination of the equations in Table 8.6 would indicate that by combining the equations for the various nodes it is possible to obtain an expression of the fan-out $n$ as a function of the parameters in Table 10.3. Table 10.3 further gives the end values of the ranges of variation of these parameters. In the Monte Carlo experiments all distributions used, except that of $\alpha_{FE}$, were assumed to be rectangular. A realistic distribution was taken for $\alpha_{FE}$ based on a large amount of data for Surface-Barrier transistors. If worst-case design is used the fan-out is $n = 3$. The resulting distribution of the fan-out $(n)$ from 3000 Monte Carlo simulated experiments is shown in Fig. 10.14. It is interesting to note that

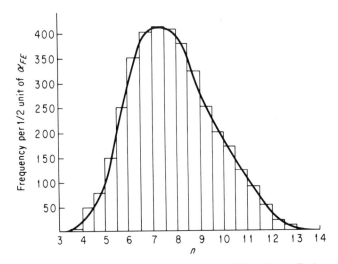

**Fig. 10.14.** Distribution of fan-out for 4000 Monte-Carlo simulated circuits.

a fan-out of $n = 3.6$ is the smallest we encountered. Only 1 per cent of the circuits had a fan-out smaller than $n = 4.2$. The mean is near $n = 7.5$.

## 10.6 DATA-PROCESSING AND SYMBOL-MANIPULATION TECHNIQUES

There exists a class of problems in the design of the computer which is particularly laborious because of the large amount of work which requires intelligent judgment. It is possible to prepare computer programs for efficient solution of problems inherent in logical design, preparation of wiring lists, and layout of circuit to conform to logical design drawings. The solution to these problems *must* be efficient, as will be indicated in the course of the discussion. Work in this area is very recent; still, results published indicate great advances in saving labor. So far, however, benefits from such data processing and symbol manipulation have been obtained through processes involving both human and machine operations. Several such applications are discussed in the following.

### 10.7 PREPARATION OF LAYOUT, WIRING, AND TEST INFORMATION*

The transmission delay increases with the length of the wire and distributed capacitances representing connectors, wires, etc. The noise pick-up (i.e., voltages and currents induced in a wire by pulses in other wires in its proximity) increases with the lengths of the wires but decreases with the total distributed capacitance on the wire. The assignment of elements on the backboard is made to reduce delay and noise pick-up.

The process is initiated by preparing a signal list. This part of the process is shown in flow-chart form in Fig. 10.15. The information from the logical

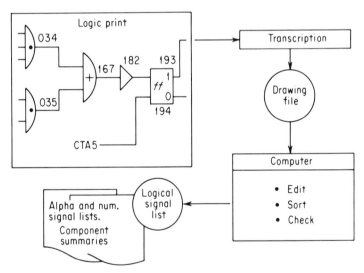

**Fig. 10.15.** Preparation of logical signal list.

diagrams consisting of gates, pulse-formers (p.f.), and interconnecting lines is transcribed and edited as shown.

In the design of UNIVAC-LARC (Ref. 7) the process was mechanized

* The contribution of Mr. T. Williams of Univac, Blue Bell, Pa., to the following two sections is gratefully acknowledged.

as follows. Using information supplied by an existing file (logical signal list) which contained all the logical connections of the computer, the logical designer decided where groups of circuit elements were to be placed on the backboard. These placements were decided on the basis of his familiarity with the general information flow path among organs of the computer, interconnecting information supplied by the logical signal list, and some engineering stipulations that specific elements must be assigned to a particular area. This partly machine and partly manual process is shown

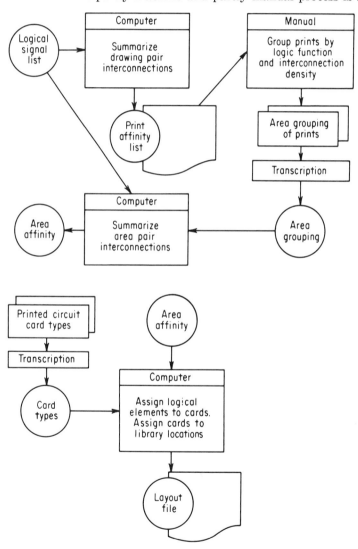

**Fig. 10.16.** Assignment of circuits to backboard (library) locations.

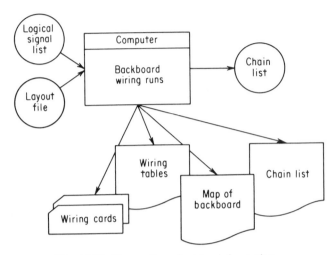

**Fig. 10.17.** Preparation of wiring information.

at the top of Fig. 10.16. The bottom of this figure shows the computer procedure assigning each circuit element to a specific printed-circuit package and assigning the packages to library or backboard locations. Wiring procedures shown in Fig. 10.17 were run on the computer to determine the consistency of the element placement, generate the wiring tables and associated documents. An iterative process described in Fig. 10.18 was used. This consisted first of determining whether bad cases (wires whose

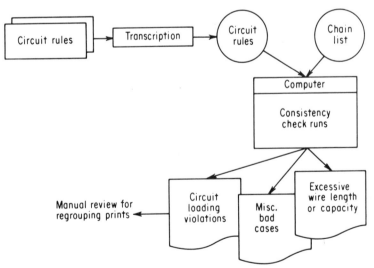

**Fig. 10.18.** Manual-machine iterative process to eliminate bad cases.

length or capacitance violated the design standard) existed. When bad cases were found, the logical elements were moved (by decision of the logical designer and/or the backboard engineer) in an attempt to reduce or eliminate these bad-case conditions.

Iterations of this semiautomatic procedure continued until wire lengths and capacitances were reduced to a tolerable level. The mechanization of the entire process may be possible as well (Refs. 8 and 9).

This procedure was designed to be flexible enough to allow the introduction of design changes into the computers. Because these changes are quite numerous during a computer's development stage, it was necessary to provide, if needed, updated tables on a daily basis. Development time and costs were reduced considerably by the use of this system.

The outputs of this process were lists and tables printed on an off-line high-speed printer and punched cards prepared by the computer. Some of the more frequently used outputs are:

(a) *Signal origin and destination table.* A table designed to aid in the reading of the logical drawings when tracing signals through the unit. This printout is arranged in signal name order and lists the source of the inputs to a logical element and a distribution of the outputs from this element.

(b) *Chain list.* A list which correlates the logical information and the backboard wiring information. All transistors and wires used in the system are indicated in this list. This printout has proved to be invaluable to the test engineers.

(c) *Printed-circuit production list.* This information is printed out so that it is useful for assembly-line personnel, instructing them what printed-circuit packages are to be prepared, how many, and how they should be designated to identify each individual package, including the necessary keys to assure that each package fits in only one place in the machine.

(d) *Location of spare circuits.* This information is necessary to inform the engineer testing out the system on the availability and location of spare circuits, so that he can use them, making appropriate connections when and if he finds it necessary.

(e) *Wiring tables.* This information, ordered by wire length and showing the pin or terminal locations of the two ends of the wire, is provided to the wiring personnel.

(f) *Socket edit.* A list in backboard-connector order which lists all the pins on this connector which are used and the points to which they are connected. This list is valuable for inspection purposes and for locating the other end of a loose wire.

(g) *Logical drawings.* From the information in the wiring list the logical drawings can be generated and printed out by the computer, thus providing updated drawings very rapidly for the use of the engineers testing a computer.

## 10.8 SIMULATION AS A TOOL TO CHECKING LOGICAL DESIGN

This procedure provides a relatively simple procedure for quick, thorough, and accurate testing of computer design *prior* to wiring. Although this tool is of primary interest to the logical designer, its use may have the further effect of drastically reducing the number of wiring changes to be made after the test period has begun.

The first step in a process for simulating a newly designed machine A, on an existing computer B, consists of making the necessary mathematical models. These are: (a) a model of system A—namely its logical design, and (b) programs to be run on computer B to simulate any machine. These two models are stored in machine B. The following steps must be followed in order to store and evaluate the logical design of machine A in the memory of B.

(a) Set down in usable form those logical equations which represent the circuitry to be simulated.
(b) Establish a set of initial signals or parameters which represent the "known" quantities in the logical equations.
(c) Solve the equations for the "unknown" quantities—in effect, the resulting signals.
(d) Compare the computed results with the expected results to determine whether an error exists.
(e) Modify the logical equations as necessary to reflect any resulting corrections in design.
(f) Solve the new equations using the same initial signals.
(g) Compare the new results with the expected results to determine whether the error has been corrected.

This process is illustrated by a specific procedure as follows.

*Preparation of Logical Equations.* For various reasons associated with convenience and ease of computation, the strict Boolean form of logical equation (e.g., $F = AB' + C + D'E$ or $G = ABCD$) has not been employed. Instead, equation data are abstracted from the already available logical signal list, routinely prepared for backboard wiring purposes.

Inasmuch as this file is maintained in numerical rather than logical sequence, levels of logic must be computed and the data resequenced accordingly (Fig. 10.19). The edited table of maximum and minimum levels which is obtained as a by-product of this operation may be reviewed by the designer for an indication of possible sources of design error. If errors are found, it is of course desirable to make corrections immediately, before proceeding further.

*Preparation of Parameters.* The initial signals or parameters are the starting values of the pulse-formers (p.f.) or equivalent level zero signals. These must be specified by component number and signal. If the number of signals to be so specified is small, the data are transcribed directly. If the

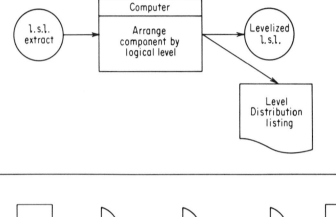

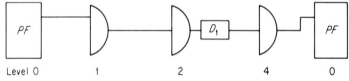

**Fig. 10.19.** Arrangement of logical signal list by logical levels.

number of signals is large, or the signals must be set and reset during the period of computation, the parameter generator is used instead. With the generator, signal parameters for any number of runs and time periods can be prepared from only a few words of specification (Fig. 10.20).

*Simulation.* Once equations and parameters have been prepared in usable form, it is only necessary to insert the parameters and solve the equations. One set of solutions—i.e., each equation solved once—represents the action of the circuitry during one time period. Successive time periods may be calculated from the current state of pulse-former signals, or from new parameters inserted at this time and/or at the beginning of later time periods. The number of time periods calculated in any one run is limited only by practical consideration of the computer time required.

At conclusion, the values of all signals for every time period are available for analysis. Generally, only a few must be examined for evidence of correct design. Those signals which the designer specifies as of interest are tabulated (and printed) for his inspection. If an error appears that makes

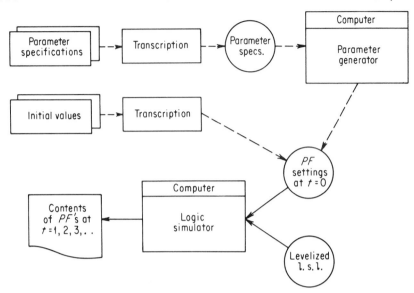

**Fig. 10.20.** Flow chart of the logic simulation process.

examination of intermediate results desirable, this information may be obtained in tabular form as well.

### 10.9 LOGICAL DESIGN BY COMPUTER

Logical design usually consists of the human logical designer translating input and output specifications into logical equations and/or logical drawings, so that the number of circuits and their costs are minimized. Computers are capable of performing processes of this type with much greater speed than humans; therefore, many more solutions can be considered using techniques that eventually converge toward minimized logical networks. This approach is still in the research stages and involves the theory of minimization of Boolean functions, the application of mathematical techniques, such as linear programming, to such minimization, etc. The subject matter is beyond the scope of this book.

### REFERENCES

**1.** Remington Rand Univac, Division of Sperry Rand Corporation, *Statistical Techniques in Transistor Evaluation, Final Report*, Contract NObs-72660, April 1959.*

**2.** Kaskey, G., N. S. Prywes, and H. Lukoff, "Application of Computers to Circuit

* Available from ASTIA (see also Ref. 2).

Design for UNIVAC/LARC," Paper presented at the Joint IRE-AIEE-ACM
Computer Conference, Los Angeles, Calif., May 9–11, 1961.

3. Ezekiel, Mordecai, *Methods of Correlation Analysis* (2nd ed.; New York: John
Wiley & Sons, 1941).

4. Johnson, P: O., *Statistical Methods in Research* (Englewood Cliffs, N.J.: Prentice-
Hall, Inc., 1944), Chap. 5.

5. Hildebrand, F. B., *Introduction to Numerical Analysis* (New York: McGraw-
Hill Book Co., 1956), p. 429.

6. Lehmer, D. H., "Mathematical Methods on Large-Scale Computing Units,"
*Harvard University Computation Laboratory Annals*, **26** (1951), 141–146.

7. Remington Rand Univac, Division of Sperry Rand Corporation, *The Univac
Prepared Engineering Document Program*, T. Williams, Remington Rand Univac,
Philadelphia, Pa.*

8. Remington Rand Univac, Division of Sperry Rand Corporation, *The Backboard
Wiring Problem: A Placement Algorithm*, L. Steinberg, Remington Rand Univac,
Philadelphia, Pa.

9. Lee, C. Y., "An Algorithm for Path Connections and Its Applications," *I.R.E.
Transactions on Electronic Computers*, **EC-10**:3 (Sept. 1961), 346–365.

## PROBLEMS

**1.** Using d-c worst-case design, determine the resistors and the minimum transistor
current gain ($\alpha_{FE}$) for the following circuit:

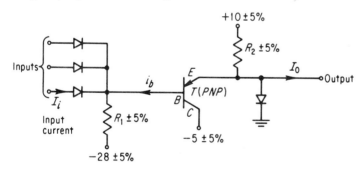

**Fig. P10.1.**

Input current $I_i$ is at least 1 ma when $T$ is "off," and not more than 50 $\mu$a
when $T$ is "on." Output current is to be not less than 6 ma when $T$ is "off"
and not more than 50 $\mu$a when $T$ is "on." $V_{CE}$ when $T$ is "on" is 0.3 v. $V_{BE}$ when $T$
is "on" is 0.5 v. The drop of a conducting diode is 0.3 v. $i_c \leq 50$ $\mu$a at $i_b = 0$
(assume $i_b = 0$ at $V_{BE} = 0$).

* Available from its author.

**2.** In the circuit of Prob. 1, on a worst-case basis find the minimum required transistor current gain ($\alpha_{FE}$) if $R_1$ and $R_2$ have respectively the mean values of 47 K and 1.5 K. Also find the minimum required value of $\alpha_{FE}$ for a 0.1 per cent failure probability assuming that the voltages have the mean values as in Prob. 1, and both voltages and resistances have standard deviations equal to those of rectangular distributions of ±5 per cent about the mean. Assume $\alpha_{FE}$ is independent of voltage and current.

**3.** Discuss the logical capabilities of the circuit from the point of view of whether or not it can be used as the only logic circuit in a computer. If you think it can be so used, show how; and if you think it can't, show why not and/or show what is lacking. Also, discuss in the same way the electrical compatibility of this circuit with others of identical construction in a computer.

**4.** In the circuit of Prob. 1 using the resistor values of Prob. 2, compute one of the response times to an input step (rise time, fall time, or storage time) when unloaded if $f_T = 20$ mcps, $\alpha_F = 0.99$, and $\alpha_R = 0.8$.

**5.** When packaged, the circuit of Prob. 1 occupies a 1-in. cube. Packages are to be made by stacking $n$ of these cubes as below.

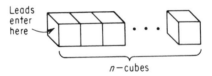

Leads enter here →

$n-$cubes

Fig. P10.2.

The backboard is square and the packages are mounted as below.

$n-$cubes

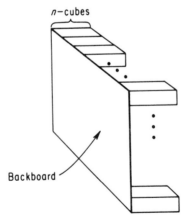

Backboard

Fig. P10.3.

Signal leads pass through the package to the backboard, across the backboard to the appropriate package, and through that package to the appropriate circuit cube. Determine the backboard size and the number of cubes in a package that minimizes the length of the longest possible signal lead if there are 1000 circuits to be mounted on the backboard. What aspect of efficiency does this optimization affect?

6. If the output current of the circuit is 6 ma, as in Prob. 1, and the voltage swing is 5 v with a rise time of 10 nsec, estimate the crosstalk between two of the longest possible signal leads in the structure of Prob. 5 if there are ten cubes in a package. Assume that backboard wiring is 1 in. above the backboard which is used as ground plane. No. 22 wire is used and the two wires are ½ in. apart. Assume the crosstalk in a package is negligible (how can this be achieved?).

# INTRODUCTION TO

# SEMICONDUCTOR DIODE THEORY

## I.1 QUANTUM MECHANICS

A thorough treatment of the theory of solid materials requires the use of the formal methods of quantum mechanics. The starting point is the Schrödinger wave equation, which leads through various interpretations to a description of the behavior of electrons in the crystal lattice of a solid. It can be justified as the result of the application of Fourier analysis to mechanics.

Consider the question of wave-particle duality. If a particle is considered to be distributed in space with a density $g(x, y, z)$, the total energy of the mass in a volume element $dv$, moving with the volume element with a velocity $u$ and with a potential energy $dV$, is

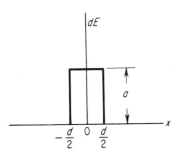

**Fig. I.1.** Distribution along the
x axis.

$$dE(x, y, z) = \frac{1}{2}gu^2 \, dv + dV \quad (I.1)$$

Consider $dE(x)$ distributed along the $x$ axis as in Fig. I.1. The Fourier transform of $dE$ is

$$F(k) = \frac{1}{2\pi} \int_{-d/2}^{d/2} ae^{-jkx}\, dx$$

$$= \frac{a}{\pi k} \sin \frac{kd}{2}$$

By using the inverse Fourier transform, $dE(x)$ may be written

$$dE(x) = \int_{-\infty}^{\infty} \frac{a}{\pi k} \sin \frac{kd}{2} e^{jkx}\, dk \qquad (\text{I.2})$$

The quantity $dE(x)$ has been expressed in Eq. (I.2) as a sum of standing waves each having an amplitude

$$F(k) = \frac{a}{\pi k} \sin \frac{kd}{2}$$

That is, the Fourier integral makes it possible to express particle characteristics in wave form. The elementary waves are of the form

$$\psi = e^{jkx} \qquad (\text{I.3})$$

The differential equation that $\psi$ satisfies in three dimensions is the Schrödinger wave equation for the electron

$$-\frac{\hbar^2}{2m} \nabla^2\psi + V\psi = E\psi \qquad (\text{I.4})$$

where $\hbar$ = Planck's constant $\div 2\pi = 1.054 \times 10^{-34}$ joule sec
  $m$ = electron mass
  $V$ = potential of field in which electron is immersed
  $p$ = momentum of electron
  $k = p/\hbar$
  $E$ = total energy (here a constant)
This fact can be verified by substituting Eq. (I.3) into Eq. (I.4) and comparing with Eq. (I.1) after integration of Eq. (I.1) over the particle.

## I.2  ENERGY LEVELS

If Schrödinger's equation [Eq. (I.4)] is properly set up and solved for the single electron in the hydrogen atom or for a single electron in the outer electronic shell of a more complex atom, it is found that $E$ can have only discrete values, called "energy levels." These are shown, schematically, in Fig. I.2 analogous to the different resonant modes in a resonant transmission line. The energy levels can be interpreted as being the allowable energies which the electron can possess. The lowest energy that the electron can have (ground-state energy) corresponds to the case where the electron calmly sits in an undisturbed atom. Electrical forces can cause the electron to gain energy and thus occupy one of the excited states. If it ever loses energy, it loses it in discrete amounts, giving it out as radiation whose angular frequency is given by $\omega = \Delta E/\hbar$. In the excited states, the electron is bound to the atom. However, if the electron is given an energy greater than $E_{max}$ in Fig. I.2, it will be removed from the atom, which would then be ionized.

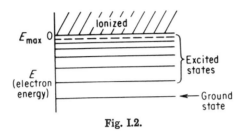

**Fig. I.2.**

## I.3  ENERGY BANDS

There is a principle enunciated by Pauli which states that no two electrons can be in the same state simultaneously. Perhaps this may be understood by the coupled-resonant-circuit analogy, wherein each of two identical coupled resonant circuits has twice as many modes of oscillation as it would have alone. If we plotted the energy levels for either of the two electrons under consideration in two atoms a distance $x$ apart versus $x$, we would get something like Fig. I.3.

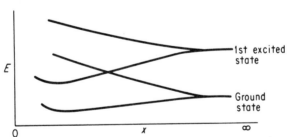

**Fig. I.3.** Two energy levels as a function of atom separation for two atoms.

Now the atoms in a crystal lattice are arranged in a regular and periodic array. Let $x$ be the distance between any two atoms. If the lattice were assembled from infinity retaining the same periodic structure, the energy levels we have been talking about would split into a very large number of levels in the lattice. This is shown in Fig. I.4. The shaded areas are densely occupied by the multitude of energy levels. The parameter, $E_g$, is called the gap width. If $E_g < 0$, the material is a conductor. If $E_g > 0$, the material is a nonconductor. In insulators, the gap width may be several electron-volts; in semiconductors, useful at room temperature, the gap width would be in the vicinity of one electron-volt. Approximate gap widths are 0.7 ev in germanium, 1.1 ev in silicon, and 7 ev in diamond. Diamond is an insulator while silicon and germanium are semiconductors.

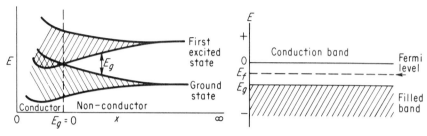

**Fig. I.4.** Two energy levels as a function of atom separation for a solid.    **Fig. I.5.** Semiconductor band structure.

## I.4 INTRINSIC SEMICONDUCTORS

In a perfectly pure semiconductor, the energy levels that an electron may occupy form several bands as we have seen. This band structure is shown in Fig. I.5. $E$ is taken to be zero at the bottom of the conduction band. The filled band represents those valence electrons that are bound to their atoms ($E < E_g$). Only the lower edge of the conduction band is shown, as it may represent the result of the overlapping of many higher-energy bands. Electrons that are free to move around in the lattice have energies in the conduction band ($E > E_g$). At temperatures above absolute zero, some electrons will be in the conduction band. Using Fermi-Dirac statistics, the number of electrons in the conduction band can be shown to be proportional to

$$\exp\left[-\frac{|E_f|}{kT}\right], \qquad E_f < 0 \tag{I.5}$$

where $k$ is Boltzmann's constant ($1.38 \times 10^{-23}$ joule/°K), $T$ is the absolute temperature, and $E_f$ is the Fermi level. The Fermi level in intrinsic semiconductors lies about in the middle of the energy gap. The probability that an electron has an energy greater than $E_f$ is $\frac{1}{2}$, which serves to define the Fermi level. The conductivity turns out also to be proportional to Eq. (I.5).

## I.5 IMPURITY SEMICONDUCTORS

The above discussion has been confined to the case of perfectly pure semiconductors. However, if impurities are introduced into the semiconductor, interesting and useful effects occur.

If a valence-5 impurity atom such as antimony or arsenic is introduced into the crystal lattice (Fig. I.6), the extra electron furnished by this impurity atom (n-type impurity or "donor") is not involved with the electron-ion bonds holding the crystal together and little energy is required to remove it from its parent atom, which then acquires a unit positive charge. This electron is then free to move about in the crystal lattice. In the energy-band picture this state of affairs is represented by the existence of an energy level in germanium about 0.01 electron-volts below the bottom of the conduction band (see Fig. I.7). The level is occupied only when the electron is bound by the field of its parent donor atom.

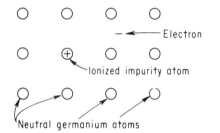 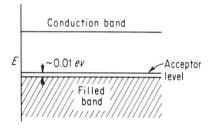

Fig. I.6. Showing a donor atom in place in a germanium crystal lattice.

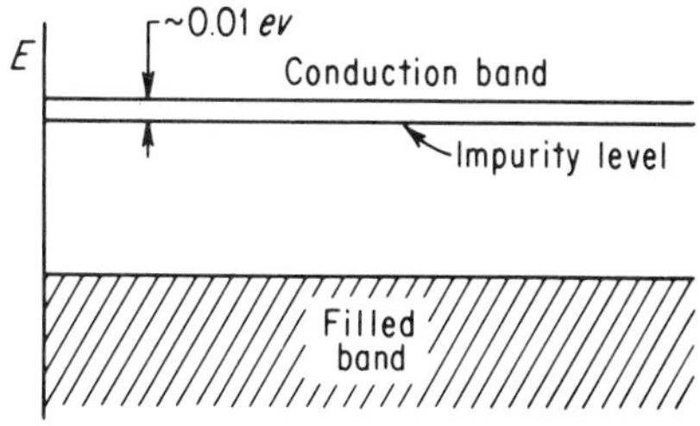

Fig. I.7. Showing energy level introduced by presence of a donor atom.

If a valence-3 atom such as an atom of boron or indium is introduced (p-type impurity or "acceptor" atom) into the crystal lattice, the vacant bond or "hole" at the impurity site can borrow an electron from nearby, filling the vacant bond but transferring the "hole" to another location (Fig. I.8). In this way, a hole may move through the crystal lattice. In

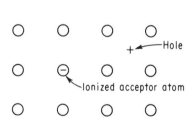

Fig. I.8. Illustrating a hole in a crystal lattice.

Fig. I.9. Band structure with an acceptor atom in the crystal lattice.

many respects, holes behave in a crystal lattice like positively charged electrons and can be conceptually treated as such. The presence of the impurity atom introduces an additional energy level in germanium about 0.01 electron-volts above the top of the filled band. (See Fig. I.9.) When the hole is separated from its parent atom, this level is filled, leaving a vacancy in the multitude of levels in the filled band corresponding to motion of the hole in the crystal lattice.

When more than one donor or acceptor atom is present, the single acceptor or donor level is replaced by a group of closely spaced levels at about the same energy occupied by the single level.

Electrons in n-type material or holes in p-type material are referred to as *majority carriers*, as they can be the charge carriers in an electric current flowing in the material. Thermal, radiative, or other energy sources can give an electron enough energy to put it in the conduction band, leaving a hole in the filled band. If this occurs in n-type material, the additional electron is not significant, provided only relatively few are produced by the thermal, etc., energy sources compared to the majority carriers already present. However, the hole produced can carry charge and is referred to as a *minority carrier*. In p-type materials, the minority carriers are electrons. Minority carriers may also be injected at junctions with materials having large numbers of carriers that are minority carriers in the material under consideration. This last instance gives rise to the phenomena that are made use of in the transistor and-exist to some extent in p-n junction diodes.

Minority carriers existing with a carrier charge density per unit volume, $\rho_c$, in a semiconductor decay to an equilibrium carrier charge density, $\rho_{c0}$, at an exponential rate with a time constant, $\tau$, called the *lifetime*, such that

$$\frac{\partial \rho_c}{\partial t} = -\frac{(\rho_c - \rho_{c0})}{\tau} \qquad (I.6)$$

Equation (I.6) holds only if the minority carrier charge density is independent of position. However, any current that flows is due to diffusion or an applied field **E** such that

$$\mathbf{J}_c = \sigma \mathbf{E} - D\,\nabla\rho_c \qquad (I.7)$$

where $\sigma$ is the conductivity for minority carriers and $D$ is the *diffusion constant* for the particular minority carrier. $D$ is defined by Eq. (1.7). From Eq. (I.7) and the equation of continuity for minority carriers,

$$\nabla \cdot \mathbf{J}_c + \frac{\partial \rho_c}{\partial t} = 0$$

we have for the case in which $E$ is negligible

$$\frac{\partial \rho_c}{\partial t} = D\,\nabla^2 \rho_c \qquad (I.8)$$

Equation (I.8) gives the contribution of diffusion to $\partial \rho_c/\partial t$. Combining Eq. (I.6) with Eq. (I.8) yields

$$\frac{\partial \rho_c}{\partial t} = -\frac{(\rho_c - \rho_{c0})}{\tau} + D \, \nabla^2 \rho_c \tag{I.9}$$

which is known as the *diffusion equation* for minority carriers in a semiconductor. Division of every term in Eq. (I.9) by the electronic charge gives the form usually encountered in the literature, wherein the independent variable is the minority carrier density (the number of minority carriers per unit volume) since each carrier is assumed to carry a charge whose magnitude is equal to the electronic charge.

### I.6 THE P-N JUNCTION DIODE

In n-type material the Fermi level is a little below the bottom of the conduction band, and in p-type material it is a little above the top of the filled band. Since the Fermi level must be the same throughout two solids in thermal equilibrium, we have the band structure, charge, and electrostatic potential distribution shown in Fig. I.10 at zero bias. Holes and

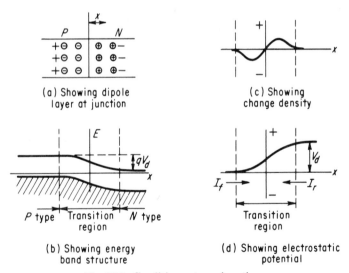

(a) Showing dipole layer at junction

(c) Showing change density

(b) Showing energy band structure

(d) Showing electrostatic potential

Fig. I.10. Conditions at p-n junction.

electrons flow across the junction until an electrostatic potential of amount $V_d$ (the diffusion potential) is built up, stopping further net charge flow.

A hole current, $I_f$ [Fig. I.10(d)], consisting of those holes which are able to pass the potential barrier as determined by statistical mechanics,

$$I_f = I_p e^{-[(q/kT)(V_d - V)]}$$

where $V$ is an applied voltage, $I_p$ is a constant, $k$ is Boltzmann's constant, and $q$ is the magnitude of the electronic charge. A current, $I_r$, of thermally generated holes flows in the reverse direction. Since $I_f = I_r$ when $V = 0$,

$$I_r = I_p e^{-(q/kT)V_d}$$

The net current from left to right in Fig. I.10 is

$$I_f - I_r = I_p e^{-qV_d/kT}(e^{qV/kT} - 1)$$

A similar expression can be derived for electrons such that the net current becomes

$$I = I_s(e^{qV/kT} - 1)$$

where $I_s = I_{s0}e^{-qV_d/kT}$ and $I_{s0}$ is a constant depending on the material and on the junction area.

By differentiation of $I_s$, we obtain

$$\frac{dI_s}{I_s} = \frac{qV_d}{kT^2} dT$$

At 300°K if $V_d$ is assumed to be 0.7 volts,

$$\frac{dI_s}{I_s} = 0.09 \, dT$$

which indicates $I_s$ doubles every 11°C if $V_d = 0.7$ volts. This approximates the temperature dependence of the saturation current in germanium diodes.

## REFERENCES

1. Van der Ziel, A., *Solid State Physical Electronics* (Englewood Cliffs, N.J.: Prentice-Hall, Inc., 1957).

2. Shockley, W., *Electrons and Holes in Semiconductors* (Princeton, N. J.: D. Van Nostrand Co., 1950).

# STATISTICAL CONSIDERATIONS

Some of those elements of probability theory which are needed in the text will be outlined here, in the hope that the interested reader may be stimulated to pursue the subject further.

## II.1   RANDOM EXPERIMENTS AND RANDOM VARIABLES

Consider an experiment in which a circuit is constructed of components taken from stock and then the amount of delay for a step input is measured; then another circuit is constructed and the same measurement is made, and so forth. Assume that 100 circuits are constructed and delay measurements are made. Since no two circuits will have corresponding components with exactly the same component values, a range of delay measurements will be obtained. To the accuracy of the measurements, let us say that 7 circuits out of the 100 give a delay of 20 nsec. Then the fraction of circuits that yield a delay, $T$, of 20 nsec is $7/100 = 0.07$. By this procedure we have attempted to experimentally measure the probability that a circuit will have a delay of 20 nsec when built from our stock of components. If our stock of components has been used up completely by building 100 circuits, then we have determined that the probability of a circuit's having a delay of 20 nsec is 0.07. However, if we have enough components to build another 100 circuits, the figure 0.07 is clearly only an approximation to the probability that any circuit in the 200 will have a delay of 20 nsec. Definition as a fraction or "frequency ratio" is the modern mathematical definition of probability. A variable that can be obtained from an experiment such as that described above is called a "random variable," and the experiment is called a "random experiment."

The problem in statistical design is to design so that at some instant the fraction of circuits in a computer that will not work because of out-of-tolerance components and/or voltages is no greater than some defined limit. That is, we wish to make the probability that a circuit will not work at the specified instant no greater than the defined limit. The first step in making a design is to obtain this probability for a circuit. This can be done in several ways, such as:

1. By performing the random experiment (building many circuits).
2. By simulating the random experiment—for example, on a computer (Monte Carlo method).
3. By calculation from known distributions of component values using probability theory.

## II.2  ELEMENTARY RULES

The statement that "the probability that the delay, $T$, is 20 nsec is 0.07" will be denoted by

$$P(T = 20 \text{ nsec}) = 0.07$$

Since probability is a fraction or frequency ratio, $0 \leq P \leq 1$. Also, if there are two events that can occur in a random experiment either singly or simultaneously, then clearly

$$f_{A \text{ or } B} = f_A + f_B - f_{A \text{ and } B}$$

where $f$ is the frequency ratio for the occurrence of an event (such as $T = 20$ nsec) in a random experiment. Therefore,

$$P(A \text{ or } B) = P(A) + P(B) - P(A \text{ and } B)$$

If events $A$ and $B$ never occur simultaneously (mutually exclusive events), $P(AB) = 0$ so that

$$P(A + B) = P(A) + P(B) \tag{II.1}$$

## II.3  CONDITIONAL PROBABILITIES AND INDEPENDENT EVENTS

If $P(B \mid A)$ is the probability that $B$ occurs, on condition that $A$ has occurred (conditional probability), it is easily shown from frequency ratios that

$$P(B \mid A) = \frac{P(AB)}{P(A)} \tag{II.2}$$

If $A$ and $B$ are independent events, then $P(B \mid A) = P(B)$ and Eq. (II.2) becomes

$$P(AB) = P(A)P(B) \tag{II.3}$$

which is a very important relationship.

## II.4 DISTRIBUTION FUNCTIONS

In the case of the circuit experiment above, if we wished to write "the probability that $T \leq 20$ nsec" we would write

$$P(T \leq 20 \text{ nsec})$$

If it is known $P(T \leq x)$ for all $x$, the "probability distribution" of $T$ is known and

$$F_T(x) = P(T \leq x)$$

is the "distribution function."

By the addition rule [Eq. (II.1)]

$$P(T \leq b) = P(T \leq a) + P(a < T \leq b)$$

since the events $T \leq a$ and $a < T \leq b$ are mutually exclusive events and their simultaneous occurrence is $T \leq b$. Hence

$$P(a < T \leq b) = P(T \leq b) - P(T \leq a)$$
$$= F_T(b) - F_T(a) \qquad \text{(II.4)}$$

## II.5 DISCRETE DISTRIBUTIONS

Distributions can be discrete, continuous, or mixed. As an example of a discrete distribution, suppose that measurements of circuit delay are made to the nearest 5 nsec in the experiment mentioned above and the results in Table I.1 are obtained. The distribution function and the probabilities

**TABLE I.1**

| Delay (nsec) | 10 | 15 | 20 | 25 | 30 | 35 | 40 | 45 | 50 | 55 |
|---|---|---|---|---|---|---|---|---|---|---|
| No. of circuits having delay | 1 | 4 | 7 | 20 | 25 | 19 | 12 | 6 | 4 | 2 |

are plotted in Figs. II.1 and II.2. The heights of the steps are equal to the probabilities as given by Eq. (II.4).

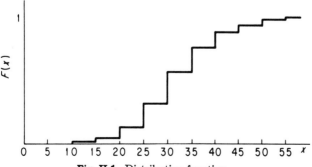

**Fig. II.1.** Distribution function.

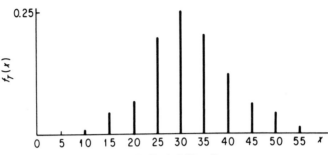

Fig. II.2. Probability diagram.

## II.6 CONTINUOUS DISTRIBUTIONS

Only continuous distributions as approximations to discrete ones will be considered. What this means is that large numbers of circuits are of concern, so that the steps in $F_T(x)$ are small enough so that with little error $F_T(x)$ can be replaced by a continuous curve.

If $F_T(x)$ is continuous, Eq. (II.4) may be written

$$P(x < T \le x + dx) = \frac{F_T(x + dx) - F_T(x)\, dx}{dx} = \frac{dF_T}{dx}\, dx$$

$$= f_T(x)\, dx$$

where $f_T(x)$, the frequency function, is defined as $dF_T/dx$. Hence

$$P(a < X \le b) = F_X(b) - F_X(a) = \int_a^b f_X(x)\, dx$$

and

$$P(X > \epsilon) = \int_\epsilon^\infty f_X(x)\, dx$$

$$\int_{-\infty}^\infty f_X(x)\, dx = 1$$

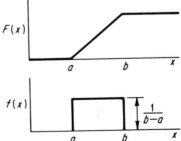

Fig. II.3. Rectangular distribution.

## II.7  THE UNIFORM DISTRIBUTION

An example of a continuous distribution is given in Fig. II.3. This is the "uniform" or "rectangular" distribution, which often is a good distribution to take for component values when only the worst-case limits are known.

## II.8  JOINT DISTRIBUTIONS

If in an experiment two quantities such as the width and amplitude of a pulse are measured, a function of interest is

$$P(V_1 < V \leq V_2, T_1 < T \leq T_2)$$

Corresponding to this there is the joint distribution function of $V$ and $T$

$$F_{V,T}(x, y) = P(V \leq x, T \leq y)$$

and in continuous distributions

$$F(x, y) = \int_{-\infty}^{x} \int_{-\infty}^{y} f(x, y) \, dx \, dy$$

and

$$\int_{-\infty}^{\infty} \int_{-\infty}^{\infty} f(x, y) \, dx \, dy = 1$$

If the variables are independent, then $F_{T,V}(x, y) = F_T(x)F_V(y)$.

## II.9  THE MEAN

The mean of a continuous distribution can be defined, by analogy to the well-known process for determining the arithmetic mean of a discrete distribution, as

$$m = \int_{-\infty}^{\infty} xf(x) \, dx = E(x)$$

If $Y = g(X)$, the mean value of $Y$ is

$$E(Y) = E(g(x)) = \int_{-\infty}^{\infty} g(x)f(x) \, dx$$

It is easily shown that

$$E(aX + b) = aE(X) + b$$

$$E(X + Y) = E(X) + E(Y) \qquad \text{(for a joint distribution)}$$

$$E(XY) = E(X)E(Y) \qquad \text{(if } X \text{ and } Y \text{ are independent random variables)}$$

## II.10 MOMENTS

The absolute moments of order $n$ are $\alpha_n = E(X^n)$ so that $\alpha_0 = 1$, $\alpha_1 = m$ (the mean), etc. The central moments of order $n$ are $\mu_n = E[(X - m)^n]$ such that

$$\mu_1 = E(X - m) = E(X) - m = 0$$

$$\mu_2 = E[(X - m)^2] = E(X^2) - 2mE(X) + m^2 = \alpha_2 - m^2$$

and so on. The standard deviation is $\sigma = \sqrt{\mu_2}$.

## II.11 SUMS OF INDEPENDENT RANDOM VARIABLES

If $X_1$ and $X_2$ are independent random variables which are distributed with mean and standard deviations which are respectively $m_{X_1}$ and $\sigma_{X_1}$, and $m_{X_2}$ and $\sigma_{X_2}$, then the mean and standard deviations of $X_1 + X_2$ are

$$m = E(X_1 + X_2) = E(X_1) + E(X_2) = m_{X_1} + m_{X_2}$$

$$\sigma^2 = E[(X_1 + X_2 - m)^2]$$

$$= E(X_1^2 + X_2^2 + m^2 - 2mX_1 - 2mX_2 + 2X_1X_2)$$

$$= E(X_1^2) + E(X_2^2) + m^2 - 2mm_{X_1} - 2mm_{X_2} + 2E(X_1X_2)$$

But $X_1$ and $X_2$ are *independent* so that $E(X_1X_2) = E(X_1)E(X_2)$. Hence

$$\sigma^2 = E(X_1^2) - m_{X_1}^2 + E(X_2^2) - m_{X_2}^2$$

$$= \sigma_1^2 + \sigma_2^2$$

This may be generalized to $n$ *independent* random variables $X_1, X_2, \ldots, X_n$ where $X = X_1 + X_2 + \cdots + X_n$ and then

$$m = m_{X_1} + m_{X_2} + \cdots + m_{X_n}$$

$$\sigma^2 = \sigma_{X_1}^2 + \sigma_{X_2}^2 + \cdots + \sigma_{X_n}^2$$

The distribution of the sum of two independent random variables $X = X_1 + X_2$ may be obtained from the convolution integrals which can be derived using the joint distribution concept,

$$f_X(x) = \int_{-\infty}^{\infty} f_{X_1}(x - v)f_{X_2}(v) \, dv = \int_{-\infty}^{\infty} f_{X_2}(x - u)f_{X_1}(u) \, du$$

where $f_{X_1}$, $f_{X_2}$, and $f_X$ are respectively the frequency functions for the distributions of $X_1$, $X_2$, and $X$.

## II.12 CHARACTERISTIC FUNCTIONS

The characteristic function (c.f.) of the distribution of any random variable $X$ is defined

$$\phi_X(t) = E(e^{itx}) = \int_{-\infty}^{\infty} e^{itx} f_X(x)\, dx$$

Thus

$$|\phi_X(t)| = 1, \qquad \phi_X(-t) = \phi_X^*(t)$$

If $X = X_1 + X_2 + \cdots + X_n$ and the $X_i$ are independent random variables, and if the c.f.'s of the $X_i$ are $\phi_{X_i}(t)$, $i = 1, \ldots, n$ and $\phi_X(t)$ is the c.f. of the distribution of $X$, then it is easily shown that

$$\phi_X(t) = \phi_{X_1}(t)\phi_{X_2}(t) \cdots \phi_{X_n}(t) \tag{II.5}$$

Equation (11.5) will be used later.

## II.13   THE NORMAL DISTRIBUTION

The normal distribution is defined by

$$f_{m,\sigma}(x) = \frac{1}{\sigma\sqrt{2\pi}}\, e^{-(x-m)^2/2\sigma^2}$$

and

$$F_{m,\sigma}(x) = \int_{-\infty}^{x} f(x)\, dx$$

$$\phi_{m,\sigma}(t) = e^{mjt - (1/2)\sigma^2 t^2}, \qquad j = \sqrt{-1}$$

From $\phi_{m,\sigma}(t)$ it follows that the distribution of the sum of $n$ normally distributed random variables having means $m_{X_i}$ and standard deviations $\sigma_i$ is also normally distributed, with mean and standard deviations given by

$$m = m_1 + m_2 + \cdots + m_n$$

$$\sigma^2 = \sigma_1^2 + \cdots + \sigma_n^2$$

## II.14   CENTRAL LIMIT THEOREM

If $X$ is the sum of $n$ independent random variables which are *not* normally distributed, and no one random variable contributes an excessive amount to the sum, then for large $n$, $X$ is approximately normally distributed with mean and standard deviations given by

$$m_X = m_{X_1} + m_{X_2} + \cdots + m_{X_n}$$

$$\sigma_X^2 = \sigma_{X_1}^2 + \sigma_{X_2}^2 + \cdots + \sigma_{X_n}^2$$

If $n$ is infinite, the error in the approximation is zero.

## II.15   SAMPLING

If there are $N$ values $x_1, \ldots, x_n$ of the random variable $X$, the mean and standard deviations are

$$m = \frac{1}{N} \sum_{j=1}^{N} x_j, \qquad \sigma^2 = \frac{1}{N} \sum_{j=1}^{N} (x_j - m)^2$$

If a sample of size $n$ is taken without replacement, and the mean and standard deviations of the $s$th sample are

$$m_s = \frac{1}{n} \sum_{j=1}^{n} x_j, \qquad \sigma_s^2 = \frac{1}{n} \sum_{j=1}^{n} (x_{sj} - m_s)^2 \qquad (\text{II.6})$$

then the mean and standard deviations of the distribution of the sample means $m_s$ are

$$E(m_s) = m \qquad (\text{II.6a})$$

$$\sigma_{m_s}^2 = \frac{N}{N-1} \frac{n-1}{n} \sigma_s^2 \qquad (\text{II.6b})$$

Thus, assume there are 10,000 circuits in a computer and 100 of these have their delays measured and are tabulated in Table II.1. The mean of the sample is, from the first of Eqs. (II.6),

$$m_s = \frac{1}{100} \sum_{j=1}^{100} T_j = 31.85 \quad \text{nsec.}$$

By Eq. (II.6a) this is an approximation to the mean delay of the 10,000 circuits. However, the standard deviation of the distribution of the sample means is, from Eq. (II.6b),

$$\sigma_{m_s}^2 = \frac{10,000}{9,999} \frac{99}{100} \sigma_s^2 = 0.99 \ \sigma_s^2$$

For discussions of other types of sampling and for the meaning of terms such as AQL, the reader should consult the references.

## II.16  SUMS OF INDEPENDENT RANDOM VARIABLES

A simple method (simple in that it is routine) will now be developed for the computation of the frequency function of a random variable $X$ which is the sum of $n$ independent random variables $X_1, X_2, \ldots, X_n$ whose distributions are known and which can be piecewise approximated (using straight line segments or using segments of polynomials).

## II.17  HEURISTIC APPROACH

It will be assumed that frequency functions for $X, X_1, X_2, \ldots, X_n$ exist and are continuous except possibly at a finite number of points in a finite interval. Then, if the $X_i$ are independent random variables, the frequency function of $X$ can be obtained by repeated evaluation of the convolution integral: i.e., if $f_{X_1+X_2}(x)$, $f_{X_1}(x)$, and $f_{X_2}(x)$ are the frequency functions of $X_1 + X_2$, $X_1$, and $X_2$ respectively, and $X_1$ and $X_2$ are independent random variables, then

$$f_{X_1+X_2}(x) = \int_{-\infty}^{\infty} f_{X_1}(x - z)f_{X_2}(z) \, dz = \int_{-\infty}^{\infty} f_{X_2}(x - z)f_{X_1}(z) \, dz \quad \text{(II.7)}$$

Thus if three independent random variables have each the rectangular frequency function

$$\begin{aligned} f(x) &= 0, & x < -\tfrac{1}{2}, x > \tfrac{1}{2} \\ f(x) &= 1, & -\tfrac{1}{2} < x < \tfrac{1}{2} \end{aligned} \quad \text{(II.8)}$$

then the sum of two of these random variables has the frequency function (triangular) obtained by the use of Eq. (II.7)

$$\begin{aligned} f(x) &= 0, & x < -1, x > 1 \\ f(x) &= x + 1, & -1 < x < 0 \\ f(x) &= 1 - x, & 0 < x < 1 \end{aligned} \quad \text{(II.9)}$$

Application of Eq. (II.7) to Eqs. (II.8) and (II.9) yields the frequency function for the sum of the three random variables (three parabolas):

$$\begin{aligned} f(x) &= 0, & x < -\tfrac{3}{2}, x > \tfrac{3}{2} \\ f(x) &= \tfrac{1}{2}(x + \tfrac{3}{2})^2, & -\tfrac{3}{2} < x < -\tfrac{1}{2} \\ f(x) &= \tfrac{1}{2}[(x + \tfrac{3}{2})^2 - 3(x + \tfrac{1}{2})^2], & -\tfrac{1}{2} < x < \tfrac{1}{2} \\ f(x) &= \tfrac{1}{2}[(x + \tfrac{3}{2})^2 - 3(x + \tfrac{1}{2})^2 + 3(x - \tfrac{1}{2})^2], & \tfrac{1}{2} < x < \tfrac{3}{2} \end{aligned} \quad \text{(II.10)}$$

This is a direct procedure and could be applied to

$$X = X_1 + X_2 + \cdots + X_n$$

except that the labor involved in the evaluation of the convolution integrals is excessive. An indirect procedure involves the use of characteristic functions. If the frequency function of $X_i$ is $f_{X_i}(x)$, its characteristic function is

$$\phi_{X_i}(t) = \int_{-\infty}^{\infty} f_{X_i}(x)e^{jtx} \, dx, \qquad j = \sqrt{-1} \quad \text{(II.11)}$$

If the $X_i$ are independent, the characteristic function of $X$, the sum of the $X_i$, is $\phi_X(t)$ where

$$\phi_X(t) = \phi_{X_1}(t)\phi_{X_2}(t) \cdots \phi_{X_n}(t) \quad \text{(II.12)}$$

and the frequency function of $X$ is given by

$$f_X(x) = \frac{1}{2\pi} \int_{-\infty}^{\infty} \phi_X(t)e^{-itx} \, dt \quad \text{(II.13)}$$

However, the evaluation of Eq. (II.13) involves contour integration in the complex plane and is also quite laborious. Nevertheless, the form of Eqs. (II.11), (II.12), and (II.13) suggests the existence of an operational method.

Consider the function

$$f(x, x_0, k) = 0, \qquad\qquad x < x_0$$
$$f(x, x_0, k) = \frac{(x - x_0)^k}{k!}, \qquad x > x_0 \tag{II.14}$$

The frequency function for the rectangular distribution is then, from Eq. (II.8),

$$f(x, -\tfrac{1}{2}, 0) - f(x, \tfrac{1}{2}, 0)$$

Equations (II.9) may be written

$$f(x, -1, 1) - 2f(x, 0, 1) + f(x, 1, 1)$$

and Eqs. (II.10) may be written

$$f(x, -\tfrac{3}{2}, 2) - 3f(x, -\tfrac{1}{2}, 2) + 3f(x, \tfrac{1}{2}, 2) - f(x, \tfrac{3}{2}, 2)$$

The characteristic function for the frequency function given by Eqs. (II.8) is, using Eq. (II.11),

$$-\frac{e^{jt(-1/2)}}{jt} + \frac{e^{jt(1/2)}}{jt}$$

and for Eqs. (II.9) it is, either by (II.11) or by (II.12),

$$\frac{e^{jt(-1)}}{(jt)^2} - 2\frac{e^{jt(0)}}{(jt)^2} + \frac{e^{jt(1)}}{(jt)^2}$$

and for Eqs. (II.10)

$$-\frac{e^{jt(-3/2)}}{(jt)^3} + 3\frac{e^{jt(-1/2)}}{(jt)^3} - 3\frac{e^{jt(1/2)}}{(jt)^3} + \frac{e^{jt(3/2)}}{(jt)^3}$$

Comparison of the above pairs of frequency functions and characteristic functions suggests the transform pair

$$f(x, x_0, k) \longleftrightarrow (-1)^{k+1}\frac{e^{jtx_0}}{(jt)^{k+1}} \tag{II.15}$$

Note, however, that substitution of Eq. (II.14) into Eq. (II.11) yields a divergent integral. A rigorous proof of Eq. (II.15) will be given later. If, on the other hand, one defines:

$$g(x, x_0, k) = \frac{(x_0 - x)^k}{k!}, \qquad x < x_0$$

$$g(x, x_0, k) = 0, \qquad\qquad x > x_0$$

then

$$g(x, x_0, k) \longleftrightarrow \frac{e^{jtx_0}}{(jt)^{k+1}} \tag{II.16}$$

Equations (II.15) and (II.16) form the basis of the operational method.

## II.18  RIGOROUS APPROACH

Assume that the frequency function in Fig. II.4 is piecewise approximated with critical points $x_1 < x_2 < \cdots < x_n$. Let

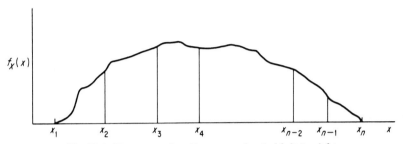

$f_X(x)$

$x_1$     $x_2$     $x_3$     $x_4$          $x_{n-2}$  $x_{n-1}$  $x_n$     $x$

**Fig. II.4.** Frequency function approximated left to right.

$$f_X(x) = P_1(x - x_1)u(x - x_1) + P_2(x - x_2)u(x - x_2)$$
$$+ \cdots + P_n(x - x_n)u(x - x_n) \quad \text{(II.17)}$$

where

$$u(x - x_k) = 0, \qquad x \leq x_k$$
$$u(x - x_k) = 1, \qquad x > x_k \text{ and } f(x) = 0, \quad x < x_1 \text{ and } x > x_n.$$

The characteristic function is

$$\phi_X(t) = \int_{-\infty}^{\infty} f_X(x)e^{jtx}\,dx = \int_{x_1}^{x_n} f_X(x)e^{jtx}\,dx$$

or

$$\phi_X(t) = \int_{x_1}^{x_n} P_1(x - x_1)u(x - x_1)e^{jtx}\,dx + \int_{x_2}^{x_n} P_2(x - x_2)u(x - x_2)e^{jtx}\,dx$$

$$+ \cdots + \int_{x_{n-1}}^{x_n} P_{n-1}(x - x_{n-1})u(x - x_{n-1})e^{jtx}\,dx$$

or

$$\phi_X(t) = \int_{x_1}^{x_n} P_1(x - x_1)e^{jtx}\,dx + \int_{x_2}^{x_n} P_2(x - x_2)e^{jtx}\,dx$$

$$+ \cdots + \int_{x_{n-1}}^{x_n} P_{n-1}(x - x_{n-1})e^{jtx}\,dx$$

Denote

$$\int^{x_s} P_k(x - x_k)e^{jtx}\,dx = I_k(x_s) \quad \text{(II.18)}$$

Then

$$\phi_X(t) = I_1(x_n) - I_1(x_1) + I_2(x_n) - I_2(x_2) + \cdots + I_{n-1}(x_n) - I_{n-1}(x_{n-1})$$
$$\text{(II.19)}$$

Let $I_1(x_n) + I_2(x_n) + \cdots + I_{n-1}(x_n) = K(x_n)$. Then

$$\phi_X(t) = -I_1(x_1) - I_2(x_2) - \cdots - I_{n-1}(x_{n-1}) + K(x_n) \quad \text{(II.20)}$$

Comparison of Eqs. (II.17) and (II.20) shows the following correspondences:

$$P_1(x - x_1)u(x - x_1) \longleftrightarrow -I_1(x_1)$$
$$P_2(x - x_2)u(x - x_2) \longleftrightarrow -I_2(x_2)$$
$$\cdots$$
$$P_{n-1}(x - x_{n-1})u(x - x_{n-1}) \longleftrightarrow -I_{n-1}(x_{n-1})$$
$$P_n(x - x_n)u(x - x_n) \longleftrightarrow K(x_n)$$

According to Eq. (II.14), let

$$P_0(x - x_0)u(x - x_0) = C_0 \frac{(x - x_0)^k}{k!} u(x - x_0) = C_0 f(x, x_0, k)$$

Then

$$C_0 f(x, x_0, k) \longleftrightarrow -I_0(x_0)$$

where

$$-I_0(x_0) = -\int^{x_0} P_0(x - x_0)e^{jtx}\, dx = -C_0 \int^{x_0} \frac{(x - x_0)^k}{k!} e^{jtx}\, dx \quad \text{(II.21)}$$

Evaluation of the integral II.21 yields

$$-I_0(x_0) = C_0 \frac{(-1)^{k+1}}{(jt)^{k+1}} e^{jtx_0}$$

Hence

$$f(x, x_0, k) \longleftrightarrow \frac{(-1)^{k+1}}{(jt)^{k+1}} e^{jtx_0}$$

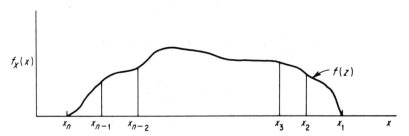

**Fig. II.5.** Frequency function approximated from right to left.

may be regarded as a transform pair [see Eq. (II.15)]. If the frequency function is approximated as in Fig. II.5, where

$$x_1 > x_2 > \cdots > x > x_n$$

and    $$f_X(x) = \hat{u}(x_1 - x)\hat{P}_1(x_1 - x) + \cdots + \hat{u}(x_n - x)\hat{P}_n(x_n - x)$$

where $\hat{u}(x_0 - x) = 1 - u(x - x_0)$, then it is easy to show that

$$\hat{u}(x_0 - x)\hat{P}_0(x_0 - x) \longleftrightarrow \int^{x_0} \hat{P}_0(x_0 - x)e^{jtx} \, dx$$

If one sets

$$\hat{u}(x_0 - x)\hat{P}_0(x_0 - x) = \hat{C}_0 \frac{(x_0 - x)^k}{k!} \quad \hat{u}(x_0 - x) = \hat{C}_0 g(x, x_0, k)$$

then it follows that

$$g(x, x_0, k) \longleftrightarrow \frac{e^{jtx_0}}{(jt)^{k+1}} \tag{II.22}$$

may be regarded as a transform pair [see Eq. (II.16)].

An interesting consequence of Eq. (II.22) is the following pair of relations:

$$\phi_X(t) = \sum_{i=1}^{n-1} \hat{C}_i \frac{e^{jtx_i}}{(jt)^{\alpha_i}}$$

if

$$f_X(x) = \sum_{i=1}^{n-1} \hat{C}_i \frac{(x_i - x)^{\alpha_i - 1}}{(\alpha_i - 1)!} \hat{u}(x_i - x), \qquad x > x_n \tag{II.23}$$

The second of these relations may be recognized as a general form for a frequency function piecewise approximated from right to left. The first of these relations is recognized as the result of replacement of terms using Eq. (II.22).

The probability that $X > \epsilon$ may be obtained as follows:

$$P(X > \epsilon) = \int_{\epsilon}^{\infty} f_X(x) \, dx$$

Substitution of Eq. (II.23) in the above yields after integration

$$P(X > \epsilon) = \hat{C}_i \frac{(x_i - \epsilon)^{\alpha_i}}{(\alpha_i)!} \hat{u}(x_i - \epsilon) \tag{II.24}$$

In particular if $\epsilon$ is a critical point $x_s$, Eq. (II.24) reduces to

$$P(X > x_s) = \sum_{i=1}^{s-1} \hat{C}_i \frac{(x_i - x_s)^{\alpha_i}}{(\alpha_i)!}$$

## REFERENCES

1. Cramér, H., *Elements of Probability Theory* (New York: John Wiley & Sons, 1955), pp. 57–65, elementary notions; 71–86, means, moments, general functions; 108–116, normal distribution; 253–262, sampling and quality control.

2. Cramér, H., *Mathematical Methods of Statistics* (Princeton, N.J.: Princeton University Press, 1946), p. 185, characteristic functions; pp. 244–246, sums of uniformly distributed random variables.

3. Gray, H. J., "An Application of Piecewise Approximations to Reliability and Statistical Design," *Proceedings of the I.R.E.*, **47**:7 (July 1959), 1226–1231. Material of Secs. II.16 ff.

# LOSSLESS AND ALMOST LOSSLESS

# UNIFORM TRANSMISSION LINES

The equations for the instantaneous voltage and current on the uniform transmission line shown in Fig. III.1 are

$$\frac{\partial v}{\partial x} = -Ri - L\frac{\partial i}{\partial t}$$

$$\frac{\partial i}{\partial x} = -Gv - C\frac{\partial v}{\partial t} \tag{III.1}$$

where $R$ and $L$ are respectively the resistance and inductance per unit loop length (two wires) and $G$ and $C$ are respectively the shunt conductance and capacitance per unit length.

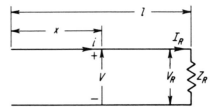

**Fig. III.1.** Uniform transmission line.

If Eqs. (III.1) are transformed with respect to time and the initial conditions are neglected, then

$$\frac{dV}{dx} = -ZI$$

$$\frac{dI}{dx} = -YV \tag{III.2}$$

$$Z = R + sL$$

$$Y = G + sC$$

Solution of Eqs. (III.2) yields

$$V = Ae^{\Gamma x} + Be^{-\Gamma x}$$

$$Z_0 I = -Ae^{\Gamma x} + Be^{-\Gamma x} \tag{III.3}$$

where

$$\Gamma = +\sqrt{YZ} \qquad \text{(propagation constant)}$$

$$Z_0 = +\sqrt{\frac{Z}{Y}} \qquad \text{(characteristic impedance)}$$

In a lossless line, $R = G = 0$ so that $\Gamma = s\sqrt{LC}$ and $Z_0 = \sqrt{L/C}$. The total delay is $l\sqrt{LC}$. Equations (III.3) become

$$V = Ae^{s\sqrt{LC}x} + Be^{-s\sqrt{LC}x}$$

$$Z_0 I = -Ae^{s\sqrt{LC}x} + Be^{-s\sqrt{LC}x} \tag{III.4}$$

Each of Eqs. (III.4) can be interpreted as the sum of two waves. Remembering that if $F(s)$ is the Laplace transform of $f(t)$, then the inverse transform of $F(s)e^{-sT}$ is $f(t - T)$, which is $f(t)$ delayed by an amount $T$, each of Eqs. (III.4) can be interpreted as the sum of two waves: an advanced wave and a retarded or delayed wave. Hence the second terms in Eqs. (III.4) represent a wave propagating from left to right in Fig. III.1 without change of shape or amplitude, while the first terms represent a wave propagating from right to left. At the load, the second terms represent the *incident* wave and the first terms represent the *reflected* wave.

In almost lossless transmission lines, $\Gamma$ becomes

$$\Gamma = \sqrt{(R + sL)(G + sC)} = \sqrt{s^2 LC}\left(1 + \frac{R}{sL}\right)^{1/2}\left(1 + \frac{G}{sC}\right)^{1/2}$$

$$\cong s\sqrt{LC} + \frac{R}{2Z_0} + \frac{GZ_0}{2}$$

where $Z_0 \cong \sqrt{L/C}$. Hence, on almost lossless lines, signals are propagated without change of shape but with attenuation.

At the load,

$$x = l, \qquad V = V_R, \qquad I = I_R = \frac{V_R}{Z_R} \tag{III.5}$$

Substitution of Eqs. (III.5) into (III.3) yields, after solution for $A$ and $B$,

$$A = \frac{V_R - Z_0 I_R}{2} e^{-\Gamma l}, \qquad B = \frac{V_R + Z_0 I_R}{2} e^{\Gamma l} \qquad (III.6)$$

The ratio of voltage to current for the incident wave is, from Eq. (III.3), equal to $Z_0$.

The voltage reflection coefficient at the load is [from Eqs. (III.4), (III.5), and (III.6)]

$$r_V = \frac{\text{reflected wave}}{\text{incident wave}} = \frac{A e^{\Gamma l}}{B e^{-\Gamma l}} = \frac{Z_R - Z_0}{Z_R + Z_0}$$

The current reflection coefficient at the load is

$$r_I = \frac{\text{reflected wave}}{\text{incident wave}} = -\frac{A e^{\Gamma l}}{B e^{-\Gamma l}} = \frac{Z_0 - Z_R}{Z_0 + Z_R}$$

The voltage transmission coefficient at the load is

$$t_V = \frac{\text{transmitted wave}}{\text{incident wave}} = \frac{V_R}{B e^{-\Gamma l}/Z_0} = \frac{2 Z_R}{Z_R + Z_0}$$

The current transmission coefficient at the load is

$$t_I = \frac{\text{transmitted wave}}{\text{incident wave}} = \frac{I_R}{B e^{-\Gamma l}/Z_0} = \frac{2 Z_0}{Z_R + Z_0}$$

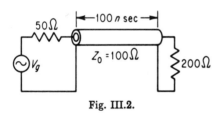

Fig. III.2.

With knowledge of the delay per unit length, the characteristic impedance, and the above coefficients at both ends of the line, any transient problem can be solved on any lossless transmission line.

For example, consider the circuit in Fig. III.2. $V_g$ is a 9-volt step. The reflection and transmission coefficients are as follows.

*Sending end:*

$$r_V = \frac{50 - 100}{50 + 100} = -\frac{1}{3}$$

$$r_I = \frac{1}{3}$$

$$t_V = \frac{2 \times 50}{50 + 100} = \frac{2}{3}$$

$$\dot{t}_I = \frac{2 \times 100}{50 + 100} = \frac{4}{3}$$

*Receiving end:*

$$r_V = \frac{200 - 100}{200 + 100} = \frac{1}{3}$$

$$r_I = -\frac{1}{3}$$

$$t_V = \frac{400}{200 + 100} = \frac{4}{3}$$

$$t_I = \frac{200}{200 + 100} = \frac{2}{3}$$

At $t = 0$, the incident wave (input of line) is

$$\frac{100}{100 + 50} \times 9 = 6 \text{ volts}$$

At $t = 0.1$, this arrives at the 200-$\Omega$ resistor. $6 \times r_V = 6 \times \frac{1}{3} = 2$ volts is reflected and $6 \times t_V = 6 \times \frac{4}{3} = 8$ volts is transmitted (see Fig. III.3) and appears across the 200-$\Omega$ resistor. The reflected 2-volt step travels from right to left and at $t = 0.2$ is incident on the 50-$\Omega$ resistor. $2 \times (-\frac{1}{3}) = -\frac{2}{3}$

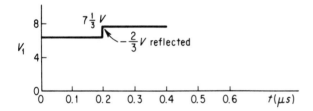

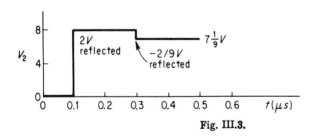

$V_1$ = sending end voltage

$V_2$ = receiving end voltage

**Fig. III.3.**

volt is reflected and $2 \times \frac{2}{3} = \frac{4}{3}$ volt is transmitted and appears at the sending end in addition to the 6 volts already present. These results, plotted in Fig. III.3, show the sending- and receiving-end voltages approaching the eventual steady-state value of 7.2 volts.

## REFERENCES

1. Goldman, S., *Transformation Calculus and Electrical Transients* (Englewood Cliffs, N.J.: Prentice-Hall, Inc., 1949), Chap. 10.

2. Millman, J., and H. Taub, *Pulse and Digital Circuits* (New York: McGraw-Hill Book Co. Inc., 1956), Chap. 10.

# INDEX